# THE FIGHT FOR LIFE

# THE FIGHT
# FOR LIFE

BY PAUL DE KRUIF

HARCOURT, BRACE AND COMPANY

NEW YORK

*Typography by Robert Josephy*

PRINTED IN THE UNITED STATES OF AMERICA
BY H. WOLFF BOOK MFG. CO., NEW YORK

*to Rhea*

# ACKNOWLEDGMENTS

PHILIP S. ROSE has been the principal guide and collaborator during the six years it took to gather the facts for *The Fight for Life*. Many adventures here told appeared in a preliminary form in *The Country Gentleman,* of which Rose is the editor. It was only during the past year that it became possible to re-write them around the central theme that the death fight has become the whole people's fight for life. The collection of the materials would have been impossible without Philip Rose's generous support. His understanding of science helped in the first selection of adventures from today's profusion of discoveries that stir the excitement of the reporter of science. His insight helped greatly in the final clarification of this book's challenge: that mankind's inheritance has now become the right to live. Best thanks, friend Philip!

Thanks are due to Bruce and Beatrice Blackmar Gould for inciting this reporter to look into the reasons for the disgrace of the needlessly high maternal death rate in our country, and into the causes at the bottom of our inability to stamp out syphilis. The results of these investigations appeared in a preliminary form in *The Ladies' Home Journal,* of which the Goulds are the editors.

Finally, the officers of the Curtis Publishing Company deserve thanks for their generosity which has permitted the writer to devote a large part of his time, during the past two years, to unpaid service as Secretary of The President's Commission for Infantile Paralysis Research. Without this support the facts for the present hopeful fight against the maiming death could not have been gathered.

PAUL DE KRUIF

# CONTENTS

## Part Four: THE GHASTLY LUXURY

*Prologue*

# FIGHTERS ALL

THE common inheritance of mankind has now become the right to live, and this is the story of the deeds and dreams of certain modern men and women—fighters all—who have faith that this is true.

It cannot be a safe, a Sunday-school, a bedtime history of amusing scientific discoveries by famous searchers now long dead and gone. No, it is the chronicle, seen at first hand by this reporter, of a small part of an adventure that is as portentous as any upon which mankind has embarked since learning to walk upright, since finding out how to tame fire.

The game these fighters for life are playing makes the discoveries of Leeuwenhoek, first of the microbe hunters, seem like a boy's game of marbles. This is true, too, of the adventures of Pasteur and Robert Koch. For the story of today's death-fighting men and women is much more than a saga of achievement inside stuffy laboratories. This tale reports the beginning of man's attempt at the impossible, of his aim not to control, mind you, but to wipe out certain deaths. These have from the beginning of recorded time lain in wait to kill babes in their cradles, to rob children of their mothers, to leave families fatherless. Our fighters for life now have the science to obliterate these miseries, so that at last even history will have forgotten them.

By known science, these deaths are already needless. They are without question preventable. Then why not now begin to wipe them out forever?

That is the high stake for which the men and women of this story—with hesitation, with doubts—have begun to gamble. Those of them with the deepest insight are beginning to

3

realize how stern the game will be. These modern defenders of our right to live are not—like lucky Leeuwenhoek or happy Pasteur—mainly responsible to themselves. Our moderns do not own their science. Nor do the people own the science of those now dedicated to fight for the lives of all. Yet this new adventure upon which our fighters for life are now embarking must be democratic to the limit. It is the people's death fight or it is nothing. And, before the struggle can be engaged, the whole people must be told of it, must understand it, must feel its glorious promise. Having felt it, the people will then fight for the right of their searchers to use their science to give mankind the right to live.

This is the burden of the story. That's why this science can no longer be the cozy hobby that old Antony van Leeuwenhoek made it two hundred and fifty years ago. Compared to these present not-yet-famous-searchers, the great Dutch drygoods-store-keeper was lucky. He was no meddler with the fates of men. He was esteemed to be only a harmless peeper into an amusing new subvisible world, where cute little microscopic animals lived their astounding, silly, insignificant existences. What, in the 17th Century, did Leeuwenhoek's new microbes mean to mankind? Nothing. And so, the supremely sharp-eyed Dutchman could remain simply a discoverer. He did not have to be a fighter. His microbes were merely playthings for the fine gentlemen of the Royal Society of London.

But now today, for our present adventurers, these microbes hold strange, complicated, ominous meanings. Now their deadliness is realized. Now our searchers have found how marvelously this deadliness is controllable, yes, eradicable. Now against their subvisible, mortal sting, life can be promised. Now today this promise—because of human greed and human folly—is denied. And in certain high places it is actually doubted that the defeat of this needless death and suffering will be for the good of men!

So you see, the present history cannot be pretty, and the fighters for our lives will have other enemies than mere miserable deadly microbes and physical disease. For today's inheritors of Leeuwenhoek's great pioneering, these microbes are much more than material for elegant scientific argument, or for the condescending ohs and ahs of fine English gentlemen, and of the intellectual élite of Europe. That is all these microbes were for the Abbate Lazzaro Spallanzani. That fantastic Italian padre took the torch of microbe-hunting from the Dutch trail-blazer. He proved that all microbes must have parents, that every microbe must come from a microbe before it, that the yarn about germs generating spontaneously was a myth, a scientific howler. Yes, all life comes from life!

But what did that deepest biologic truth mean, for Priest Spallanzani? Only that he too was lucky, and could live and die, not frustrated, but reasonably happy, in his ivory tower of science for the sake of science. Proving that all today's life must come from the original life created by God in the beginning, this Spallanzani—underground friend of the impious imp, Voltaire—was on the safe side of an argument that was pretty dangerous in the 18th Century. No inquisition would jail, torture, or burn this experimenting priest for proving that the Pope was right. Nor did anyone at all, in those 18th Century days of the then so hopeful sunrise of science see anything of good or sinister significance for mankind in this highbrow doctrine that microbes must have parents.

Then came Pasteur, the scientific nonpareil, the microbe-hunting one-and-only. He proved to the hilt—it was brilliant if a bit bombastic—that microbes are a menace. That was their one meaning to Pasteur and so he too was lucky. This way you can sum up his happy history: he proved *publicly,* what Spallanzani knew before him: that microbes must have parents. He discovered, and sold the world, what Spallanzani never dreamed of: that certain microbes are a menace to the lives of men. And then, inspired, letting himself go all out, to the highest peak of aspiration yet reached by any human being, Pasteur shouted this battle cry—

"It is in the power of man to make parasitic maladies disappear from the face of the globe, if the doctrine of spontaneous generation [of microbes] is wrong, as I am sure it is!"

If all microbes, including all those murderous to men, must have parents, then let's begin right now to wipe out the vicious forebears and there'll be no more deadly children. It was just that simple. It was true without question. No scientist could gainsay Pasteur's bringing this hope for the lifting of one of mankind's greatest miseries. There is none yet to deny him. So he died with the hoorahs of scientific big shots, statesmen, nabobs of wealth, and the plain anonymous millions ringing in his ears. And now he lies, the first saint of science, in a little chapel in the Institut Pasteur in Paris.

## II

". . . To make parasitic maladies disappear from the face of the globe . . ."

That was the challenge. And you ask was Pasteur's dream, his prophecy, utopic? He himself had the far-ahead-looking insight of genius, and as an experimenter he was uncannily resourceful. Was he a thousand years ahead of his time? Could the absolutely needed technical weapons for this most epic of mankind's wars be fashioned, now, by lesser men?

Without a question they already have been. The forty-two years since the old Frenchman's dying have been a blooming, golden age of death-fighting science. Against that lance-shaped pneumonia microbe first spied by Pasteur, today's doctors and microbe hunters have invented most powerful, life-saving serums. Against it, too, they have forged a fantastic short-wave electric fever. They have discovered, as well, how the little assassin sneaks from man to man. Pasteur would turn over in his tomb with happiness if he could know the power of these weapons. In Pasteur's time there was scientific excitement at the discovery of the TB microbe by Robert Koch. But today our doctors have the use of Roentgen's marvelous magic eye, that can see into the inside of a sick victim's chest before he himself even suspects that he is endangered. And our surgeons then can cure this early consumption, can prevent the waxy TB microbe from spreading its white horrible death to others. Old Robert Koch would growl guttural approval of this death-conquering science. Against the dreadful, life-sapping pestilence of syphilis our lab-men have devised marvelous blood tests. They can spot all those infected; and, with an eerie power of peering into a man or woman's future, they can foretell that in five, or ten, or twenty years this person may be doomed to the madhouse and demented death. Better still, fever, thought to be man's enemy, has now been turned into his friend to forefend this syphilitic madness. And, best of all, our chemists have cooked up cunning chemicals to kill the syphilis microbe in the human body and so prevent its infecting of other men, women, innocent children. Outdoing Leeuwenhoek, Pasteur, and Robert Koch in experimenting wisdom, today's searchers have penetrated into a weird subcellar of life to discover deadly little beings too small for the strongest microscope to see. They have followed the subvisible sneaking of the infantile paralysis virus that maims little children. And, experimentally in their laboratories, they have devised a powerful yet simple chemical blockade that they hope may guard our children's bodies from the attack of this tiny, dastardly marauder. So sure and strong is their science against the streptococcus killing mothers in childbirth that, in the filthiest hovels, thousands of women in succession can bring the world new life without one mother's dying from childbed fever. By a just-discovered chemical death-fight, they can now cure streptococcus infections formerly deadly. Our experimenters are endlessly resourceful; and can prove that plagues once thought to be microbic, like pellagra, are nothing more than slow starvation—

So there's no denying it; our modern searchers have not failed Pasteur, the prophet. Why then are our doctors, healthmen, public health nurses, not right now in full cry to wipe out all deaths that are, beyond scientific doubt, preventable, needless? Why do so many hundreds of thousands go on needlessly dying? Forty years ago there was hope in laboratories, in hospitals, among all death-fighters, that they could quickly take up Pasteur's challenge. What now has damped the fire that Pasteur's own white-hot hatred of suffering and death stirred in his thousands of scientific disciples?

Why do the majority of our present scientific leaders speak carefully, modestly, of *controlling,* instead of wiping out all preventable death and suffering?

Why is the white plague, consumption, though eradicable, now on the upgrade in many of our large cities?

Why does syphilis—which could still more easily be made an evil memory—show no sign of a general down trend?

Why does any American mother at all have to die of preventable childbed fever?

To find the answers to these questions has been for the past three years the duty night and day of this present reporter. The search has taken him into strange places: at midnight into the hovels that are miscalled homes in Chicago's slums; and to the White House to listen to our President's wisdom on the political angles of these tragic enigmas. Stirring days have been spent in a fantastic house of science, part hospital, part engineering laboratory; and here your chronicler has tried to find out why a new gift of life is not more quickly at the disposal of the sick human mass. He has been attentive, too, at scientific conclaves held in magnificent offices of insurance companies. Here he has listened to a little gang of our leading men of science—at their wits' end to keep the flame of possible life-guarding research from flickering out. He has visited great houses of healing, asking poor people smiling weakly, but smiling because they've just been snatched from death, whether they feel good to be alive. He has been present and has taken part in night-long arguments, plottings, plannings, with health commissioners, tuberculosis controllers, surgeons, syphilis-fighters. And the burden of their plaints has been: "We-could-wipe-this-damn-thing-out, if only—" Your reporter has invaded the leaky, ramshackle cabins of share-croppers black and white; he has been awed to observe Negro mothers, aunties, black as night and primitive, at their groping grasping for the rudiments of a simple new science that can now save them and their own from dying—

And from this three-years-long hegira your chronicler has brought back these preliminary answers—

The people, the mass of humanity, do not object to living, to get new strength to go on living. If they only know.

And this, too, is not to be doubted: that our microbe hunters, doctors, healthmen, nurses—if given truly adequate weapons, means for the great new battle—will fight it with a selflessness and an enthusiasm that will make the final victory sure.

### III

What then is the dead hand that holds back our defenders of the new right to live? This reporter began first to get a hint of what it was from his observation of those curious events of the past twenty years, that may properly be called the rise and the fall of pellagra.

A child can understand what causes this sickness and there is no other death that is so simple to prevent. For no other sickness does there exist such a cheap, powerful cure, even in its last desperate stages. Pellagra is starvation. Of all nations we are the greatest shouters about our possible abundance. Our President himself has soothed us, saying that it will be seen to that nobody shall starve, and indeed, that nobody now is starving. What are the facts about this red death that is nothing else but slow hidden hunger?

At the peak of pellagra's raging, in the chicken-in-every-pot days of 1928 and '29, at least seven thousand Americans, yearly, in our Southern States died of this sickness. 1935, which is the last year of record, this preventable and curable plague killed at least three thousand citizens, black and white. And, for every human being dying of it, you can find thirty-five others, miserable, unable to do a decent day's work to eke out what is with a pretty euphemism called their living. So, you see, in 1935, there were more than one hundred thousand inhabitants of our romantic Dixie who were no worse than half-dead. Though about the desirability of this state of existence there is justifiable argument. For, as famed Surgeon Edward Francis of our Public Health Service puts it, "Which man is worse off, the man who has to drag out his life, half-dead, or the man who is dead completely?"

There is, of course, this hopeful angle to this red shame of pellagra: the number dying from it has gone down remarkably since the boom days of the late 1920's. There is this, too, that the men who fight it know: the red hunger may very well return to be a leading killer of lowly southerners, if those boom days come again. But what power of science is it that smashed the pellagra death rate so sensationally, dropped that death rate faster in less time than for any other mortality whatsoever? And why is it that the death-fighters against this sickness, and the southern doctors, and the citizens of the South, are up in arms, right now, to rub out the red death for good and ever? This could be accomplished in a few years' time, no doubt of it.

Why this will almost surely not be done can be understood from the following record of events, random happenings, high opinions that would be truly droll, if they were not such examples of human ignorance and folly.

It was a national disaster that jolted our pellagra-fighting science into action to begin to save the lives of red-rashed, forgotten men and women. This was the Mississippi River flood of 1927 that spread its terror over the cotton-raising Delta region of the South. It drove thousands of hidden, sick, pellagrous wretches—of whose existence our self-satisfied respectable citizens had no idea—out of their miserable cabins into Red Cross camps. So the flood was really a high-powered advertising agent of neglected human misery. So this good disaster put the red horror before the eyes of our volunteer Red Cross workers.

Agonized by the sight of this mass agony, these Red Cross volunteers appealed to Mr. James L. Fieser, the Red Cross Vice-Chairman in Charge of Domestic Operations. What to do? The able veteran manager of disasters called on Dr. William De Kleine, who had just been appointed temporary medical director. And this raw-boned Michigander, tall with a fighting glint in his pale gray eyes and with a kind of Lincolnian homeliness, hurried to the late Dr. Joseph Goldberger, of the United States Public Health Service. De Kleine admitted at the outset that he knew nothing at all about pellagra. And now all that day, in Goldberger's little paper-bestrewn office in the Hygienic Laboratory, the old Red Brick Building on the Hill in Washington, De Kleine sat enthralled by the veteran pellagra fighter.

The brilliant Goldberger, Jewish, wise, gentle, yet the boldest of scientific desperadoes, told a saga of cold fact-finding to De Kleine. Facts that could quickly wipe out this southern death, if only anybody cared about its forlorn victims. But who'd ever given a tinker's damn about them till now? Now that their misery and dying was unconveniently under the feet of our good citizens?

You see, for ten years the Jewish genius had known precisely how to conquer pellagra, had seen his science as forgotten as the very victims whose misery he so well knew how to end. This, to put it bluntly, is what Goldberger had discovered: the difference between southern folks who rot to demented death from pellagra and the folks who never get it is that pellagrins are poor.

Almost invariably. Goldberger, stalking stoop-shouldered, peering, questioning, through southern mill-villages, plantations, asylums, orphanages, superficially prosperous cities, found this drastic difference between the well-off and the poor—

The prosperous eat what the poor can't afford to buy.

Before Goldberger, the orthodox theory was that pellagra was epidemic, catching. But, in an insane asylum where the red death was killing six out of every hundred inmates, our searcher saw that the doctors, orderlies, nurses, never got it! To Goldberger's super-commonsense this fact immediately made the germ theory of pellagra seem fishy. And he stayed there watching, in that asylum, and he saw this: that it was not the sick inmates who got the milk, the nice cuts of meat. Through squalid, feudal mill-villages our doctor prowled. And yes—

Where the red rash on their hands and necks, where the nervous weakness, the gnawing indigestion, sent poor people to demented deaths, there the staff of life was the "3 M's": meat, meal, molasses. It was polite to call it meat. It was white meat but not the white meat of turkeys or chickens. It was sow belly and fat back devoid of lean.

Then, in two Mississippi orphanages, where the youngsters were strangely well-behaved, listless, and gently playful because of pellagra, Goldberger got permission to feed these little ones daily milk and lean meat. Of course the U. S. Public Health Service put up the wherewithal, since this was strictly a scientific experiment and not in any sense a matter of our Government's keeping no-good people alive with public money. Goldberger fed these children. Pellagra vanished. The kids became mischievous, and now were a pleasure to their teachers, who remarked upon their strange new brightness.

But this science of Goldberger's was too simple for many a scientific highbrow, so he answered these doubting Thomases by a human experiment at the Rankin Prison Farm, Mississippi. Feeding nothing but the "3 M's" to sundry embezzlers, rapists, murderers, for months, he gave these volunteers for scientific martyrdom what was, beyond doubt, pellagra. In return they got their freedom. But even now powerful scientific authorities insisted that pellagra was contagious, like typhoid fever. With exact and white hot scientific passion, Goldberger now fed himself—himself alone first of all!—the discharges of dying pellagrins; he injected himself with their excreta, their blood. Then in these latter injection experiments he was joined by his wife, Mary, and by his assistants, by many devil-may-care death-fighters of the Public Health Service, turning themselves into human guinea-pigs.

And no. Pellagra was not contagious.

And yes, a little less mass poverty, a half-dollar-a-day more, for lean meat, for milk, and not very much public money for the workers who could instruct poor southerners, and pellagra would be only an evil memory. This was the story Goldberger told William De Kleine, now worried about thousands of obvious, scandalous pellagrous flood victims. This had all been cold, hard, and utterly impractical fact, for ten years now.

IV

It was just that simple and unattainable. But what, in this 1927 present emergency of flood, could the horrified lay members of the Red Cross chapters do for these forlorn farmers, who'd flocked to the camps, with bleeding hands, with vacant eyes, bedraggled and many of them balmy. More than 50,000 were believed to be pellagrous in the flood area of Mississippi, Arkansas, Tennessee, Louisiana. What can we do *now?* That was what practical public health man De Kleine asked dreamy Joseph Goldberger, who smiled and said:

"Just feed them!"

But William De Kleine was one of America's top practical men in public health activity, knew human beings, and told Goldberger you couldn't, overnight, change the old "3 M's" eating habits of millions of people. Let's be sensible. For Godsake, let's be practical! When the disaster victims had been returned to those sickening shanties called their homes, the Red Cross simply wouldn't have the *money* to go on feeding these myriads lean meat, milk—why, they were luxuries!—and the idea of feeding them was, for our nation, economically unsound, et cetera.

All right, said Goldberger, who smiled, and stayed patient with our harassed Red Cross Medical Director. All right. Don't worry. Don't get excited. Just search out the surely pellagrous people. Then simply feed them brewer's yeast, pure powdered yeast, two teaspoonfuls three times a day, in a little water. You see, years before, Goldberger, though in no sense an economist, had faced his nation's economic unsoundness, its economic incompetence. He was no master of our economists' money mumbo-jumbo. He admitted he was a mere doctor. He couldn't find the fifty cents a day to guard the myriads who, mysteriously (?), went into debt the deeper the more diligently they tilled the soil and the longer hours they slaved at the textile mill spindles. Goldberger was neither a prophet of a spurious plenty nor an economy-howler bellowing for balanced budgets at the expense of human masses; and, being a mere scientist, the Jewish genius retired to his stinking laboratory basement that reeked of sundry dogs he had recently made pellagrous, black-tongued with the "3 M's" diet—

Now bankers, mortgage-foreclosers, planters, mill proprietors, shocked Red Cross volunteers, and sick sharecroppers, here is pure powdered yeast! It doesn't taste very good, mind you. It is bitter. But it costs only 17¢ a pound. It is more powerfully curative, for a sick pellagrin, than the finest food is powerful to prevent your getting sick with it in the first place. Two cents a day per head will save the lives of all those wretches whose present visible agony is a bother to good citizens. Goldberger smiled at De Kleine whose pale gray eyes narrowed and now were gleaming—

Did two cents per head per day for a life seem economically sound? Could America afford it? Could the Red Cross manage it?

De Kleine records that this was the best day of his life, that far. He walked out of Goldberger's scientific den and over to the office of Judge John Barton Payne. He walked out of Payne's office on air, he said, when that gruff Red Cross Chairman gesticulated like a Führer and snapped: "Sold!" to De Kleine's respectful plea for $25,000, for yeast for all, for all threatened in the Delta region. Now, pronto, State Health Officers wired to De Kleine yes of course they'd try the new yeast cure. And now near the town of Marked Tree, Arkansas, Healthman Bill De Kleine leaned down, looking at his first case of pellagra—

With him were Red Cross Nurse Annie Gabriel, and an old country doctor who had forgotten how many people he had seen die of pellagra but who knew mighty well when he was looking at one who had not long to live. Here lay an eighteen-year-old Negro girl. She was a bag of bones at the end of pellagra's final starvation. She could not hold food on her stomach. Her mouth was half-open and her eyes were a blank. Asked questions, she answered with an unintelligible, high-pitched whining. Her neck, arms, feet, were covered with flies feeding on her oozing ulcers, not bandaged.

"You wouldn't mind our trying this yeast, Doctor?" asked De Kleine. Of course not. Why not try anything, so long as

she hadn't more than a week or ten days to live. The old
doctor was tolerant of any remedy, however new-fangled, in
this extremity. And who blames him for his being skeptical,
in view of this yeast's commonness, its simplicity? It had no
jawcracker scientific label. It had been tied up too long with
plain beer and bread. Now followed a teaching of new ultra-
modern, homespun science. Now De Kleine made the dying
girl's mammy, herself, measure out the two spoonfuls of the
yeast powder, then stir it up in an old cup in a little water.
"Mind you do it just that way, Mammy, three times a day,
two spoons three times *every* day, three times."

"Yas, suh, Ah'll see she get it," said Mammy.

And now, at the first try to make her daughter drink it,
there was a retching— It was no go— "All right, now mix up
some more. Just try it again, Mammy—"

So all that day De Kleine, Nurse Gabriel, and the old
country doctor went from cabin to yet more dilapidated
hovel. Was this medical science? They didn't themselves
quite believe in what they did, not even De Kleine, who
trusted and revered Joseph Goldberger. Then De Kleine
crossed the Mississippi to spread this new yeast science further. He left faithful Annie Gabriel to do the follow-ups in
Arkansas, to go back and back to every cabin, to teach, to
cajole the inmates. Then in less than two weeks De Kleine
came back to Marked Tree. To that first cabin he came with
Nurse Gabriel and now the ex-dying girl was sitting up in
bed. Her sores had healed. Her eyes were bright. She was
hungry. Now she could keep down all she ate. Now she was
no longer starving.

No, it wasn't happenstance, this miracle, said matter-of-
fact Annie Gabriel, now bubbling over. It was what was
happening to all of them, all who got this yeast, all were
better, many already out of bed, and working.

This was the first field test, under practical conditions,
under the worst possible scientific surroundings, of a cure as

powerful and as sure as any in death-fighting's history. So De Kleine, the State health officers, doctors, nurses, nutritionists of the Delta region, began their sowing of the seeds of knowledge of this dirt-cheap science. It was the deepest down-to-the-grass-roots mass sowing because only the lowest of the human mass was threatened. Yes, the flood was a good disaster.

But was pellagra conquered by it? Not by a long shot. Simple, powerful as it was to cure, this powdered yeast was not a food. It was a rather disagreeable-smelling, bitter-tasting medicine. Here was the catch in it: let it work its magic cure in six weeks. All right. Feeling new life, the victims would no longer feel the need of this yeast medicine. Then they'd stop taking it. Then, back on their 3 M's diet, they'd again be in danger. And, despite the yeast, in 1928, and 1929, the pellagra death rate kept on rising. Then came the great drouth of 1930, and who could call that a blessing, or say it was in any sense a good disaster? All that late summer and early autumn of 1930, De Kleine, now permanently in charge of the medical affairs of the American Red Cross, went on foot, by automobile, on horseback, through country where no green spear of grass existed, past dead mules and cows gaunt and dying, into cabins from which even the 3 M's were vanishing from the cupboards, into shacks dismal with the dust from blasted fields of cotton. In the hot coppery sunset of one such day, on the way back into Little Rock, Arkansas, De Kleine—tough Dutchman though he was and is—fought to hold back his tears of anger. He had for the first time been face to face with the beginning of mass human starvation.

This was before the New Deal's coming, mind you. This was still in those days when Government head men feared that Government feeding of millions—even though they were famished—might destroy their rugged individualism, their spirit of American independence. And wasn't it better for them to die, still upstanding citizens, than to go on living on a Government dole? It was up to the Red Cross. Never before disappointed in our famed American mercy-in-emergencies, the Red Cross asked the American people for a drouth relief fund of ten million dollars, got five hundred thousand dollars more than the ten million. So the Red Cross mass-fed, that autumn, more than five hundred thousand families, more than two million people. But again, this was only a makeshift against the pellagra of the Delta region of the South.

That terrible year—despite this Red Cross mercy, despite the Red Cross food that was on the whole better than any the sharecroppers got in normal times, despite the yeast, distributed by hundreds of thousands of pounds—nearly seven thousand died of pellagra.

In these desperate days the volunteers of the Red Cross chapters, substantial white collar citizens, again became pellagra-fighters. They became that, not knowing it. Not to fight pellagra, but to stave off actual starvation of the rural southern masses, the men of the Red Cross chapters distributed hundreds of thousands of pounds of garden seeds. They were guided by the Federal and State Departments of Agriculture, and our rulers of those days are to be congratulated on this lapse in their stand for ragged individualism. For shouldn't the starving tenant farmers have found the seeds themselves, and learned for themselves the almost lost art of gardening? You see gardening had become a lost art with many of the sharecroppers and tenant farmers, because, to get the last penny out of the cash-crop, cotton, many planters, landowners—themselves near ruin—forbade their toilers space and time to raise their own garden truck on the soil round their own cabins.

But now the Red Cross helped these gaunt people to put in fall gardens; and the planters co-operated, because they were face-to-face with their toiler's mass starvation, which was more spectacular, more educational to planters, than the chronic, the perennial, submerged, diffused disaster of pellagra. So now, with farm bureau agents directing it, with Red Cross chapters doing the leg-work of distributing seeds, with the Red Cross women, helped by Home Demonstration agents holding canning bees among the farmers, all joined the threatened lowly to fend off their starvation.

So not knowing it they fought pellagra.

For you see, in his laboratory, Joseph Goldberger, helped by G. A. Wheeler, by William H. Sebrell, his associates of the Public Health Service (though none of them were economists), down there among their barking dogs, they had another triumph in their long, humdrum science. On the dogs, made pellagrous by the 3 M's diet, they had tested all available foodstuffs. *In order to find the cheapest food the southern land might grow!* Now here at last was dirt-cheap prevention: kale, collards, mustard greens, green cabbage, tomatoes, eaten regularly—result: no pellagra! Again, it was just that simple.

You see, this was the deadly rhythm of pellagra: it was in the spring with the rising of the sap, the blooming of the magnolias, that the red death always began raging. Because people had no greens to eat all winter. But what to do? Who could expect poor folks, sharecroppers, to buy the fruit jars needed to can their winter pellagra-preventing foodstuffs? Weren't fruit jars—economically unsound? Hold on. Just a moment, said Goldberger. Here were turnip greens. They were most powerful against pellagra. In the South turnip greens will grow all winter. Wouldn't you be willing to live on turnips in the winter so that in the spring you'd not get sick and maybe die?

**v**

Now the drouth was over, with the fall rains that came at last in the late 1930 autumn. Now, 1931, seven years since pellagra had begun its deadly upsurge, by the death records

of the Bureau of the Census, there began an event that was
at first mysterious and not explainable. Pellagra deaths were
no longer on the up. In certain Delta states there was even
a little dropping of the death curve. But how could this be?
For, all over America, there was now a drouth more sinister
than lack of rain: this drouth was the drying up of money,
of the wherewithal which is the blood circulation of the
human mass. Now here in 1931 was mass poverty, at its most
exquisite in American history. So what now, in view of what
had been the time-honored true saying: "Pellagra attaches
itself to poverty as the shadow to the body?"

Yet here in Washington sat Red Cross healthman Bill
De Kleine, scanning the 1931 death records. He saw that
pellagra was nowhere on the upgrade, no. How sad it was
that Joseph Goldberger couldn't have lived to see it. For
De Kleine, roving up and down the southland, could have
given the great Jewish searcher a reason for this apparent
mystery. But Goldberger was dead now. And his best biog-
raphy, terse and bitter, is that written to your chronicler in
a letter by Goldberger's comrade in the Public Health Service, famed microbe hunter Edward Francis—an implacable
truth hunter among American death-fighters—

*"When Goldberger began his pellagra studies, he told me
that for two centuries pellagra had been in the hands of the
school of impressionistic research—which he defined as the
school in which the researcher after turning in his chair and
looking at a long distance out of the window solemnly announced his mature impressions as scientific facts.*

*". . . He said that during the entire reign of the impres-
sionistic school and its bungling science nobody had ever
tried the curative effect of diet alone as the sole factor and
that he proposed to try that one simple experiment.*

*"In that impressionistic school were always the believers
in the ease and frequency of mining pure gold, believers that
the problem was a matter for the brain rather than for the*

*hand and that the intricate processes of refinement were un-
necessary.*

*"Goldberger told me that his own refining process in
pellagra was simple and that the dictum which was to hold
first place in analyzing his results was this: If you get a prom-
ising result once, that is probably due to accident; and if
you get the same result twice, it may be only a coincidence;
but if you get the same result three times, then you have got
proof positive.*

*". . . In regard to the word 'Jew' as applied to Gold-
berger, in all the years from 1903 when I first met him in
Vera Cruz to the morning of his death in January 17th, 1929,
in a room at the Naval Hospital directly across the hall from
my room, I never heard anybody apply that word to him in
a disparaging sense because of personal appearance, personal
traits, scientific greed, scientific inaccuracy, or financial
grasping. . . . The louder his critics spoke, the softer was
his reply. . . .*

*"The Public Health Service paid Goldberger during his
life"* (in nearly thirty years) *"$125,000.00. If scientists were
purchaseable, I would recommend the purchase of forty
Goldbergers in lieu of $5,000,000.00 worth of stone labora-
tory buildings. . . ."*

So Edward Francis in estimate of his dead friend, and so
Goldberger was not now here, in 1931, to observe and to be
stirred, in his peculiar, very quiet, philosophical manner,
about this first recoiling of the red monster, the killer, pellagra, before the blows of his own science in the hands of
the human mass. Yes, deplorable; but truth's immortal; science lives and grows after its discoverers; and now the news
of the life-saving yeast, of the life-guarding gardens, had
spread through the south, not so much by scientific publication, or at learned medical conferences, as by word of mouth
from man to woman and to pickaninnies and poor white
children. It was a grapevine sort of science. It sneaked into

the thoughts of planters, doctors, nurses, Red Cross volunteers, health men. And into the heads of those tenant farmers and sharecroppers who themselves were the human guinea-pigs in this totally unorganized, southwide, mass experiment against pellagra.

There was, to Bill De Kleine investigating it, no question that the ferment of Goldberger's truth, first broadcast by the Red Cross, had begun working. In Sunflower County, Mississippi, a black pellagra spot where, in 1931, as many as 1,313 cases of the red sickness had been reported, that year 890 pounds of yeast had been distributed. Only 331 cases were reported in 1932. In North Carolina, where in 1930 the red death had reached its peak, a vigorous "live-at-home" campaign, a fight for home gardens was fought, for and by the poor farmers. In 1931 the deaths were only two-thirds as many as in 1930. Yet, how could pellagra, southwide, be decreasing? Cotton prices were now going down and down. A map of the Delta region of the State of Mississippi, pictured by learned Howard Odum, showed this correspondence: where the percent of land in cotton, and where the total tenancy was highest, there, too, the red death was by far the most formidable killer. Nobody denies this deadly hook-up. Yet, in Mississippi, between the peak death rate year of 1928 and the peak poverty year of 1932, pellagra deaths had gone down by half, and more!

There is, alas, no scientific explanation that is airtight, that would satisfy such implacable truth masters as Goldberger, and his friend Edward Francis. But, all over the pellagra belt, from Florida to Oklahoma, there had arisen a movement that was not so much an organized death-fight as an upheaval of what might be called social conscience. For a time it seemed as if this concern of the more fortunate few for the less fortunate human mass might be a net gain to transcend the depression's money losses. Then, in the desperate days of the early 1930's, the tenant farmers and share croppers were considered to be human beings by their betters. Were Tennessee farmers too poor to buy fruit jars to can their garden truck? Then women, like Mrs. N. E. Logan, Executive Secretary of the Knox County Red Cross chapter, finagled half-gallon Mason jars, captured by John Law from moonshiners, bootleggers—

Then Mrs. Logan wrote to Red Cross headquarters in Washington—

"It's a tragedy to these people. It's pathetic to see them when we say we can't supply them with yeast. Some cry like babies."

What the Red Cross had so well begun was now taken up by farm and home demonstration agents, and by State and County health departments. Doctor Spencer, of Chatahoula Parish, Louisiana, wrote to Dr. Bill De Kleine—

"There has not been a pellagra death in our parish since dietary benefits were popularized."

This reporter knows of no down-trend of the mass death rate of any human sickness following so swiftly upon any death-fighting discovery as this of Joseph Goldberger. By 1935, South Carolina, Arkansas, could boast of seventy-four percent less pellagra deaths than those occurring in the peak years just before the depression. The drop, for all the South, by 1935 had touched a percentage of sixty! Yet we must not be too prejudiced in favor of truth hunter Joseph Goldberger, nor of this beautiful mass human use of his simple science. Public Health Service Surgeon G. A. Wheeler—he was Goldberger's most tried and true right-hand man from those first days when the great Jew was laughed at—Wheeler predicted this marvelous drop in the death rate. And not because of science, no, but for more mundane reasons.

Wheeler said the pellagra death rate would begin to drop very soon after it began to pay less to grow cotton. When they grew less cotton, they'd grow more greens, to live.

So when, and if, the boom days come again? When the

white fields of cotton in dear old Dixie begin to grow again right up to the doors of the shabby cabins of the share-croppers—what then?

That is why Surgeon Wheeler, and Edward Francis so zealous for the fame, for the universal coming-true of his comrade Goldberger's science, both of them insisted that a smashing demonstration was now demanded. An Exhibit A, as Francis puts it, to show America that, in a given area, not a single case of the red sickness need exist, nor any single human being need die of it, for a period of so many years. Independently of the Public Health Service men, De Kleine had dreamed this same demonstration; and it was maybe the innocent notion of all of them that, if you could show America a region absolutely free of the red death, the rest of the South, of America, would then be ashamed to allow pellagra to go on raging!

## VI

This May, 1937, your chronicler was present at a little council of war to plot this scheme. De Kleine was there, and Sebrell, now Goldberger's successor in the Public Health Service. The State Health Officers of Tennessee and Arkansas were present, and the State Epidemiologist of Mississippi. Battle plans were laid for a giant demonstration that pellagra could be liquidated, completely, in the then worst pellagra county existing in each of these three states. For these powerful Exhibits A, the Red Cross was prepared to furnish funds and the morning was memorable because there was here planned a new, democratic kind of death-fight. There were to be adequate technical experts, yes, but these were to be aided by men and women lay volunteers, from the Red Cross chapters, PTA's, and women's clubs. The farm and home demonstration agencies were to co-work with all. Plain citizens—non-medical—were to make a house-to-house dragnet to search out every single case of pellagra in each of the counties in question. This dragnet, supervised, of course, by

nurses, doctors, was to put all those threatened instantly
under doctor's care, with yeast free for all in danger. And,
more basic: to prevent it—where no gardens: gardens. It was
a lovely blueprint for a new kind of war for life for the lowly.

Budgeted, the cost of this enterprise turned out to be low.
Aside from the pay and travel allowances of U. S. Public
Health Service experts who'd direct the battle, not more
than $6,000 yearly was estimated to be needed to wipe the
red shame out of the worst county. So the conference of
May 6, 1937, adjourned, with all enthusiastic. And next
morning we left Memphis, early, by motor to survey Sunflower County—supposed the blackest pellagra spot remaining in Mississippi. This was where over thirteen hundred
had been found pellagrous in 1931, and though the sickness
had been since that on the downgrade, yet the number suffering in 1935 was formidable. And now?

And now, alas for our plans, where was pellagra? All that
day in May we drove well over three hundred miles, from
town to town, from plantation to plantation, from cabin to
cabin, looking for pellagra. From 1931 to 1936, in Sunflower
County, it is true that pellagra deaths had gone down nine-
fold. There had been only three deaths in all in 1936. Indeed, the sickness had become so no-account that it was not
mentioned as a public health menace in County Health
Officer Hugh Cottrell's report for 1936. Yet this was May,
next to the peak month for the sickness, which was June—

That day we talked to many citizens and folks whose
citizenship is still, in the South, not even a pretense. Did the
Negro sharecroppers know about pellagra? Oh, yas, suh, we
know pellagacy. Did they know about yeast? In leaky cabin
after ramshackle shanty the dark people, mammies, aunties,
told how 'east was mighty good for the pellagacy. And
gardens? It was astounding to find so few cabins without
their fenced-in patch of green. Here was Aunt Lyra, in her
garden patch on a big plantation near Indianola. Yas, suh,

she'd had the pellagacy. Not no more. She squinted at her rows of green stuff. She said: "If Ah hadn't been doin' what Ah done heah, by this time Ah guess Ah done would've been all et up an' daid!" Then she chuckled appreciation of this simple method of survival.

That day, as the sun was setting, our search ended, by our finding one case of the sickness, unmistakable, red on the hands of a white tenant farmer.

What were the basic reasons for this spectacular decline, almost to the vanishing point, of the once deadly sickness? Was the only reason the cynical one, advanced by Goldberger's veteran helper, G. A. Wheeler? Was it only because, when the price of cotton went down, the croppers would just naturally grow more greens to live, or more accurately, to exist? This was part of it, the local experts agreed, but not all. Able State Epidemiologist, H. C. Ricks, and County Health Officer Hugh Cottrell, and Public Health Nurse Jordan, all pointed to an additional explanation of the mystery. And planters, and yes the black sharecroppers themselves, agreed unanimously—

It was a simple business of bookkeeping, of down to earth arithmetic—

If you spent a few dollars for seeds and some hours of time at your garden, then you'd likely save many times that money, in doctor bills, in days of work you'd otherwise lose, if you took sick with pellagra!

Here was a homespun economics dawning, beginning to be understood, and in this instance applied. It was maybe a cold and heartless motive for mankind's war against death and misery. But they were beginning to get it through their heads that pellagra was bad business, in the literal sense of the word business. Yes, no doubt of it, if we could only find enough of this pellagra to make our demonstration spectacular, the planters would co-operate.

They would be for it, explained Doctor Ricks—"because your planter wants his nigger to work."

Does that mean that the red shame has been conquered? No. The threats of its murderous return are several. The Federal Relief agencies, which, following the pioneering by the Red Cross, did so much to feed the poor southern people, to teach them life-guarding food habits, to teach them gardening—these agencies are now under savage attack by our budget-balancers. They are leading a hand-to-mouth existence. And there is no doubt that, to get gardening down deep into the habits of all poor southern people, you've got to subject them to a long education. Now it seems that we can no longer afford the educators. And, if war comes again, or if for some other reason there comes an idiotic boom in the prices of cotton, tobacco— What then will become of the life-guarding gardens round the sharecroppers' cabins?

But these are dark imaginings and to hell with them, for that day, May 7, 1937, in Sunflower County, Mississippi, will remain in this chronicler's memory as an experience that was most eerie. Because it was more than this vanishing of pellagra that we observed that day, for Hugh Cottrell and his nurses were bringing the supreme power of science to bear upon many another misery and death of the southland's lowly. In the Negro church at Inverness, Mississippi, we saw rows of cleanly clad Negro mothers, with their pickaninnies very clean, bright-eyed, and quiet, sitting waiting on the church benches. They were this morning participants in a service that was—to this reporter—prophetic of the religion of mankind's future. Here was a scientific maternal health clinic. Here these Negro mothers came, from far and wide in that deep south county, to learn how to care for themselves before their babies came. And then they were here taught, too, the latest in the science of the feeding of their children, in little words that all could understand. They came, eager to have keen young Doctor Cottrell and his competent nurses give their youngsters diphtheria toxoid, and smallpox and typhoid vaccination. Tiny pickaninnies, born syphilitic, here had benefit of curative treatment. Now this is worth remarking: that there was something the opposite of condescending or paternalistic in the atmosphere of that church clinic. Cottrell and his nurses, white people, highly educated, were exactly like older brothers and sisters teaching the great power of science—not the book knowledge of it but the actual use of it—to these childlike dark mothers. And this is worth remembering: it was plain that these present descendants of a people, benighted and savage two hundred years ago, were now beginning to understand this new magic, and to depend upon its life-giving power.

This is worth asking: Why was there this evident comradeship between these two classes of humanity, the one high and scientific, the other ignorant and lowly? Was it because these young southern death-fighters were prophetic of humanity of the future, because they were not working under need of making profit by fighting human misery, because there was absolutely nothing pecuniary between them and these humble people, because they were in no sense exploiting those who were suffering?

Was this comradeship so strong because these young defenders of the right to life were paid their modest stipends for one reason—

To give these dark people a hand up, a friendly boost up, to a new, a slightly less dangerous, less painful, less miserable, way of living?

Your chronicler does not answer these questions. But this he knows: that here was a picture of the simple power of science being understood and acted upon by people just emerging from ignorance and superstition. To him for the first time it was plain how the power of science can and will make mankind brothers.

## VII

If this is true for the future, then what is it now that holds back the early victory of our defenders of the right to live?

What frustrates their science is a new spirit that is beginning to spread among American citizens of the upper brackets. For this is the tragedy: at the moment the mass of mankind begins to reach out for this life-saving science, the rulers and owners of the people begin to fear science, and even deny it.

When your reporter met the first symptoms of this foolish fear, he was inclined to dismiss them as no-account, exceptional. He laughed at this cynicism about science because it first began to be uttered by toy philosophers, intellectuals.

One of these—a writer famous in highbrow households—is reported to have been anything but thrilled by this news of the South's possible salvation from pellagra—

"No, I'll not say I'm in favor of shooting all the sharecroppers, but I see no sound reason why they shouldn't be allowed to starve to death." This was the comment of that decadent parlor oracle.

You say this wisecrack is not seriously intended, or that it is meant only to mitigate the tax-burden of the do-gooding that oppresses this intellectual—who is also a minor capitalist? No, for this reporter is now encountering more and more serious people—two years ago you would have called them people of goodwill—who now question and even deny the right of mankind to live. It used to be your chronicler's custom to regale his friends with just-observed events of the death-fight. They used to be interested, sometimes stirred by these triumphs. Now many of them become inattentive, and ask strange questions—

"But can you really *do* anything for such people?" asked one well-circumstanced mother of several children, after the story of the sharecroppers' fight against pellagra.

"Wouldn't it have been better simply to have given that baby something out of the black bottle?" asked another woman, herself the best of mothers, and scientifically learned. This was her comment on her own account of a famous surgeon. He had left a dinner party to go to try to save a dying pickaninny, who was the maybe not-wanted and the youngest of a poor family of too many Negro children.

But you say that these ex-women-of-goodwill are not influential? How can their new found fear of life have any effect upon the work of our defenders of the right to live? Their husbands, while prosperous, are only professional men, not rulers, not owners of the means of livelihood of the people. Granted. But to get a glimpse of the spirit of those who are the true determiners of life or death for the people, attend to this experience of our Secretary of Agriculture, Henry A. Wallace. To the Honorable Secretary, this reporter had conveyed the news of the new triumph against the red death, pellagra. Wallace was stirred by it. He was proud of his own department's part in it. He told the great triumph of science over death to a wealthy northern businessman, who was one of the undoubted arbiters of the lives of the people—

"His rather sarcastic comment," said the Honorable Secretary, "was that scientific triumphs of this sort *merely meant the saving of more human lives* * and that there were already too many human beings in proportion to the soil and other natural resources in the South."

This is now the deadly challenge to the science that, only a few years ago, was acclaimed as mankind's deliverer.

For if pellagra has rid the South of its now too many people, then shouldn't tuberculosis, syphilis, mortality of mothers, indeed every kind of preventable death, be allowed to go on raging throughout America?

Now our defenders of the right to live must face it; the people themselves must look this fact in the eye: that it is

* Italics this writer's.

becoming of less and less avail to appeal to the formerly
vaguely humane sentiments of those who rule and own us.
They are afraid now. And where fear enters, as it has into
so many households of the owning class and their satellites,
there sweet charity flies out the window.

But what do they fear? Why are our economic feudalists,
their well-paid henchmen, these henchmen's ladies, frightened of new life, longer life, more strength for the human
mass?

### VIII

So that he may not be accused of allowing his prejudices
in favor of the right of the underdogs to live to give the
answer, this chronicler turns to the mature thoughts of one
of the most hard-boiled of America's biologists.

He is a searcher, one of whose delights is to squirt streams
of ice-water upon the alleged life-saving exploits of many
of our death-fighters. His exposure of maybe too-easy explanations of why human life grows longer has made him
anything but popular among the rank and file of our healthmen. He distrusts half-baked expectations of humanity's
rapid uplift to a better life. Of all pretentious do-gooding he
is the implacable enemy. He has many times denounced this
present chronicler's enthusiasm for life for mankind's mass.
His criticisms have been biting, and hard to bear.

This philosopher of science, this pioneer in the biology of
human beings, is Raymond Pearl; and his devotion to truth
for truth's sake must be respected. He puts his finger upon
the true cause of the fears of those who are now getting ready
to deny life to the people. The fear is that the number of
the have-nots is beginning to get too great for the comfort
of the haves. Mind you, he does not so state it, but he
sketches a terrifying picture of the recent awesome increase
in human numbers.

"On a rough estimate," says Pearl, "there are probably
upwards of 300 billion pounds of human protoplasm in its

various forms busily engaged in living on this earthly globe, while there were probably not over 100 billions similarly occupied in 1837."

In short, in one hundred years three times as much living human bone, brain, fat, and muscle—

It appears that this sudden, tremendous spurt in the multiplying of humans is, so far as science knows, unprecedented. For maybe five hundred thousand years that mankind has occupied the earth, his rate of increase was slow. Then, mid-17th Century began an increase that was astounding; then, bang, the population curve began shooting almost straight upward.

Why? What, in terms of science, is the cause of it? The scientific cause of it is science itself.

Formerly among the weakest, most miserably equipped, physically, of the earth's inhabitants, Doctor Pearl tells how mankind has become, by science, by far the strongest. This is at the bottom of man's great leap ahead in numbers: that his machines have made him—on land, in the air, and on the surface of the water—by far the fastest and most powerful of all the earth's creatures. Now, by science, he can see through thick walls. He can look past the moon. He can talk in low voice and be understood at the four corners of the earth. He can hear a fly's gentle footfall. To his formerly feeble hands he has attached giant steam-shovels, the tractor, the combine. And his new chemistry has caused three ears of wheat to flourish where one grew before.

These machines, this science, have actually become a part of man's brain, his eyes, his ears, his muscles; and it is this science alone that has given him the chance, yes, has compelled man riotously to increase his numbers.

Now the owners of the mass of men feel the upsurge of the mass from below, and fear it, and does not science justify this terror?

Yes, partly; yes, maybe. There are records, Doctor Pearl

points out, prehistoric, dug out of sands and rocks and the bowels of the earth. They tell how, when other species of animals have for a time become strongest, most cunning, when they then have multiplied out of all proportion, it was then that these now forgotten ancients began to ride for a fall.

But should we then smash our machines, and stop researching? Or try foolishly to limit the benefits of science to those temporary aristocrats of the upper brackets?

Our distinguished biologist does not believe it. In what he calls the great Symphony of Life, the dominating music, the main theme is the urge, says Pearl, to personal, individual survival, here and now.

But does that now demand—in the face of mankind's teeming increase—that our wealthy businessman, our frightened ladies, should wish the death of myriads by denying them the right to live that science can give them? Against the pressure of clamoring populations, have the rulers and owners of the mass no other resource but this urge of I-for-mine-and-the-devil-take-the-hindmost?

Our eminent biologist explains how mankind—evolving—has surmounted this murderous necessity. Of course your own urge to survive is selfish. But the simple selfishness of the pig at the trough and the mother duck for her own brood of ducklings is right now being transformed into another kind of self-interest—enlightened. Let Doctor Pearl explain it—

"This is a belief, that for the present and until times get much worse, it will be likely to conduce more effectively to individual survival to play along with and help one's neighbors in the crowd."

Already, says our biologist, this new urge begins to overwhelm and obliterate the purely piggish urge of I-for-me. And this, your present chronicler has found, is most true among the masses of the lowly. Lest again he be accused of prejudice, let the late John D. Rockefeller, himself, bear witness—

"Probably the most generous people in the world are the very poor, who assume each other's burdens in the crises which come so often to the hard-pressed." So wrote that pious man.

And in the ranks of the masses of mankind's lowly there is a muttering, the yet indistinct rumbling growl of a new urge to mass-survival. This has been caught by the ear of writer John Steinbeck, who makes a humble worker say—

"There ain't nothing separate. Guys think they want something soft for themselves, but they can't without everybody gets it."

So a biologist, a capitalist, and a literary artist agree that the human mass is committed to we-for-ours. Does this justify the fears of those who believe that there are now already too many people for our earth to maintain—in comfort?

Doctor Pearl himself is amused at this bogey of a physical overcrowding of mankind. He points out that, even in spite of our lusty increase, there are yet only forty people to the square mile of the earth's surface; and that, if all existing living human beings were confined upon the continent of Australia, there would be well over an acre of land there for every person.

But let's grant that should a new economic order prevail on the earth, so that science would be universally unleashed in all its power, to feed, to clothe, to house, to guard the life of all mankind—let's admit that there then might occur a yet more colossal multiplication. Would we then have to prohibit by law the death-fighting adventures of our defenders of the right to live?

Doctor Pearl does not deem that such drastic measures would be necessary. If our science makes us too lusty, if our death-fighters begin to save too many, there is already at hand a counter-science that can meet the situation without letting poor devils die who do not need to.

The effects of birth control on the birth rate, says Doctor Pearl, are already plainly apparent over large and leading parts of the world's population.

We do not have to defend the efforts of our death-fighters. We do not have to apologize for their fighting the death of the least of human beings.

Now the ground is cleared for this chronicle of the fight against the death of mothers, against the maiming death of infantile paralysis, and the story of the new wars to wipe out tuberculosis and syphilis. What is the chance for victory in a nation organized for profit, not for life?

*Part One*

THE FIGHT FOR LIFE'S BEGINNING

## CHAPTER ONE

# FUNDAMENTAL TO LIFE OF MOTHERS

O F course the fight for life must start at life's beginning; and what have our searchers discovered to lift the pain and danger from childbirth, to save the lives of mothers, and let them bear their babies alive and strong?

The fighter for life who has guided your chronicler in this inquiry is Joseph B. De Lee. He is a lone wolf, a hater of death, a fighter for the lives of women who give the world new life. It can be truly said that this sums up his forty-five years of working.

Surely there is in life no more incessant need for vigilance of our death-fighters: every fourteen seconds in the light and dark of each day of all the year—in our country—some woman, somewhere, faces this ordeal that is of all human experiences most fundamental. In all the fight against death and pain few triumphs have been more stirring than those to guard women in their travail to give their babies life's good morning.

De Lee, that strange ascetic, whose wife has been the art and science of obstetrics, whose one love has been helping women not to die, has shown this reporter it is right here that science can best learn to be powerful for all women. But to effect this there is no doubt that strange and shameful secrets must be smoked out. And De Lee, kindly, gray-bearded, dark-eyed—a sort of condensation of what you think all doctors ought to be—is of all medical men most forthright about the failure of today's birth-helping science to guarantee to women their right to live.

More than fifteen thousand mothers die every year in our

country with childbirth the direct cause of their death. De Lee has made himself an annoyance by reminding the medical profession of this curious situation. He says, too, that the English physician, Blair Bell, may not be far off the track in calculating that at least a like number of mothers die from childbirth's remote consequences. These facts and calculations are not generally spread by our doctors, not to the public, not to the mothers. De Lee has kept asking—for forty years and more—how much of this mortality is needless.

This man—so stern yet gentle—has written a book of the art and science of obstetrics. This tells how—besides our annual holocaust of American mothers—more than eighty-five thousand babies lose their lives a-borning. Is this waste of life inexorable? Or could De Lee and our many able birth-helpers teach our physicians how to prevent the majority of these from dying? You may feel that, since two million and more babies are born every year, and only maybe thirty thousand mothers die as their reward, this amount of mortality should be charged up to profit and loss on life's ledger. De Lee is fanatic against such resignation.

He points out how death is by no means all the hell that women suffer in return for giving the world new life. By lectures, by marvelous movies, by writing, he gives you cause to wonder why it is—in our present state of obstetric art and science—that countless thousands of healthy women each year must begin lifelong invalidism, wretchedness. It often is of a degree that would have made their death in child-bed more merciful. Then too, there is this question to ponder: what is it that brings children, perfect in their mothers' wombs, into the world by many thousands yearly—to begin lives maimed, sightless, and, yes, bereft of reason?

Your chronicler has asked this relentless death-hater, De Lee, whether all these horrid events are due to a fate against which our fighters for life are powerless.

To these questions De Lee's answers are simple and not

debatable. He says that most of this suffering and death is now needless. He not only says it; he has proved that the overwhelming majority of mothers who die now do not have to. He is blunt about it. And this honesty is as embarrassing (to certain doctors and all others indifferent to mothers dying) as his science is subtle and indomitable. He is partial —on the side of the suffering mothers. He has prejudices— on the side of maimed and butchered babies. His work has been a lonely joy to him and he is the living example of this: that if you love life for yourself it is difficult to be tolerant of death for others.

## II

De Lee is fair. He is the first to say hoorah for the many obscure American doctors who—skillful and conscientious— have brought a thousand or more babies without death to a single mother. He is enthusiastic about the Frontier Nursing Service in Kentucky where nurse midwives—without benefit of doctors—bring babies with a death-free record the most eminent physician would envy. But why does this good art and science have to exist side-by-side with an incompetence and bungling that is not far short of murder?

He keeps reiterating the scandalous news that, in the past twenty-five years, 375,000 of our women are known to have died to bring the world new life. This is a number greater than that of all the men killed in all our wars since the Declaration of Independence. It is his merit that he does not oh and ah about such statistics of mass horror and then forget about them. Maybe this is because he has so many thousands of times seen the terror of complicated childbirth, its bloodshed, its cries of agony, so that he has been shaken to the marrow, so that he could hardly bear to look on any longer. Then he has too often seen the contrast of this awfulness transformed by the coming of the baby that, just-born, comically wrinkles its face in its first bawl of protest at having to leave the coziness of its mother. Then he has

watched the smile on the face of the mother at the cry of
the child she has risked her own life to bear. Presiding as he
has at so many thousands of these human dramas, and being
himself so human, it is not surprising that he has resolved it
shall begin to be the right of every last mother to have the
right to all the gentle power of all the science of life's good
morning.

Our good professor of obstetrics does not believe that this
killing of mothers and butchering of babies is in any way
intentional or malignant. He knows the murder is thanks to
ignorance, nothing more. What keeps so much of the now
available powerful science from so many hundreds of thousands of women is the notion that there is no need to use
it—and this is common among the people as well as their
physicians. While tuberculosis, diphtheria, are universally
feared as mortal sicknesses, having a baby is generally (and
foolishly) considered to be a normal, a natural, activity of
women. Like going to sleep or breathing—

Though he is by no means the first to have detected the
error of this notion, it is the merit of De Lee that, for forty
years, he has exposed it with fury. How, indeed, he asks, can
you call this event normal when it results in the wound-
ing, the tearing, of their delicate tissues—in the majority of
civilized women—of those passages through which their
babies must come to see the light or day? And even the nine
months of preparation for this so dubiously blessed event is
often one long sickness. What woman who has suffered the
nausea and vomiting of pregnancy can think of this as normal? What chemist, finding dangerous changes in the blood
of expectant mothers, can call these natural? What microbe
hunter can call a woman who is to have a baby healthy—
when he detects the lowering of her resistance to infections?

No, De Lee faces this fact: that if childbearing ever was
normal, much of it, most of it, has now become pathological.
How can modern childbearing be anything but profoundly

unnatural, he asks, when half of all modern women who have had children bear the marks of injury from their ordeal and will sooner or later in some degree suffer from the consequences of childbirth?

It is now clear that human reproduction should take rank as a dangerous sickness and old French Doctor François Mauriçeau was not far wrong when he wrote that pregnancy is a disease of nine months' duration. And if this brooding time is a sickness, then its culmination is often terrifying, and even more dangerous to the baby than its mother. For many infants are killed and maimed by the powerful forces of *natural* labor. De Lee makes it plain—and there is nobody to refute him!—that there is no specialty in the art and science of doctoring that demands such complicated, diversified knowledge—of diagnosis, of blood chemistry, of the art of giving anesthetics, of microbe hunting, of psychology, of the boldest wielding of the surgeon's knife in emergency.

Today, for any mother to be reasonably sure that her travail will be safe to herself and her baby, it is demanded she should be under care of a specialist in birth-helping, or at least attended by a physician who has such a specialist at his instant beck and call. And today, in America, what have you?

You have the situation that this highest of the medical arts and sciences has the lowest position in most of the medical colleges in America. So it comes about that these colleges turn out doctors who, though they may have good bedside manners, as birth-helpers can hardly be better than bunglers. And who can blame them, since they have been taught that childbirth is only normal, only natural?

You have this condition: that the responsibility of bringing babies is still permitted to remain in the hands of old neighbor women, and of untrained midwives. And how much more able than these, really, is your downy recent medical graduate who admits that he has delivered just one baby before getting his license to practice? Or those thousands of busy family doctors who still deliver the bulk of America's babies—physicians who have neither the time nor the wherewithal to go back to study the stern science of this dangerous illness of childbearing?

Women are civilized now. Most of them are no longer natural. Then is it a wonder that so much of their childbearing cannot be normal?

### III

Of course there are cynics who say no to life, who will prove that the fight for life is foolish, who will laugh at De Lee's faith that birth-helping deserves the first place, the highest dignity, of all the life-saving arts and sciences. They may ask, what, indeed, *is* normal in this business of life's perpetuation? In the long history of all living things, haven't parents served their purpose when they have sired their offspring? Among insects it is actually the rule for the female to die soon after she has reproduced her kind. The male bee is murdered by his act of fatherhood. The salmon perishes after spawning. Many cows, sheep, horses, suffer injury in the blessed event of giving life to their young—

To these no-sayers De Lee can answer by biology that is just as basic: for, if there is one thing that sets off human beings from bugs, beetles, and all other beasts whatsoever, it is this—

That human beings can take thought, that they are now beginning to escape from the inexorable, the deadly limit that nature has imposed upon the lives of all other living creatures.

This is the one fact that is fundamental to all the fight for life. De Lee knows deep down in him that no human misery or wretchedness is natural, that it cannot be allowed to remain tolerable. This is the religion of mankind's modern fight for life.

Yet, so subtle a human biologist is De Lee that he knows the pain, the misery, the death, that now afflict us because—arrogant with our young science—we've tried to go too fast away from and beyond our animal nature that's as old as life itself. Because we have been warped, weakened, as animals by that half-healthy condition called civilization.

For many years De Lee has denounced the pseudo-science that promises to make childbearing quick and easy among women for whom the dubious legacy of civilization has made it difficult and full of danger. Of course there's no doubt that women do exist among us for whom their travail is hardly to be called labor because their babies come so easily. And there are still many mothers whose babies come so quickly that their safe arrival soon drowns the memory of their short pain. De Lee has pondered this scientific riddle. He has found a hint of the explanation of it in the little-known observations of the English physician, Grantly Dick Read.

For help for civilized women Doctor Read went to savage ladies, for instruction in his birth-helping science. He believes that, among highly cultured women ten thousand years this side of barbarism, their childbirth can largely be freed —without anesthetics!—from its pain and the danger of death that then so often follows this agony. Among English women this birth-helper has found many—so he reports— for whom he has made childbirth a joy, stern it's true, but with its pain not unbearable. He imported this new science to England from the primitive women of the South Sea Islands, China, and Japan.

Doctor Read records how he witnessed the event of the coming of her baby to a native girl in the subtropics. Knowing that her time was arriving, Read saw this girl walk alone toward the undergrowth on the edge of her village. He followed her. It was permitted, it was no violation of the tribe's manners or decorum because the people of this village knew Read as "The Doctor." He sat near her, smoking his pipe, not trying to talk to her but just watching her half sitting, half lying down. The waves of her womb's contractions, plainly to be seen over her body, were much more violent than those common among European or American women—

Yet you could hardly call them "pains." The girl's face showed no pain or fear. She did look sternly expectant. She was working, yes. And now, in a very little while the head of her child appeared, and she smiled to herself, not noticing the doctor. Now in a few minutes more the child was lying there, kicking, bawling lustily. The cord from it to its mother was quickly white and free from blood. Now the girl severed the life-line with her fingers. She wrapped the baby in the cloth she'd worn round her shoulders. Then she looked at Doctor Read, and laughed.

That was the foundation of his fear-conquering science. He thought of the terror and pain that's so much a part of civilized childbirth, and of the fatal bleeding of the mothers, and of the blue babies that will not breathe, and of the wombs of women failing to contract, to close down after they have had their babies. He recalled the agony of fear he had seen so often. It was a terror the equal of that of English boys he had seen shell-shocked in the War. He looked at the native girl again. He knew he had never seen such joy, such pride and tenderness as this that lighted her face at the first cry of her child.

What was it that made it so—let's say, not terrible? It was the absence of the fiend of fear—or so Read believes—that makes the coming of a baby to a savage woman a stern work, yes, yet all but painless. Your savage woman grows up in a life where from babyhood she is trained to meet hunger, where she's got to be tough against hardship and all kinds of pain, where human life is cheapest and where she's never far from the threat of death. But for the most civilized mothers the travail of the coming of their first babies is usually the first fundamental event of life that they cannot put off on to others, from which they cannot run away. These civilized ladies, by their own mothers, by their women friends, are showered with "Oh-you-poor-darling" sympathy. Our girls meeting this first bringing of new life have their brains—they not realizing it!—soaked with yarns of an impending awfulness.

And what can this do but pull the trigger, at the time of final crisis, to stir that most powerful of all human instincts: fear. And it is this fear, exploding in the brain cells, that sends powerful waves of nerve-energy down to the sympathetic nerves leading to the muscles of the womb. These are the muscles that work not when you will them to but willy-nilly. They are the muscles that hold back, that hinder the work of expelling the baby that the womb must do. And this —or so Read believes—is at the bottom of childbed's pain. So Doctor Read now treats the minds of civilized women who are expecting babies. Before their ordeal begins, yes, at the beginning of their pregnancy, he begins to set up brain barriers, thoughts against these fears. Then, when at last their travail has started, he still further builds up his women's courage. He obliterates the fear reflex by telling the laboring woman how she soon will have the reward of hearing her baby's first cry.

This, so says Grantly Dick Read, is more powerful than any anesthetic that has ever been discovered—and safer. And there is no question that our English birth-helper's new art has the backing of the science of the Russian, Ivan Pavlov. It was in the evening of his life that this Pasteur of the human brain and heart discovered fear to be the most fundamental of all the instincts, the basic reflexes. It was then, too, that Pavlov showed how fear can be conditioned out of animals, of people, in short—how it can be conquered.

But today, alas, in the opinion of De Lee, this hopeful new art must be called an art of the future. For our mothers who must have their babies now, Grantly Dick Read is a lonely pioneer in this new knowledge that a woman's brain is of an importance at least equal to that of her body. De Lee says there is no doubt that this English trail-blazer has proved you can bring some civilized women back to the fearless naturalness of savages. De Lee himself has practiced it, and has accomplished it. And this chronicler has seen its power, as he watched De Lee's band of young birth-helpers bringing babies—with a never before heard-of safety!—to the poor women in Chicago's dingy hovels.

Yet this science is new, and it would be interesting to take a census of the skilled obstetricians of America who have so much as heard of this English pioneer, let alone attempting to use this safest of all anesthetics. De Lee asks whether this fear is, all of it, implanted in civilized women by their oh-you-poor-darling mothers and companions. Hasn't it become hereditary, hasn't it become part of the very brain-stuff of women no longer savage? And won't it take generations of a new life, of a new sort of civilized savagery let's call it, to correct this defect that has existed in civilized women since before the Bible was written?

## IV

De Lee does not wait for a utopia of fearless mothers. He has dug into the present available science of life's beginning to test and weigh all it now promises against this curse of childbed's pain. It is astounding how short a time our doctors have been at the job of even trying to fight this ages-old horror. "In sorrow shalt thou bring forth thy children." That was the Bible's dictum, that was its cruel science. And when you ponder the agonies of uncounted millions of mothers who have had to bear that last supreme example of man's inhumanity to woman, that science made no recorded effort—in all history—to still that pain till 1847.

Is it that, till these past one hundred years, humankind was so bad-hearted that even its best medical men wanted to see women tortured? No. There is a sounder explanation for their wait for the soothing of childbirth's pain. Till past the Middle Ages, men, physicians, were not allowed at childbed's side while women had their babies. As a last resort, doctors were called in only when the labor was most difficult, when the baby wouldn't come at all, when mothers were about to die from pain and exhaustion. Then the ministrations of these physicians, their obstetrical science if you want to call it science, consisted in using long sharp hooks to pull a mutilated baby from its mother who would then almost surely die. Even so, religion demanded that mothers be considered secondary to their unborn children.

When their travail was hard, they were tied down and jumped upon to shake the baby from its place. Or, to hasten childbirth, the childbed was lifted up and then let down, wham, upon the floor. Until at last, the obstetrical forceps were invented, and that began the turning of birth-helping into a respectable art, into a new kind of surgery. So that, at last, shortly after 9 o'clock on the evening of January 19, 1847, a Scottish doctor, James Y. Simpson—his face beamed like a full moon from the middle of a funny encircling fringe of beard—gave the first recorded whiff of pain-killing ether to a woman in her last extreme of agony.

She was one of those unfortunates whose pelvis was so deformed that, when her first baby wanted to be born, its head had to be crushed before the child could be taken from her. Now, against her doctor's advice, she had risked the coming of a second child. Now again it was no go. Again it was unbearable. So that our full-moon-faced Scotchman Simpson made bold to hold an ether-soaked handkerchief over her face at the moment of that recurring hell of her pain.

There was a sigh—could there be a sound more wonderful? —and then, oblivion. There a hitherto unheard-of nirvana. And then Simpson reached in and turned that

baby's body inside the mother's womb without her ever
knowing, and now here at last was the baby, born, and gasping. "She quickly regained consciousness—and talked with
gratitude and wonderment of her delivery—and of her not
feeling the pains of it," wrote James Y. Simpson.

Before he tried it he had had nights of doubts and worry.
Would the pain-killing power of ether, would its sleep-
producing magic, kill the womb's work as well? Now Simpson tested this new pain-killer upon woman after tortured
woman. He worked in an entranced enthusiasm. Then, with
never a doubt, he published his discovery, he told the
world: "Physical suffering is annulled, but the needed mus-
cular contractions are not interfered with—" Or so he believed. And he reported upon identical miracles wrought
upon one hundred and fifty women, with no damage to
mother or baby!

Now there arose a hue and cry, first from eminent divines.
They, of course, not themselves able to have babies, found
it hard to understand the annoyance that mothers suffered.
What about the Bible's dictums? What about the primeval
curse? What about: "In sorrow shalt thou bring forth thy
children." But James Y. Simpson was not a Scot for nothing.
Though professionally a doctor he was—like most Scots—
a stout theological argufier. He shouted that the word "sorrow" was a bungling translation of the original Hebrew.
He confounded the dominies by expostulating that, if to
abolish childbirth's pain was wicked, then the whole art and
science of medicine must be abandoned! For, in the primeval
curse of Adam, was not man doomed to die? Then he tossed
a final theologic bomb among the reverends: Wasn't it ex-
traordinary, under the Christian dispensation, that "the God
of Mercy should wish for, and delight in, the sacrifice of
woman's screams of pain"?

Before the sadistic men of God were routed, a few old-
fogey physicians—who again as males could not feel this

agony—tried to kill the brave new science. They argued that the pain of childbirth was "a salutary manifestation of the life force." Simpson answered their pseudo-science with yet more dubious theology. He pointed out that God had used an anesthetic upon Adam, casting that primordial gentleman into a deep sleep, when he was de-ribbed for the creation of lovely Mother Eve. But Simpson blasted them with examples from their own art and science, too. He reminded them of the horror, in days not long gone, of victims who had to have their legs cut off, and who, to be saved from fatal bleeding, were forced to have their flesh seared with hot knives, or the ends of their limbs dipped into boiling pitch.

The pain of childbirth, argued Simpson, was comparable to this. And did any surgeon, asked this knight against women's suffering, now any longer oppose the use of ether in his amputations?

But Simpson's best co-workers were the mothers. "I have not had a single patient who has not afterward declared her sincere gratitude for its employment," wrote Simpson in regard to this new use of ether. Now Simpson chuckled. Let the doctors try to stop it! While every one of his women was now setting out, "like a zealous missionary to persuade her friends to avail themselves of the same measure of relief in their hour of trial and travail."

Alas, again, as in the case of most discoveries, it was not that simple. Simpson again like all first rank discoverers suffered from this defect: he was human. And the human eyes, ears, senses of touch and smell, and the human brain, *at the moment that they discover,* seem able to see, to hear, to feel, to scent, to understand just by an absolute yes or no. A new find seems black or white. It is never gray. So it is that discoveries thought perfect have a trick of turning on their finders. They may even take a toll of victims from the very ones the searchers have toiled and sweat to save. So now

Simpson had to back water. He had to warn doctors that this new pain-killing discovery could not be peddled by every medical Tom, Dick, and Harry.

The pain-killing trick was not simple, it was subtle. It was tight-rope walking, because you had to keep the mother unconscious of her pain, yes, but not so far under the ether that her womb's contractions would be interrupted. Simpson groped about for a better anesthetic than this ether. He thought for a time he had found it in chloroform; and now chloroform is going out of use—because of the many mothers it has done to death.

All this began ninety years ago; and now today, in spite of an ingenious try-this-try-that-try-everything, and a long cudgeling of brains by an army of chemists and birth-helpers, a perfect anesthesia for childbirth's torture is not yet with us. De Lee has been a great experimenter with, and an open-minded weigher of this scientific mercy in its many forms. He still says we possess no drug that is completely without danger to mother or child. He points out the perils lurking in the gentlest pain-killers. He uses them, yes, but he advises this limitation: That all anesthetics require expert obstetricians to ward off the dangers while retaining the blessings of this killing of childbed's pain.

But this is idealistic, utopic, impossible! There are surely one hundred times less expert obstetricians than there should be, in our country, to bring or to supervise the bringing of all our country's annual two million babies. Then why not train more experts? Silly suggestion! *How would these experts make their livings,* specializing in the bringing of babies? This must above all be remembered, that in our system of society we must deal with a profit for the doctor, not with what's best for the life of mothers and their babies.

So it comes about that the New York Academy of Medicine, in its recent investigation of the scandal of the excessive dying of New York City's mothers, reports that it is "the

opinion of many observers that increase in the use of anesthesia is a factor in keeping the maternal mortality rate sta-
tionary."

So, to be blunt about it, in addition to killing pain, these
pain-killers help to kill the mothers.

The mothers are responsible too. They cry for painless
labor, so forcing their doctors' hands. They insist that their
agony be shortened. They do not seem to care that the killing of their pain makes it possible for doctors more easily
to put their hands, their instruments, into the wounded
passages to hurry the baby's coming. They do not seem to
mind that this makes it possible—too often—for the doctors
to put in death.

V

The worst enemy of mothers in childbed isn't pain, but
death, or lifelong misery. It is a bitter coincidence that, the
very year Simpson learned to kill this pain, the fundamental
discovery against the worst of childbed's deaths was made.
It is a paradox that these two discoveries fought against
each other. For the killing of pain has maybe done more than
any other one thing to hold back the conquest of childbed
fever.

While Simpson first heard a mother's screams of agony die
away under his ether-soaked handkerchief in Edinburgh,
Ignaz Semmelweis was becoming enthusiastic, obsessed, and
a nuisance to his fellow doctors by a terrific scrubbing of his
hands, a pernickety cleaning of his finger nails, a washing of
the very scent of death off his hands, a making of quadruple
sure by an epic soaking of his hands in strong chlorine
water—

Before those hands touched the inside of any mother
wounded during the coming of her baby.

By that simple science Semmelweis had solved the riddle of
the massacre of mothers in his own maternity division of the
Vienna General Hospital. For years it had been a medically

ethical secret that women in the midwives' maternity division were five times as safe from childbed fever death as women delivered by famous professors, by Semmelweis and his medical students.

Semmelweis seemed to be the only one of the faculty who cared about it, and caring, he saw this: that from the autopsy room from mothers dead of childbed fever, and from all kinds of sick, infected patients, he himself was carrying death into healthy women about to have their babies.

By means of his own contaminated hands and instruments.

Having publicly denounced himself as a mother-murderer, the wild Hungarian sent the death rate from childbed fever down by ten times, next year, in 1848.

Only because his hands and instruments were scrubbed, and reeked of chlorine.

You'd ask what doctor with heart or conscience could now refuse to join him in this saving of mothers' lives?

Well, while pain-killer Simpson was knighted by Queen Victoria for making the coming of her own babies easy and painless, Semmelweis died still sneered at in a Vienna madhouse. He was the real founder of the anti-microbe fight that has made not only obstetrics but all surgery safe for those who follow his stern and simple science. Yet his mother-saving science against childbed fever has had hard sledding.

In his own time, was it that it was too silly to believe you could wash a death—unknown—off your hands before delivering a woman? Maybe. But then the cause of this death was discovered. Pasteur, a generation after Semmelweis, proved it was the streptococcus the honest Hungarian had washed off to keep mothers from dying.

Yet today, sixty years after Pasteur's find, this childbed fever death, while abated in our country, is still the chief killer of women who try to give the world new life. So our competent and honest obstetricians are now fighting for a victory that was won ninety years ago!

This fever death may sneak into a childbearing woman anywhere they have their babies—in home or hospital. But in one especial place women must face the gravest threat of its lurking. Here is the chain of events, as De Lee sees it, and it's a science as clear, simple, and certain as it is ghastly—

Pain-killing made childbirth a quicker, easier business for doctors and surgeons. Women wanted childbirth surgical because that way its agony would be shorter. Becoming surgical, childbirth took place more and more in general hospitals. And what—asks De Lee—can these general hospitals be, if not places where all sorts of sick, germ-laden, infected people are gathered? They are, so insists this master-birth-helper, unless administered with the super-exact care of a microbe-hunting laboratory, only too often cesspools of infection.

With the co-working of Dr. Heinz Siedentopf, De Lee tore the lid off this medical scandal in a powerful scientific paper in *The Journal of the American Medical Association.*

Doctor Siedentopf was a skilled German birth-helper. De Lee picked him as his co-worker because he was more than simply unprejudiced. He actually did not think, when he began, that childbed fever was any longer a serious menace. What he then found was terrible.

From his investigation it was clear that, all over the world, more and more women were having their babies in hospitals, in the obstetric wards, usually, of *general* hospitals. Had this resulted in better welfare for the mother and child. In less loss of life?

One glance, reported the German birth-helper, at the mortality statistics from many parts of the world showed the contrary. During the past years the maternal death rate in many countries has been on the up, even when you excluded the cases occurring after abortions, to which certain doctors like to pass the buck as an explanation of our excessive maternal dying. It was clear, from Siedentopf's study, that childbed fever made the profession of being a mother, today, more dangerous than any masculine profession. In certain countries the shocking death rate of mothers was viewed with consternation—

Two hundred and fifty-two maternal deaths occurring in ten years in Aberdeen were investigated by the Scottish doctors, Kinloch, Smith, and Stephen. Twice as many mothers delivered by physicians died as mothers who were delivered by midwives. And the deaths of mothers delivered in hospitals were five times the number of those delivered by midwives. The Scottish observers found that this was not by any means only because hospitals got the most difficult cases. Childbed fever was the arch-killer. This was true not only for Scotland, but in New York City death's danger has recently been found to be five times as great in mothers delivered by operations—usually in hospitals—as in women bearing their children by their own natural powers.

Of course, at this point, there come those objectors who will blame the mothers. Why—if operations are dangerous —do they demand to go to hospitals to have their babies? Siedentopf makes answer that, for example in Germany, the reason is not the foolishness of mothers. They are victims of our economic system. The poor pregnant woman may have her baby in what seems to be a good public hospital without charge, while delivery at home means trouble and expense. And in America, too, with mass poverty deepening, hundreds of thousands of women have had to abandon expensive private physicians and choose charity hospitals—

This was certainly part of the reason why, roughly, 6,000 women were yearly dying—needlessly—from childbed fever.

De Lee and Siedentopf were blunt and plain about the danger of women having their babies in many of our general hospitals. The peril lies in infection sneaking from wards devoted to medicine, surgery, gynecology, pediatrics, and from the autopsy rooms that are veritable pest-holes of microbes, and from laboratories as well. The truth is that our doctors—some of them—have become too offhand, too sure of the power of their so-called aseptic science to scotch the invisible comings-and-goings of deadly microbes. Not enough is known yet about the nature of dangerous bacteria, and about their resourcefulness in slithering from the sick to healthy, but wounded women, lacerated by the ordeal of having their babies.

Subtle are the habits of deadly microbes, and much of what was thought science about them, that made it seem safe to disregard them, is now being demolished. Pus and other infected fluids are spilled on the floors of operating and autopsy rooms. Here they may dry to powder, be ground up by the traffic of the hospital, and in the form of a fine, deadly dust be spread through the hospital by swirling air currents or even by ventilating flues. It is known that many dangerous microbes retain their infectious power for many hours, and some of them for weeks and months. Microbes, carried to the wounded mother by dust, or in droplets of saliva thrown out in coughing, laughing, sneezing, by doctors, nurses, orderlies, may then settle into the field of operation, into the open wounds the baby makes in its mother by its very act of being born.

Germs may lurk upon the catgut used to sew those wounds. And it is now known, too, that surgeons, nurses, can cause infections—fatal—by unwittingly spitting microbes from their throats, spraying them from their noses onto the supposedly sterile instruments they use for their operations. There is often too much faith put in the gadgets that are supposed to make dressings and instruments free from all microbic deadliness. And in many hospitals it is not enough remembered that surgeons, nurses, orderlies, are human. Being human, they all are prone to slips of technique, to fits of negligence—in a business that demands all the exact care, the constant alertness, the super-cleanliness of a microbe-hunting laboratory. So De Lee refined the science of Semmelweis.

What then is the remedy? De Lee says there is only one: to make the coming of babies as nearly as possible foolproof. If babies must be delivered in a hospital, then it must be a hospital *built for that one purpose only,* far away and free from other sickness and death.

For many years De Lee has maintained this in the face of medical fury and professorial indignation. Other birth-helpers in our country have been and still are his equals in skill and science, but few have come near him in his Semmelweis-like self-accusation, his honesty. For more than forty-five years now, his blasts against maternal death from infection have been playing upon careless doctors, dangerous hospitals. He begins by acknowledging his own fatal errors. Many years ago he had his first bitter experience with childbed infection. In quick succession in one hospital four of his patients caught childbed fever. One died, and another developed a crippling pelvic abscess. He tried to fight the death by being super-cleanly, by using rubber gloves in all deliveries of babies, by keeping childbearing mothers apart —though in the same hospital building—from medical and surgical cases of sickness.

It was no go. De Lee compiled scandalous dossiers of information of epidemics of childbed fever in many general hospitals: disasters of which the public is usually not informed or which are even covered up by questionable explanations. Here are examples of the way death may lie in wait for mothers having their babies among collections of sick infected people—

General hospital, Class A, ten cases of childbed fever, six severe, three deaths . . . General hospital, maternity ward on same floor as surgical, five mothers and six babies seriously ill, three mothers and three babies died of infection . . .

General hospital, with maternity ward forming part of a floor housing medical and children's cases: fourteen cases of child-bed fever, three deaths . . . Class A Hospital, Boston, twenty to thirty cases of childbed fever, six deaths . . . Maternity ward of the famous Toronto General Hospital, eight fatal cases of childbed fever occurring in three weeks' time . . . And in De Lee's own experience, among his own patients, delivered in a famous Class A general hospital: one of the just-born babies died of erysipelas; one of the mothers developed a fatal streptococcus blood-poisoning; another died of a pyemia in this institution . . . In another general hospital, with its maternity at the end of a general ward floor, shut off by a vestibule with two doors between, epidemic blood poisoning carried off ten new-born babies. The ward was closed then, and disinfected and painted. Within three months another epidemic carried off nine more babies . . . Even rich women—who can afford private rooms—are not safe having their babies in these general hospitals when they are on floors near patients with other sicknesses in other private rooms. De Lee is in possession of evidence of one epidemic where five of these rich women had breast abscesses at one time . . . And, finally, the childbed fever epidemic in a great New York maternity hospital in 1927 is notorious. Here the flaming fever attacked twenty-five mothers, killing nine before it ended.

Of course there are in our country many expertly admin-istered general hospitals where such needless disasters do not happen; but how are mothers, and their husbands, to know which hospitals these are? How many general hospitals re-port these catastrophes, and make a public acknowledgment of their occurrence?

What hospitals, in what cities, are required to make ac-counting to the people? And which ones, though not re-quired, do so of their own will?

## VI

Yet we must not be too severe upon the hospital authorities and those physicians who may assure fathers and mothers that they can have their babies safely in such places.

We must blame the mothers. Women now know their ordeal can be made much less painful in hospital, because in most hospitals every last wrinkle of the art of pain-killing is at the quick command of doctors. It isn't alone that mothers are ready to run the chance of dying rather than suffer their long pain. No, our mothers are shrewd as well. They know that in these general hospitals there are marvelous ways of saving life from other threats of death in childbirth. After all, the childbed fever microbes have formidable rivals in mother murder. There is the danger of fatal bleeding before, during, and after the baby's coming. Against this mortal danger there has grown up a brilliant hospital art and science. On the operating tables in hospitals, doctors can ingeniously—thanks to the birth-helping Englishman, John Braxton Hicks—turn the baby within its bleeding mother so that the child itself with its own little body stops the fatal flow of blood. They can insert curious rubber balloons into the womb's mouth to stanch dangerous bleeding. Bled white, yes, dying, women can now be saved, and best in hospitals, by the great new art of blood transfusion.

It is in hospitals that modern mothers know all these powerful life-guarding weapons are closest by. In hospitals they can be applied with promptest skill. So, not only for their comfort and less agony, but for safety from the terror of the bleeding death, women tend to forget about the fever death that is most terrible and frequent of all the mortalities of childbearing women.

But what kind of an insane situation is this: that to dodge death from bleeding, women must risk death from infection?

Can't all these pain-soothing, hemorrhage-fighting devices

be installed in hospitals that are infection-free, absolutely isolated from all sorts of sickness, and built especially for mothers in childbed? It takes no medical genius to answer that query. And there are such hospitals in existence in our country—to take care of a pitiful few of the two million mothers who each year give our nation its new life.

Is De Lee alone in insisting upon the need of special maternity hospitals? By no means. As long ago as 1925, the Joint Committee on Maternal Welfare, under the chairmanship of able Dr. Fred L. Adair, advocated a detached and separate maternity service for childbearing mothers, with its own special personnel, in all general hospitals admitting pregnancy cases. This Committee also recommended, *as an ultimate ideal,* that physically separated buildings be provided for this purpose *when practical.*

Yes, as an ultimate ideal and when practical, and the italics are this chronicler's. Here is the clue to the continuing slaughter of mothers with childbed fever: that cursed word "ideal." Because the word "ideal," in our American language, means only one thing: a goal that will never be attained. And by practical is meant this: what's practical for our birth-helpers in their fight for life is only what our present economic system will permit the doctors to do. Our doctors and birth-helpers do not run and do not own their hospitals. They do not own their present marvelous death-fighting science, nor do the people own it. And this is the question that mothers, and their husbands who do not want their wives to die, must ask of the rulers and the owners of the people—

If special maternity hospitals where mothers will be safe, if these are physically attainable, then why are our doctors not permitted to attain them?

And what is more practical than the giving to our doctors of all the equipment, all the construction, that will save the lives of all the babies and mothers science now knows how to save?

What dead hand is it that makes it idealistic and impractical to give all this science to all mothers? De Lee has the simple answer. When his proposals for separate, safe, special maternity hospitals were met, as they were, by protest, it was not because his mother-saving science was in error. No.

It was only because of this: that the building of safe, separate, special maternity hospitals was too expensive.

When De Lee advised the absolute segregation of clean—
—not infected—childbearing women as the one practical remedy, a stormy discussion followed at every medical meeting where he brought up this question. All who took part emphasized the financial aspect of the situation. Segregation was too costly.

De Lee, alas, had no economics. He kept saying only this: that nothing compares in value to human life.

Now towards the end of his life he begins to see that there are two kinds of life, two kinds of life-guarding science. The special maternity hospitals where childbed fever does not lurk are in the main for those of the top life, for the haves, who can pay for all the science and art of death-free, comfortable childbirth. The other kind of life-guarding science is for the have-nots, the mass of our mothers of the bottom life. In the main they cannot pay, or pay only a little.

Yes, we must for the present be practical in the orthodox economic tradition. And we may ask: haven't our death-fighters maybe found some new trick of science that is cheaper than the building of special hospitals? Science is wonderful!

Aren't there new dirt-cheap tricks to fight the fever death in general hospitals as they exist today?

## CHAPTER TWO

# THE MICROBE BURNER

IS the power of science infinitely deep, endlessly resourceful? Can this power of our science outwit the poverty of
our economic order that makes special maternity hospitals
not practical? Can this power of our science out-smart human
frailty itself? Has our science become so strong that it can
now say to our humanly negligent, every now and then careless birth-helpers: All right, go ahead and be careless, go
ahead and put streptococcus into wounded mothers, it
doesn't matter, because here is science to blast this microbe
before his murder, his maiming, is accomplished?

It begins to seem as if there may be such power of science,
indeed our fighters for life are beginning to take pot shots
at the mother-murdering streptococcus and his less deadly
yet nasty microbe cousins. This new science has more than
one string to its bow. There is a simple science of heat that
now fights these microbes maiming and murdering mothers;
and there is an exceedingly complicated science of chemistry. The hot science is simple but its use for endangered
mothers is complicated, requiring great nursing skill. The
chemical science is complicated but its use is extremely simple, yet, for some mothers, it may be dangerous. It must be
understood at the outset that both of these inexpensive
sciences are still experimental. They are undeniably cheap
as compared to the building of special hospitals. Will they
both be too dear for the organized poverty—called civilization—that frustrates the fight for life?

Charles Robert Elliott was the founder of the hot science
against mother-murdering microbes. Elliott himself would

be the last to put himself forward as a scientific genius, and seventeen years ago, in San Francisco, he was simply a rank-and-file practicing physician. If he had been more than that, if he had been even a moderately good microbe hunter, he would never have become a pioneering microbe burner. When Elliott invented his new trick, it was only to try to soothe a certain very sick woman's pain. He was only trying to allay that woman's agony, and the discovery that followed sneaked up on him, hit him on the head, and stunned him so that he couldn't himself believe that he had made it.

In San Francisco Elliott was distinguished mainly for being a blunt honest kind of doctor. He was peculiar as a physician because his helplessness in the face of suffering and death kept galling him, kept sending him into fits of moroseness. He couldn't take it, and not being able to shake off the memory of the suffering he saw, he had periodic recourse to John Barleycorn. You can imagine that it was also somewhat annoying to patients desperately needing him, yet his patients adored him. They felt him worrying with them, fearing death with them, fighting death with them—in a bungling manner, yes—but always fighting it. He was an insomniac. Like the famous English physician, Addison, he'd get up and go back to the hospital after midnight—though powerless scientifically—to fight death emotionally at sick people's bedsides. So they forgave Elliott his lapses of conduct and his scientific powerlessness, remembering only what he so deeply felt for them. It is not disputed that he was a good doctor.

A nurse recalls other doctors smiling at the way Elliott wouldn't give up his hopeless cases. "You're going to get up and walk out of this hospital and I'll walk out with you," he'd assure them. He would tell them that even when they had hardly a Chinaman's chance of living till next morning; and sometimes they actually did live to leave the hospital, well and walking. But, mind you, this was not thanks to the power of science but to a sort of force in this little dark-eyed man's personality that put a fighting spirit into his patients.

It was a Semmelweis-like, De Lee-like fury at women's woes that started Elliott on his way to wallop mother-murdering microbes when they were already inside women's bodies and already far along in their maiming and deadly mischief. He began his dreaming of this new science way back in 1909—many years before his first experimenting. Among his patients were many women into whom streptococcus, staphylococcus, gonococcus, and heaven knows what other microbe marauders had sneaked—thanks to the carelessness of doctors and abortionists, thanks to the sinfulness of their husbands or to their own traffic in sin. Elliott considered that all of his patients were human, fine ladies as well as prostitutes, elegant ladies as well as street girls who peddled romance for their bread and butter.

In those 1909 days it was the fashion of surgeons to rush brilliantly with the knife into women suffering from pelvic infections. Some lives were saved that way, perhaps. Many were lost by a stirring up of the dangerous infection, by spreading it about through women's bodies. In that very year came a grim report by a surgeon named Simpson. He proved that, if you didn't operate, but simply waited for those tortured women finally to get well, only one out of every hundred would die. Instead of fifteen to twenty out of a hundred who passed on despite operations.

This treatment by simply waiting was called expectant treatment. It was a long painful hoping. This was what griped Elliott: to watch women bite their lips to stand the pain that gnawed low down inside them. They might get up from their beds at last, with fevers cooled, only to come back a little later with stooped shoulders and careful steps, holding the lower part of their abdomens. The healing forces of old Mother Nature are strong, and are extolled especially by doctors who themselves do not have to do the suffering, but too often, against the microbes, nature was not enough.

But what could you do? Ice-packs soothed the pain a little, sometimes, maybe. Then there was the exact opposite: there was heat. Heat was an old thing. Every practical nurse, every old bedside handy neighbor woman, would hurry to a sick sister with a hot water bottle. Heat was a very ancient pain-killer. Old Doctor Hippocrates had prescribed hot douches for such pain-smitten women two thousand years ago. Now it was a curious fact that the delicate membranes of people's mouths, and of any other passage into the human body, can stand much hotter water than their outside skins. So while the hot water put in by douches might comfort the insides of these tortured women, it burned their skins when it ran out, and when not hot enough to burn them, it was too cool to still the pain. So what to do?

Then one day, in 1909, Elliott was fussing with an inflated toy balloon, idly, woolgathering. He remembers he happened to depress the rounded, upper end of the little balloon with his finger, and immediately—

Immediately that child's toy took the exact shape of the passage that leads from the outer world towards a woman's womb. He recalls that he looked at it, and immediately he saw how easy it would be to insert a cork in the bottom of this little rubber bag, a stopper with an inlet and an outlet, so that you could pass running water through it, circulating hot water—

This was his invention of the idea of something new in human record—an internal hot water bottle.

## II

It took him eleven years—till 1920—to get up his energy to really try it. On the very day he had first had this hunch he had cut out a model of the shape this proposed hot water bag should be, out of paper. His idea went to sleep then, to wake, to haunt, him every time he had to treat a woman racked with the pain of pelvic infection. Now it was 1920, and here in San Francisco he came home one evening to tell his wife of the case of a miserable woman, very poor, who had aborted her baby because of her infection with gonorrhea. Her fever was up over 104. Her pulse was fast and thready. Her faced looked pinched and livid. The inflammation low down in her pelvis was blowing up into a general peritonitis. The jig seemed all but up with her. Again he might have done nothing about it, but now, next morning, his wife Lillian handed him a list of rubber companies. She told him not to come back without that internal hot water bottle he had been dreaming about all these years.

Elliott was absolutely no mechanic, not even a decent whittler, but he now sat down and from a cigar box cover with his jack-knife he cut out a crude model of the form this rubber contraption should have. Then he tramped up and down the San Francisco hills from one rubber store to another till at last he found a man willing to cut out two pieces of sheet rubber, to lay one piece under and the other over that bit of cigar box cover, to take a broad rubber band and use it to cement these two pieces of rubber together with an acid cure. He hurried from the rubber man to a drugstore and bought a two-holed rubber stopper. Then he got a couple of those little glass drinking-tubes people use when they're too sick to raise their heads. He stuck them through the stopper's holes. He bought two long pieces of rubber tubing and a can to hold hot water. With his now assembled contraption he hurried to the hospital to the woman's bedside. She was still living. She was certainly no better.

"We're going to try to make you feel a little easier," Elliott told her. He introduced the flat little hot water bag into the passage to her womb. Close by was the can filled with hot water, a long thermometer sticking out of it reading 110 degrees, Fahrenheit, exactly. "Now we're going to distend the rubber bag inside you just as far as we dare, just so it don't hurt you, tell us whether it hurts you," Elliott said. Now higher and higher, slowly, to get more and more water pressure, Elliott raised the hot water can . . . "That hurts, Doctor," the woman said. Elliott lowered the can ever so little. "That's all right now," the sick woman muttered. At this exact level, Elliott, while a nurse held the reservoir, drove a nail into the wall and hung up the hot water can.

"Is that too hot?" he asked her.

"No, it feels all right, Doctor," the woman answered.

Three minutes passed. Then the clamp on the outlet tube was opened to let the water drain away from inside the woman. Now into the can Elliott poured water heated just a wee bit hotter. And so on, three minute period following three minute period, with each time hotter and hotter and hotter water distending the rubber bag inside the woman. Till the thermometer read 125 degrees. This was much hotter than any human skin can bear—

Elliott turned to the woman who lay quietly. "No, it's comfortable. I feel a little better. The pain's less," the woman said.

Nine hundred and ninety-nine doctors out of a thousand would have stopped right here. On the basis of all experience and the physiology of a woman's delicate internal membranes, this was hot enough. Common sense should have told Elliott to put his finger into the water in the can, now 130 degrees, Fahrenheit, to prove how unbearable was this temperature—

Elliott put in still hotter water.

"The pain's much better now, Doctor," the woman said, smiling. He kept looking back and forth from the woman to his thermometer, kept ordering the nurse to heat the water a little hotter, kept saying, "That's a little too hot isn't it?" He kept asking, "Do you think you could stand it just a little hotter?" The woman kept answering: "It feel good, it's all right. My pain's much less." Elliott's description of this strange hour by that woman's bedside was this:

"The temperature of the water was gradually raised from 110 to 145 degrees Fahrenheit—at which point it was maintained."

It was the simple essence of Elliott the experimenter that he didn't let himself know more than the tender, inflamed members inside the sick woman could tell him. He simply followed her feelings as that water got more and more unbearably, impossibly hot. He had the nerve to go past every scientific impossibility depending on nothing but that sick woman's sensations for a measuring instrument. He let the fact of the woman's comfort lead him. And now what happened was too good to be true.

All that day and into the night this sick woman felt her pain leaving her. Next morning her fever was lower. Her pulse was much stronger and slower. And now again this cumbersome impracticable pouring of hotter and hotter water at the woman's bedside. And again the following morning. And now the woman's fever was gone and she kept telling Elliott she felt much, much better, stronger. Her face had lost that livid look, described as prophetic of death by old Doctor Hippocrates. This is Elliott's own account of the outcome—

"After one daily treatment for a period of one hour for thirty consecutive days I had the satisfaction of seeing my patient permanently free from pain and fever, with a feeling of well-being. Examination showed no apparent disease. I followed this patient for many years and there was no recurrence."

### III

But who would, in 1920, believe this hot miracle? Only the patient herself, who didn't believe it, who simply knew it. Only this cured woman, and Mrs. Elliott who had driven her husband to this curious experiment. Elliott had stoked up a terrific, local fever deep inside this woman who was already generally feverish. It sounded like carrying coals to Newcastle, it sounded nonsensical in the extreme. For what was fever—then!—but mankind's enemy? Just three years before this, the Austrian Julius Wagner-Jauregg had dared to use the fever of malaria to fight syphilis, the general paralysis of the insane. But nobody in the scientific world, Wagner-Jauregg himself included, believed it was the *heat* of the fever of malaria that cured this incurable insanity. And even so, what had this insanity to do with pelvic infections in women after abortion, after childbirth?

Elliott for a while never mentioned this first triumph to anybody excepting his wife, Lillian. He was ashamed of it. He was afraid, he said, of making a damned fool of himself with the doctors. It was the best of luck for our microbe burner that neither his wife, Lillian, nor the poor woman he had cured, were burdened with scientific knowledge. The poor woman's reasoning was just this: she had felt the devils of hell gnawing inside her. She knew death was reaching for her; and when this dark-eyed kind little doctor then came with his funny hot water bottle and took away her pain and lifted her back to strength again—well then, she would not be impressed by any scientific authority that would question or high-hat her savior. Lillian, Elliott's wife, had reason that was still less scientific. It was blind faith that he was a great man, neglected . . . Both of these women were Elliott's co-workers.

They shamed him out of being ashamed of this first lone cure that was too good to be true. Now cautiously he tried his new hot science on other infected women; and it was Lillian who poured the hot and hotter water into the can above their bedsides. It is no wonder that Elliott failed to appear before medical societies to announce his growing number of successes. His treatment was ponderous, sloppy, had no scientific justification, and was risky. It was long hard work to cure people this way. Not only doctors but the nurses—Heaven knows they have to work too hard anyway—wouldn't enthuse about this time-consuming messy pouring of dangerously hot and hotter water into threatened women, already feverish.

The one thing sure was that the patients liked it. Woman after woman kept getting better. They should have remained invalids. Some should surely have died. It wasn't only against the gonorrhea microbe the heat proved powerful. Women, afflicted with pelvic abscesses, post-childbirth, post-abortion, caused by various microbes that had invaded them by way of doctors' hands and instruments, kept coming to Elliott. More and more of them found out how this intense, local heat of the internal hot water bottle could cool the fevers that were burning them all over, how it could still their abdominal torture, how at last it made strength surge through them again. It was lucky for them that Elliott was no microbe hunter. It was good for science that he was the merest doctor. How otherwise would he have had the simplicity to try his water bottle upon these sick women, no matter what the microbe that was torturing them? If he had been a microbe hunter he would have reasoned that, while his hot science might cook the gonorrhea germ that can't stand it to be hot for long, yet it would be powerless against the streptococcus that is tougher and doesn't mind heat so much.

It was, moreover, scientifically on the face of it idiotic to suppose that his hot gadget could battle all these various bugs infecting women, when serums, vaccines, chemicals cooked up by distinguished scientists, had failed to destroy any of them. Elliott went on curing them. He didn't even keep records in those early days. "Records," he would shout to his wife, Lillian. "What the hell's the use of keeping records? Nobody'll believe me anyway!"

Yet, in the course of months, there now began to come to the laboratory of a certain microbe hunter in a San Fran-

cisco hospital a succession of thin slips of glass. On them, so
it was reported, had been streaked purulent discharges from
infected women. On these bits of glass the searcher saw microbes in myriads. Then on succeeding days as these women
got better, the evil germs on their succeeding specimens became more and more hard for our microscopist to find.
Finally they often faded away completely. Who was doing
what to these infected women? Hadn't the microbe hunter
heard? Elliott treatment. Internal heat. The laboratorian
hunted up our little doctor. Where was Doctor Elliott *getting* these specimens? Not from the same women who'd been
so heavily infected? This with a cynical smile.

Elliott flared. Damn him, let him go take the specimens
himself if he didn't believe it. The cynic did go and take
them, day after day, from Elliott's patients getting better.
Then the microbe hunter stopped smiling.

### IV

Now a gossip began in San Francisco medical circles.
There was talk of cases of peritonitis, unquestionably mori-
bund, now okay. No operation. Elliott treatment. Elliott
acquired one prominent supporter from the medical faculty—distinguished Doctor Cookingham, who actually tried
Elliott's internal heat upon seriously infected women. He
acknowledged the curious healing power of this heat that
was so hot it should have burned them. But this did not
mean recognition for Elliott, no. Well-meaning medical
friends came to Elliott, not arguing against the truth of his
unorthodox science, yet advising him to give up his clumsy,
sloppy hot water treatment. It wasn't that they weren't happy
to see him save women from dying when no serum, no drug,
no surgery, could save them . . . No, the rank and file of doctors are willing to see human beings kept alive, if possible . . .
No, their counsel to Elliott to lay aside his strange treatment was based on economic reasoning. It was no different

from the hatred of livery-stable proprietors of the horse-and-buggy days for the new-fangled auto. Here were surgeons, gynecologists, who had spent many thousands of dollars to be trained in their specialties. And now, here was the threat of this much cheaper hot water treatment which might take away the revenue from their operations. Not only so, but, even granting Elliott was skillful in this hot science, wouldn't careless doctors, nurses, burn women with this heat of 145 degrees Fahrenheit? It wasn't foolproof. It was cumbersome and messy. It was terribly time consuming—

There was enough sense in these remonstrances to make Elliott furious. Like Semmelweis before him, he nearly went off the deep end into danger of being denounced in high ethical medical circles for dubious practice. Like Semmelweis who talked to prospective parents—perfect strangers!—on street corners, our little lonewolf now went to the rubber company, had wooden models made so that the company could manufacture seventeen hundred hot water bottles with which Elliott proposed to teach husbands to treat their own sick wives. He bought bathtub thermometers by the gross for this proposed home treatment. Then he had to give up the project, finding these cheap instruments had errors of as much as ten degrees.

So for seven years he lonewolfed it.

He had treated over one hundred and fifty cases of pelvic infection, of women invalided, threatened by the various microbes that invade them after childbirth, after abortion. Not one woman had died. Yet, hoping for medical applause, Elliott faced—daggers. It was as if some good dog had saved a child from drowning, and had then been kicked instead of being patted and thrown a bone. It was confusing to our doctor's reflexes. At last he left San Francisco and went to Seattle.

This was in 1927; and now who was this Dr. Charles Robert Elliott announcing that he was ready to demonstrate the cure, by nothing more than hot water, of incurable gonorrhea. What could he do for certain unfortunate girls, women of the streets, derelict, and confined to the City of Seattle Intern Hospital, as menaces to society? These girls were prisoners to put it plainly. They had been proved to harbor this gonorrheal infection, which, to quote a U. S. Public Health Service Report, is, for women, "a devastating curse, whose complications—sterility, invalidism, obstinate infection, and mutilating operations—are responsible for a major part of the work of the specialist in the diseases of women."

This gonorrheal infection is present, so says Joseph B. De Lee, in fully fifteen percent of all women coming to public maternities to have their babies. It is found in ten percent of those rich enough to pay for private care. The test that Elliott now faced was formidable. Here were women whose incurable infection had smoldered on in spite of as many as seventy-seven local treatments with argyrol, to say nothing of repeated electrical cauterizations.

Under the strict control of city health authorities, on the 14th day of September, 1927, Elliott began to give his heat treatment to seven of these hapless women, for an hour a day.

Within a month and eight days, the last one of them was freed from this prison-hospital, discharged as cured, according to the evidence of the bacteriological tests demanded by the City of Seattle.

Along with the internal hot water bottle, these girls had got chemical treatment, too. "If you let me use the heat alone, I'll show you I can cure them faster," said Elliott.

So he began internally heating thirty more of such infected prostitutes in October and November—using his little rubber gadget, nothing more. While some of them needed twenty days to get rid of their infection, others were completely free of it after treatment of four or five days in succession.

Their cure, proved by best bacteriologic methods then available, was certified to by Health Commissioner E. T. Hanley, by his assistant, Dr. Adolph Weinzirl, and by Dr. L. W. Whitlow who was the chief of the Intern Hospital's Visiting Staff. Though this experiment was never scientifically published, yet exact records of it do exist, and, to the best of this present chronicler's knowledge, this is the pioneer experiment in the cure, by heat, of gonorrheal infection.

You would think that this would have started our obscure microbe burner to scientific fame, but now he began to find out how sound had been the warnings of his San Francisco colleagues. Other physicians failed to duplicate Elliott's unquestioned cures. They applied the water too hot to begin with. Or it was just too much trouble to watch the thermometers closely. Or it was a nuisance to see to it that the internal hot water bottles were properly distended inside the women. So, several women were pretty badly burned internally. Elliott showed these doctors that he could cure these burned membranes by this same internal heat, applied at a slightly lower temperature. But he got into fights with his detractors. He hinted that they considered it a personal slam that anybody could cure these infected people so much faster than they themselves could. "I'm not going to stay here curing burns all the rest of my life," Elliott told Health Commissioner Hanley. The experiment petered out. Elliott was broke. He disappeared from Seattle.

### V

Again he had failed to attain scientific respectability, let alone fame or eminence— Now it was 1929 and there appeared, knocking about the offices of doctors in New York City, a certain little fanatical physician, one Dr. Charles Robert Elliott. He carried with him a strange contraption, that he said he had invented, along with an unknown elec-

trician. It was a bizarre-looking metal box, a gadget, ther-
mostatically controlled, heating water, up and up, minute by
minute, gradually, till just so hot and not any hotter. It was
connected by rubber tubes to the Elliott internal hot water
bottle. Patent applied for.

At this time Elliott hadn't even a license to practice in
New York City, and he was adventuring in a dangerous twi-
light zone of medical ethics, falling—as he now had done,
alas—into the hands of gentlemen who were going to make
a great commercial venture out of his hot mercy to suffering
women. He knocked about from the office of one specialist
in the disease of women to another. It is in the highest degree remarkable that any of them would listen to this dark-
eyed man, battered by binges, by despair, by too many hopes
deferred. It is amazing that at last the celebrated gynecolo-
gist, Dr. Frederick C. Holden, looked into this new hot
science. Holden was a man said by his peers to be "particularly careful in his conclusions, very thorough, and absolutely reliable in his statements."

To Holden our little microbe burner—invincibly bellig-
erent—announced that he with his machine was ready to
undertake the cure of any kind and degree of the pelvic
inflammatory diseases of women, down to the absolutely desperate ones. "Give me the tough ones. I want the worst
ones," Elliott growled in his husky baritone, and with the
pitiful defiance of a man who has been scorned too long—

What now happened in the gynecologic wards of Bellevue
Hospital had the highest scientific sanction. It was dressed
up now in the clothes of medical respectability. During two
years, one hundred and fifty poor, dreadfully sick, pain-
racked women, with every sort and in every stage of pelvic
sickness—caused by gonorrhea, by abortions, by infections at
childbirth—were treated with the subtly increasing and now
automatically regulated heat of Elliott's new gadget. Elliott
himself, helped by young Dr. Spencer Gurnee, performed

the treatments. And, in 1931, the brilliant results were personally reported by Holden—who had observed them—before
the New York Academy of Medicine.

Holden will be remembered for his open-mindedness that
saved Elliott's pioneering from going into the limbo of lost
discoveries.

Elliott had arrived. Maybe? Now to Holden's confirmation
was added the enthusiastic approval of the late great gyne-
cologist, Dr. George Gellhorn of St. Louis. He gave powerful support to Elliott's scorn of those wielders of the knife
who—trying to repair the havoc of childbed infections—as
often killed women as they cured them.

"Those gentlemen who . . . perform numerous operations for pelvic inflammations are out of luck, because this
[Elliott] machine will help to cure a large number of cases
of pelvic inflammation, without danger, in a short time, at
very moderate expense, without the need of having special
nurses, without going through the mental agony preceding
any operation, without protracted convalescence, or the
aftermath that will follow so many cases that have been
operated on for inflammatory conditions."

This for Elliott from the enthusiastic Gellhorn.

Across America Elliott's science now began to spread, with
Elliott himself, curiously, not in the picture, not publishing
scientifically, with Elliott himself only a name, half-shadowy.
It was not Elliott but the Elliott machine, the Elliott treatment, that was saving women at the Mayo Clinic, at the
Miami Valley Hospital in Dayton, at the hands of capable
Doctor Graham in a great hospital in Brooklyn. Elliott? Oh,
yes, he was an unfortunate doctor . . . Now in the country,
resting.

The healing heat of the hot water bottle inside infected
women was used "to prepare them" for subsequent operations. Then—grotesquely—many of them were cured so that
the operation was not necessary. The Elliott machine enabled

women doomed to barrenness from pelvic inflammations to undergo a simple operation at the hands of New York's Dr. Francis Sovak. Afterwards they bore healthy children.

This brings us to the sternest question: will Elliott's healing internal heat that is so powerful against the old, smoldering infections that wreck the lives of women infected by abortion, by chidlbirth, will this heat fight the acutely fatal childbed fever, too? Would the Elliott treatment save the thousands of our childbearing women yearly stricken with the most terrible infection of all—with that acute, desperate childbed fever caused by the hemolytic streptococcus?

Would it have this power if it were used the first moment that a woman, infected during childbirth, showed the first ominous hint of this so often fatal fever's rise?

This reporter has seen the charts recording the course of the dangerous illness of a considerable number of thus threatened mothers, from the septic ward of a famous eastern maternity hospital. On these charts were the jagged lines of saw-tooth fever curves the peaks of which rose daily to 104, 105, and even 106 degrees. On them too were marked the curves of pulse rates beating 140 and 150 to the minute—

At a certain point on these charts you might see the initials "E. T." That meant that at this point the Elliott treatment was started on these gravely imperiled women. Then you could see those fever and pulse curves going down and down, gradually, with E. T. marked on them, in red initials, twice daily. Till no fever. Till pulse normal. Till notation that they were discharged as cured—

Were these cures mere coincidences? In response to this chronicler's query why these seeming spectacular events had not been published, it was said that—alas!—there had been no attempt made to see whether it was truly the hemolytic streptococcus that was at the bottom of these women's admittedly serious childbed fever. It was not considered wise to claim cure, therefore, of this most terrible of all child-bed's infections. Correct! Indisputable!

Is it that the chief birth-helper of this hospital, scientifically conservative as it is proper that he should be, thinks that these unhoped-for recoveries were only happenstances? Could it be merely coincidental that so many women recovered, in succession, with just one exception after Elliott treatment?

Why hasn't this yet been answered, yes or no? Why hasn't a controlled experiment been made—giving alternate desperately sick mothers, *in whose blood the hemolytic streptococcus has been found,* the benefit of Elliott's healing heat?

Or, if this is too scientifically cold, too heartless, why cannot some long series of stricken women be given this chance to fight their threatened death, the moment their fever begins to rise? Why can't this mass experiment be made in some great hospital like the Cook County in Chicago? Then the rate of dying of this large series could be compared with the death rates in the years before the Elliott treatment was begun.

Why isn't there now such an experiment in progress, with Elliott, the heat master, at the head of it? Elliott himself said that he has treated many women acutely ill with what was certainly true childbed fever, and he said that his internal hot water bottle has saved them. Then where is Elliott now?

Elliott is dead now. He died as obscurely as he lived, without eulogy in newspapers or journals of medical science, without position, without recognition, without any memorial except the memory of his hot miracle by women whose lives he saved and whom he relieved of pain.

Wouldn't it now be possible to demonstrate in a long mass experiment the wiping out of childbed fever death from some one great hospital where such deaths now occur?

These are strange questions, admitted, and it is stranger still that they have not been answered. While Elliott's

treatment was attaining scientific respectability, Elliott—poor
devil—was never able to enter the circles of the medically
elect. Three years ago your reporter stood by his bedside
in one of the best of New York's hospitals. The night before he had been struck by a hit-run driver. He had been
left gravely injured in the gutter in the rain. Brought to
this house of healing, left arm broken, many ribs fractured,
head battered worse than any prizefighter's and with possibility of brain concussion, our little microbe burner had
been kept on an operating table, and was not given a room
in that hospital till it was found out whether or not he had
the money to pay for his treatment and his board and lodg-
ing. If his friend, Bruce Osborne, had not guaranteed it,
gravely injured though he was, he would have been sent to
grim Bellevue Hospital where he could have been treated by
public charity.

But we must not be too quick to make accusations of heart-
lessness against these hospital authorities who have to operate
their institutions under a system where life is the one thing
cheap and where mercy is peddled to those who have the
price to pay for it. Elliott, you see, could never get over
being Elliott. If he had failed to enter the charmed circle
of death-fighting discoverers, hadn't he himself been to blame
for it? He was, like Bobby Burns, a genius, but with short-
comings. He was, in the homespun words of Boss Kettering,
of that little band of originals who are the seed corn of the
human race.

But then enough of this sentimentality about our obscure
microbe burner. Enough of the man and what of his science?
Why aren't other death-fighters now making the experiment
to save the lives of mothers with acute childbed fever? Surely
the promise of Elliott's science demands that this be done.
The answer is plain. It isn't that doctors in our great hospitals are prejudiced against experimenting with new science,
no. Indeed, your chronicler has been informed that certain

able physicians of the Cook County Hospital in Chicago were ready to put the Elliott treatment to this test.

But where would they get the wherewithal to buy the Elliott apparatus? The company that now exploits this science—in an effort entirely laudible under our economic system to make a profit—has not the money to finance the test demanded by the Chicago doctors. And here is another obstacle—we must be realists—the Elliott treatment is no quick trick of shooting a life-saving remedy into a sick woman with a syringe. It is a pernickety, long treatment, taking several hours a day. It must be supervised by expert doctors, nurses, to see to it that the delicate internal membranes of sick mothers are not burned. A corps of trained nurses would have to stay by these mothers during the subtle process of the working of this internal heat. But you ask whether the doctors, nurses, who could be trained for this new science, do not exist?

Yes, they could be found. And they would be eager to try this new fight for the lives of infected mothers. But in the budget of this great hospital there is of course not the wherewithal to pay for the nurses, the microbe hunters, the doctors who should spend full-time at this grave experiment. It is the old story, as ancient as the exploitation of mankind by man. It is the story of the speed-up, of the stretchout. As in industry. In industry, to maintain those profits without which industry would perish, less and less workers must make more and more goods faster and faster. In our houses of healing, too, not enough doctors and nurses must take care of too many sick, suffering, dying people. Not for profit, no. But because public beneficence and sweet private charity have today only just the wherewithal to keep the doors of these hospitals from closing.

But not enough to give all threatened mothers every last chance that science could give them in their fight for life.

## VI

But maybe—since there seems to be no limit to the resourcefulness of our fighters for life—there is some new hope of salvation of our yearly thousands of feverish, dying mothers, something so dirt-cheap that the poorest hospital can yet afford to use it?

If the simple science of Elliott's heat is too expensive, hasn't the complicated science of modern chemistry something cheap to offer? There is now the glimmer of a hope that this may be so. Within the past two years exciting news has been headlined in our newspapers. It tells of a new magic chemical bullet to shoot the hemolytic streptococcus that is the chief killer of mothers in childbirth. Such is the complicated, yet glory be, cheap chemical—sulfanilamide. It does not even require to be injected into sufferers from the blood-poisoning of this treacherous microbe. So many times a day you can swallow pills of it, as simply as you swallow so many aspirins. Great chemical companies are now making profits manufacturing it with it yet within the reach of the miserable budgets of our hospitals. And here's a major hope from it for mothers—

Our microbe hunters find that this magic chemical not only cures animals infected with streptococcus. No, given before infection, these animals can be prevented from sickening!

So now, in our general hospitals, when those deadly little epidemics threaten women having their babies, what's to prevent our birth-helpers giving all women in travail a few of these life-guarding pills, before, during, and for a couple of days after their ordeal? By this cheap simple trick you'd foil the streptococcus, wouldn't you? It wouldn't even be necessary for our doctors, nurses, to go through their stern, elaborate ritual of disinfections, would it? Isn't this death-defying drug going to make the super-cleanliness of Semmelweis, of

De Lee, needless? Can our hospitals now be dirty with impunity? And is the Elliott treatment going to become a back number before its maybe life-guarding science has a chance to be tested against acute childbed fever?

These are curious questions to ponder. And they demand a curbing of too enthusiastic answers. For there is a little cloud, no larger than a man's hand, on the serene sky of this new life-giving promise. Sulfanilamide is poisonous to microbes. But it is dangerous to some human beings as well. It thins the blood of some people, dangerously. It makes others ominously dizzy, sleepy. It turns yet others blue. It poisons the hemoglobin of the blood that carries the life-sustaining oxygen of the body. It is a chemical rose that, like all roses, carries thorns. It is not fool-proof. Dissolved in a poisonous solvent, the whole world now knows how the elixir of sulfanilamide is fatal. Beyond a doubt, the testing of it will demand the closest supervision of mothers, by expert nurses, doctors, microbe hunters, blood chemists. So really, in the long run, will this chemical be cheap enough to be practical in the routine attempt to prevent childbed fever death?

There is another curious question that's not scientifically nonsensical. If a lot of sulfanilamide is poisonous, then wouldn't a little of it—*used at the same time with Elliott's internal heat*—prove to be the mortal enemy of all streptococci threatening childbearing women?

Just as 606—a little of it—combined with general artificial fever, is now being found to be so powerfully curative against the doom of syphilis? Or would such experiment, again, be too expensive?

## CHAPTER THREE

# MOTHER SAVERS: 1937

YET the power of science is mighty. It would seem that there is no limit to its strength to aid our fighters for life at life's beginning. Let economic law deny them experiments with possibly new life-saving science. They can thumb their noses at economics and set fire to economy-howlers' shirttails. They have proved that they are already armed with a birth-helping art and science so economical that it is actually cheaper to save the life of every threatened mother than it is to let any threatened mother die.

This art and science now fights the three master-murderers of mothers—eclampsia, hemorrhage, infection—with such power that, if it were used all over, motherhood would now be the safest instead of the most dangerous of professions. This knowledge does not exist in theory. There is at this moment at least one large obstetric service where it is so safe to have a baby that if all our nation's babies were brought with a like vigilance and expertness, less than twenty-five hundred mothers would die yearly instead of the fifteen thousand or more who actually perish to bring new life.

This is the hope that the records of the Chicago Maternity Center now give America's childbearing women—

That it is at least six times safer to have a baby in this service than it is for the general run of all American mothers, as judged by our national maternal death rate.

The life-saving art and science of the Chicago Maternity Center is practical, and without question teachable to the rank and file of our country's younger doctors. It does not demand costly edifices of glass, white tile, and marble. It could be applied throughout America without changing the present proportion of three out of four babies who are born in their own homes. It could work its life-guarding power in spite of the disgrace of the damnably inadequate number of maternity hospitals, limited as they are by our national false economy. The death-fight by the scientific youngsters of the Chicago Maternity Center is fought in tenements, in hovels whose appointments are far below those of a cross-section of the 1,500,000 American homes in which our babies are born each year.

The comparison of their life-guarding record with that of our nationwide maternal death rate is not a phoney one, nor is it based on doctored figures. During the five years since the Center's opening, these physicians have delivered more than fourteen thousand mothers. Of these, only twelve have died from a truly obstetric cause. Less than one out of twelve hundred. As against one out of one hundred and seventy-five women who die in childbirth our country over. And while nationwide three out of four babies are born at home, the Center's physicians bring babies to nine out of ten mothers amid a squalor and wretchedness incomparably worse than that of the average home in our wealthy America.

II

The doctors of the Chicago Maternity Center first began to bring babies to forlorn mothers—the requirement was that they must be paupers—in the deep of the depression in July, 1932. Those were hectic days in that ancient building at the corner of Maxwell Street and Newberry Avenue in the heart of the ward that's called the Bloody Twentieth in Chicago. These were the days when more than one hospital in Chicago had to close down its maternity ward because it had no money. Yet, such is human optimism that babies kept on coming to mothers who were moneyless, and in homes, many of them, hardly fit to shelter dogs or cattle. Here the physicians of the newly founded Center brought an average of ten babies a day at all times of day and night. They helped three hundred lusty new lives a month to come to homes that were often dirty, bedbuggy, all over the two hundred and ten square miles of Chicago's widespread slums where you would swear not one more life was wanted.

From the very beginning the lack of maternal deaths was astounding, and you ask how could this be, what with the youth, the comparative inexperience of the doctors? Well, you see, the Center's work did not really begin with its formal founding in 1932, but had been started thirty-seven years before, in 1895. It really began entirely without buildings, or any scientific apparatus, or hardly a dollar of money. It was hatched as a dream in the head of an intern in Chicago's Cook County Hospital. He was a fledgling birth-helper, whose one equipment was a flame of hatred against the misery and death that were then—universally—the consequence of childbirth.

This intern was Joseph B. De Lee. At the County Hospital it was his duty—he thought it an honor—to help into the world the babies of hundreds of unmarried mothers. He saw them leave the hospital, their babes in their arms, with no place to go and with not a soo-markee to get there. Emerging thus, he watched them, friendless, accosted by procuresses. These put the fatherless newborn waifs on baby farms where most of them soon died. They sold the mothers into prostitution.

But De Lee was not a sob sister and his dream to help women was practical. These were barbarous days in Chicago where it was even more dangerous to have a baby than it is now. The best (!) doctors wouldn't accept confinement cases. The richest women couldn't be sure of good obstetric care. Childbed fever flamed in great, not small, epidemics as now, and even more babies than today were butchered, maimed, and blinded. From the beginning of his dreaming De Lee saw through to the heart of the scandal. He knew that doctors didn't want to kill mothers, butcher babies. He understood that they didn't know how not to. So, why not use these un-married mothers, why not organize the bringing of all babies to all women, poor though married, to teach Chicago's doc-tors whose goodwill and amiability was then exceeded only by their obstetric ignorance?

De Lee's next thirty-five years could have been written by Horatio Alger—if that worthy had left out the blood and suffering. He was non-Aryan, and proud of it, and began by begging odd charitable dollars from wealthy Jewish ladies to found his Maxwell Street dispensary. He was poor himself, and lived on the heels of loaves of bread, washed down with milk in order to give poor women—for the first time in Chi-cago's history—the benefit of the latest birth-helping art and science. He was ascetic, denying himself every luxury to keep open the four rooms of his first dispensary, spotless in a dingy tenement. Till late at night he'd plan and study, go to bed red-eyed, to get up an hour later to trudge by lantern light through snow in below-zero cold to see one more des-titute woman through her ordeal. He began to give a new twist to the mother-saving science he had learned in the great maternities in Berlin and Vienna: he showed young medical students, interns, this miracle: that such science could exert its strange power in hovels as well as hospitals.

From those first days he was—and has remained—a fero-ciously enthusiastic yet patient teacher. Meanwhile his prac-tice among the poor had made him so expert that the richest ladies flocked to him to have their babies, for which their husbands paid gladly the large fees that De Lee then turned back into his dispensary in Chicago's ghetto.

His first little maternity hospital, founded for desperate cases among poor mothers not operable in their homes, flowered at last into the most beautiful maternity in the world. Approaching the new Chicago Lying-in Hospital, you might mistake it for a cathedral. Then—at the crest of this success—came bitterness for our doctor dreamer. Now in 1931 came the money famine. The Lying-in Hospital had been attached to the University of Chicago, famous for its shrewdness in nursing its hoards through panics, in the true tradition of that hoarder of God's gold whose money did so much to found it. It was now decided—since the University could not see to it there was enough wherewithal for children to be born decently—that to support the white stone Gothic of the Hospital, the dingy Maxwell Street Dispensary must close its doors—

What would become of the thousands of poor women of that submerged class whose babies, up till now, had been brought into the world with all the care and thoroughness any hospital could show a banker's lady?

De Lee had never married. This ramshackle house of life in the Bloody Twentieth Ward was his wife and family. Three-fourths of America's babies are born at home and this old Dispensary had been the headquarters of important teaching of medical students, doctors, nurses, to turn the worst home into a replica of the safest hospital. Best of all it had taught them that mothers, poor, pious, or prostitute, are human because, for De Lee, they all were Mrs., they all were mother. This was fundamental to De Lee's science and this was what transcended it: that all women at the gates of motherhood should have all the sympathy of which the human heart is capable. He was politically a conservative, and hobnobbed with Chicago's plutocratic big shots but his maternal economics were socialistic. In any argument where it was a choice—as in our economic system it must be—between mothers' lives and dollars, De Lee's answer is—

"I will say only this: nothing compares in value with human life."

To De Lee birth-helping was more than a mere money-making art and science. So now, in the crisis of the threatened closing down of his old dispensary, he dug down into his own pocket to keep that house of life open for another year. He named it the Chicago Maternity Center, and it was independent now, and no longer a financial embarrassment to the University of Chicago. For this independence it now paid by a poverty, a hand-to-mouth existence very much like that of the women it helped to have their babies.

All this is the background, the foundation, for the remarkable record of our young doctors—in saving mothers' lives—from the day the Center opened in July, 1932. They were all students of De Lee's. They all worshiped him. They lived to make his art and science come true—for everybody.

### III

Dr. Beatrice E. Tucker is the medical director of the Chicago Maternity Center. What best sums her up is that she is a woman of the future—if, by the defeat of woman-despising, life-hating fascism, mankind is to be allowed a future above barbarism. As a birth-helper she is better than most men physicians, yet she herself is not mannish. In the first year of her directing the hectic activities of the Center, she lived in a little dark room in the basement of the building. This made room for the swarm of young interns, medical students, nurses, who crowd this ancient barracks—to watch obstetric demonstrations, to examine rows of expectant mothers, to boil urines in the miserable little laboratory, to cat-nap while they keep one ear cocked for the telephone that jangles to bring news from poor women all over Chicago, mothers whose pains tell them their time has come.

In her basement boudoir Tucker was blown upon by grime from what's as filthy a street corner as you'll find in our so-called civilized world. Sleeping a couple of hours in the gray of morning after a night of birth-helping, she'd be roused by bawling of hawkers and a terrific quacking of doomed ducks of the Maxwell Street Market. From this

old building Tucker now began to sally out, in the heat of
Chicago summer nights, in zero cold to pneumonic houses
where a fire was a luxury. She began to understand the
mockery of what's called medical progress—

She was called to frightened households where bungling
midwives had delivered babies' heads but could not bring
their shoulders. Where a baby's head had actually been torn
off by an incompetent attendant. Where an agonized mother
had been found on the floor by neighbors, with her baby
half-born and on the verge of a deadly rupture of her womb.
Here it was 1932. De Lee had worked in Chicago for thirty-
seven years to change all this. And what could have been
more futile? Where was medical science? Was this our enlightened U. S. A.—where Tucker had to plead and argue
with a dirty midwife about to tie a mother in her bed so she
could trample up and down on her body to bring the baby?

Tucker reveled in it. Here were a thousand chances to
trick death. Here she learned to make a miracle of aseptic
order, a modern operating room out of a dank lightless
kitchen where you had to spread newspapers round to keep
cockroaches and bedbugs out of the field of the operation.
Tucker is a bundle of contradictions, hating poverty and
death and glorying in this poverty that makes her death-fight
an adventure. If Chicago was not this travesty upon civilization, there would be no chance to help to civilize it. If
Chicago was utopic, her fight would be too easy. So she
gloried in Chicago's degradation. This tall woman-against-
death, always carrying her black obstetrician's satchel, might
come back tired from a triumphant vigil against a mother's
threatened disaster. In front of the building of the Center,
she'd notice a crowd of people peering at the just discovered body of a gangster done to death. She'd forget her
tiredness. This was life. She might turn from the crowd to
see forlorn vestiges of humanity prospecting in the garbage
pile in the alley next to the Maternity Center. How could

you be the enemy of this shameful hunger unless you lived in the midst of it? Tucker is a front line soldier in the fight for life.

Like all true fighters for life she is democratic. Yet she has ambitions, like De Lee, to become an ace birth-helper. But she can't help seeing this: that every woman bearing a child is a human being, feeling as poignantly, when she bears it, as does our now noble chain-store princess. She has that optimism which alone has raised mankind a little bit above its baboon forebears. Civilization hasn't yet, for all its brains and abundance, learned to provide decent shelter, food, clothing—or even work—for the desolate myriads to whom she ministered. Well and good. Tucker, and her band of young doctors, medical students, nurses, can at least see to it that strong, living babies are born to these thousands of women. With the least possible pain. With the greatest safety from invalidism and death. With less chance of dying than their otherwise more lucky pampered sisters. And after that? What fate then waits for these well-born babies and their mothers? That is not Beatrice Tucker's business.

IV

At the Maternity Center the fight for the lives of mothers and babies starts long before the baby comes. It begins with a taut alertness for all these poor mothers the moment they come to register, as pregnant, at the Center. Of all the sorts of death and disaster that Tucker and her staff know how to checkmate by their pre-natal care, they fear none so greatly as the convulsive terror of eclampsia. Next to childbed fever eclampsia is the chief killer of mothers. No poison prepared by the most fiendish murderer can bring death more horrible. No ignorance in the still crude science of medicine is greater than that of this poison whose effect is so altogether dreadful.

This eclamptic danger is most threatening in the last three

months before a woman is to have her baby. When it comes—in the one out of every five hundred mothers bearing babies whom it still does to death—it is likely to explode like a flash of lightning. The woman's pupils dilate. Her head jerks sidewise. Her whole body becomes rigid, drawing up in a dreadful spasm. Then, in a convulsion, she may be thrown from her bed, her mouth open, or her teeth clamping on her tongue. Foam, flecked with blood, may be upon her lips. Her eyes stare, bloodshot in a face that is blue and dusky. Now the convulsion dies away, and there is hardly a sign of breathing. Then there is a sigh and a jerky gasping for breath. Now like as not the woman goes into the kindly oblivion of coma, beyond fear and pain.

If she survives—as eighty out of every hundred women do—she wakes up, bewildered. Her muscles are sore and she has no memory of the fit's beginning. It seems as if the living child within her in some way poisons the eclamptic woman. With the spasm's beginning a woman's labor often comes on quick and powerful and frequently the mother is safe from danger the moment her baby sees the light of day. Again, sometimes, kindly nature takes a hand and kills the unborn child at the moment of the first convulsion. Now, at the moment of the unborn baby's death, the dangerous symptoms vanish. Such is the pre-natal terror that the Maternity Center's doctors fear more than any, and at least five thousand mothers in the U. S. Registration Area die yearly paying this penalty for their hoped-for happiness. Once the attack begins, there is no medicine surely effective to allay it. Its only treatment is its prevention. But how prevent a death of which you do not know the cause?

v

In nearly all such threatened women you can find a succession of physical and chemical danger signals; and it is of these that Tucker and her staff of nurses and doctors take the shrewdest kind of advantage. They did not themselves discover this life-guarding science. It has been known for many years. But they practice it with a drastic alertness that would seem ridiculous if it did not result in one of the most remarkable low eclamptic death rates ever heard of.

At every last woman's first visit to the Center she is questioned, cross-questioned, then questioned some more about possible fits she may have suffered before her other babies came. Or, if this is her first child, then a tendency to eclampsia in her family is looked for. The most insignificant hints are recorded on the exhaustive history charts kept for every woman in this house of life. Of course the blood pressure of all these women is routinely tested; and their urine often examined for albumin. And, at the tiniest hint of anything not healthy, not normal, this is recorded, boldly, in red, on the woman's history. Such women are told with candor about their danger, not frightened by it, but made to face it. They are given explicit dietary directions, for food low in salt, low in protein, high in vegetables, and most important of all they are adjured to keep coming back to the Center; and still better, should a woman fail to reappear, a nurse, or a young doctor, chases out to see her.

Now, if in spite of all that Tucker and her helpers can contrive, her blood pressure keeps rising, and if more and more albumin shows in her urine, if there's a sinister sudden increase in her weight, she is visited every other day in her home.

And, if she gets no better—though yet without signs of stomach pain, headache, nausea, and those flashes before the eyes that foretell the eclamptic explosion—she is taken to a hospital.

There her pregnancy is safely ended.

Since the Center's founding, an average of twelve women every month have shown signs of this looming terror. Yet, for a stretch of months from April, 1934, to October, 1935, in an unbroken succession of 4,379 women to whom the Center's birth-helpers brought babies, not one woman died from eclampsia . . . As against an eclampsia death rate of one out of five hundred in America . . . And then, one midnight in October, 1935, there was a buzz at the switchboard in the Center. Hurry call. A woman, Polish, very near her time, convulsions. By streetcar—the Center being poor—but running to the streetcar and from the streetcar to the home, an intern, medical student, and nurse hurried to the endangered woman—

Convulsions, yes, uncontrollable, then merciful coma. The woman, mind you, had never registered at the Center, had never heard of its existence. At the beginning of the frightful crisis her other children had been bundled off to a neighbor. Her husband was blind, and as helpless as the unborn baby within his dying wife. Neighbors had called a near-by great hospital. Sorry, but they couldn't take her. You see, she hadn't registered. Better call the Maternity Center. Yes, they take anybody. So said the voice at the hospital end of the wire.

Now it is the law at the Center that, when the intern, medical student, nurse, find danger, they call Tucker or her Assistant Director, Dr. Harry Benaron. So now, at 3 A.M., that quiet, cool, quizzical young birth-helper walks into this two-room home. He finds the woman, comatose, gasping, half-buried in a feather bed. He sends the intern out pellmell to call an ambulance. Yes, the hospital will take the woman now that Benaron guarantees her case is desperate—

Now a quick shot of morphine. Then, delicately, a slow careful injection of a big dose of glucose solution into the dying woman's arm-vein . . . But three hours later this mother died, her babe unborn, in the hospital that couldn't take her because she had not registered . . . Told the details of that night, your chronicler asked Benaron how the blind husband had taken it? Had he reached out, groping, when his wife had been carried to the ambulance? Benaron had had no time to note such sob sister details. "You see," he said, "I was too busy trying to bring her through and give them a live baby."

Not that another child was needed in this desolate household, but Tucker and Benaron never concern themselves with such Malthusian reflections. What struck your chronicler in the nights and days he spent with them was their accent on life, first for mother, then for child, always for both if possible. What now was curious was the self-accusation—on the part of Tucker and Benaron—about their responsibility for this death you'd swear was no fault of theirs at all. They hadn't so much as heard of this woman till six hours before she died. Yes! But they'd have saved her if she'd only come to the Center three months before. All right! But she didn't know about the Center. Yes, but the fact remained she died while under the Center's care. So, on their records, her death is charged.

The Center accepts all cases registered there or no, and it is Tucker's rule that, whether it's a case of a woman dying a minute after they first see her, or weeks after an eventless childbirth—all mothers they treat are their death. Whether they die in their own wretched hovel or in one of Chicago's finest hospitals.

That's what makes these young birth-helpers prophetic of a sterner future art of healing. Their system is the extreme opposite of dishonest. Under its discipline there is no chance to fool yourself or to pass the buck to other doctors or to pass the buck to God. It is this most natural temptation to evade responsibility for ignorance, for blunders, and to take credit not truly yours for successes, that so largely holds back the art and science of healing. When an engineer builds a railroad bridge, and if he has designed it wrongly or been dishonest in its construction, and if the bridge then collapses drowning important people—it is the engineer who very likely takes the rap. This is his discipline. This is where the doctor's profession is so different: nature is kindly as well as cruel; human protoplasm is often self-mending; sicknesses are often self-limited. Yet what is more natural, after his patient has been cured—by nature—despite his muddling ministrations, than for your doctor then to say: Look, we've pulled her through! On the other hand should the patient perish, there's always fate or God to be blamed for overcoming the doctor's powerful science. This is at the root of the *in*discipline of the art and science of healing.

The Chicago Maternity Center's birth-helpers are more like tough young engineers than doctors. They are not fair to themselves, but they sense it that if they don't fool themselves they won't cheat others. Behind their constant self-accusation there is wisdom. Their abhorrence of one single death, though unavoidable by any criterion, their loathing of one death blotting their clean page of so many thousands of mothers living—it's this fear and loathing that key them up to make the most unavoidable deaths avoidable.

## VI

Hardly a week passes that our Center's doctors do not have to make a stern choice between life for babe and mother. They pass their lives in this kind of tension, and it was this tautness that saved a Negro mother whose conduct was nothing if not suicidal. She had called the Center one midnight, March, 1935, eight and a half months toward her time. This midnight she had noticed a faint show of blood. Now next to the horror of eclampsia, a fear of blood dominates the lives of our watchers of expectant mothers. Against any little bleeding before the baby comes they plant alertness in the brains of every mother. Now this midnight it seemed a false alarm, yet this Negro mother, Mary, was hurried to the hospital. Two days later she came back home, not in labor,

not bleeding at all, everything okay, when, that same night
—hemorrhage!

This time there was a terrifying gush of blood. When
Harry Benaron made his examination, there was no doubt
of the diagnosis. *Placenta praevia.* The eight dollar medical
term for that dreaded condition when the afterbirth tries to
come first, where the afterbirth is previous, where it is not
where it should be, but lodged between the baby and the
mouth of its mother's womb. So that when the baby begins
to be born, this afterbirth, this blood connection between
mother and child, has got to be ruptured, dangerously, often
fatally. This now threatened that Negro mother, Mary.

Benaron, as always nonchalant, as always hurrying with
deliberation, packed the inside of the woman and stanched
the cataract of blood and rushed her back to the hospital.
There the doctors tried to hurry the coming of the child.
It was no go. The black lady grew bored, hauled off and hit
the nurse who tried to hold her down, bit the young doctor
who battled with her, pulled her ragged coat over her night-
dress, and fled, barefoot, back to her home—

There her bag of waters broke. Searing pains of her labor
started. Blood again gushed from her and it was nip and
tuck whether she would live or die. Her friends again called
the Center, whose doctors justly might have washed their
hands of such an ingrate. Besides she was nothing but a
clearly disreputable unmarried mother from the toughest
part of Chicago's black belt. And so, and now, with no hair-
splitting about who has the right to live and who had better
die, the hemorrhage crew from the Center snapped into
action—

With Tucker, Benaron, an intern, a medical student, and
a nurse, every implement for a last tussle with death was
lugged into Mary's tenement den. In its kitchen there was
only a stove and a rickety table. In the entire apartment
there were two chairs in all. One bedroom held a bed with

a tattered coverlet, the other bedroom did duty as the coal-bin, in which at the moment and irrelevantly, Tucker, as she hurried in, observed a mother cat nursing her kittens. Now for twenty-four hours they stayed by Mary, stanching her hemorrhage only to have it start again. For a little while one of this fighting crew left her—to recruit colored women of the region, reluctant to give blood for a possible trans-fusion. For a couple of hours Tucker was away—in the dingy little laboratory of the Center to type the bloods of these women to make sure the transfusion would be safe. Benaron never left the mother who was growing gradually weaker.

Now in that kitchen the improvised instrument table—an ironing board held up by the two existing chairs—was ready for what they knew they must face, finally. Clean news-papers were everywhere. Instruments gleamed. Their home-spun science had turned this hutch into an operating room as safe from infection as the finest hospital. Yet hours dragged by. They all sat, when not ministering to the mother, groggy tired, on newspapers on the floor. Now the mother was just barely living . . .

Deep under ether they now sent her, and like many colored women she took ether badly. Benaron kept putting her deeper and deeper under till her womb's contractions stopped, till she was relaxed till now—all of a sudden—she stopped breathing.

That was deep enough. Just deep enough for the quick hands of Tucker, now taking advantage of this relaxation that was the same as death, this relaxation that was demanded to avoid the womb's fatal rupture—

Gauze-masked, white-trousered, tall Tucker bends over. Far up inside the mother there is the deft movement of her rubber-gloved hand quickly gently and in no hurry and now in a few long seconds the baby is turned within its mother—

The baby's own body is set to stop that gush of blood that's

inevitable when the baby breaks the misplaced afterbirth in
its act of being born—

All these long seconds the mother is as good as lifeless,
with Benaron doing nothing about it, waiting, till Tucker
straightens up, signals him with a look. Then quick, artificial
respiration.

When the babe was born at last, and the mother weak,
but sighing, safe, no longer bleeding, and when this gory
kitchen battlefield of the fight for life had been made ship-
shape, then finally the hemorrhage crew started back to the
Center. Dark circles were under all their eyes. They went
away jittery, dead beat, highstrung, exalted, never wonder-
ing whether it had been worth while to all but kill this
cantankerous Mary to keep her living.

—Over fourteen thousand women have been delivered by
the Center's doctors without one dying from the bleeding of
*placenta praevia*—

Tucker and Benaron were indignant, not with ungrateful
Mary, but it was a tough break that they had had to say
good-by to that baby to save its mother. The baby's body
had stopped its mother's bleeding, but, so doing, it had cut
off its own life-blood— Yet, the Center's record for live
babies is superb—twice as good as that reported for America
as a whole. Yes, this crew will go to lengths to bring live
babies.

VII

No risk was greater, none was more unorthodox, than the
chance Tucker took, when, in the middle of one night, she
hurried sleepy-eyed to the home of an Irish woman who had
never registered at the Center. An intern from a nearby
hospital had been called—emergency!—to this woman's sudden labor. The situation was serious. The baby was trying
to be born, one little foot protruding from its mother. Yes,
this was certainly a case for the Chicago Maternity Center.
They'll take anything. They take all death responsibility.

Now here is Beatrice Tucker. Deft examination, measurements. Bad news. The mother's pelvis flat from childhood rickets. Absolutely no room for the child to be born by the normal exit. And worse news, our Irish woman is forty years old, with this her first baby, and with her having waited ten years for this happiness, and with the chance of another child a slim one.

Tucker made a quick calculation, a shrewd weighing of the chance of mother death against new life's saving. Quick transformation of the home into an operating room; thorough scrubbing up of the operating crew and boiling up of instruments—

Now Tucker reversed the processes of nature! She took the baby's foot, washed it with antiseptic, put it gently back into the passage to its mother's womb, sewed up the outer entrance to that passage . . . Now deep ether—administered by Benaron to check the powerful labor pains, to soothe the mother's agony, but most of all to keep the baby from killing itself trying to be born again . . . Then, with the siren of the ambulance shrieking for a right-of-way, Tucker sitting by the mother keeping her deep under the ether, they jolt, bounce, and sway on a wild journey to the maternity hospital.

Here the Porro Caesarean operation is done by the hospital's obstetricians who are waiting and ready. They take out baby, womb, and all—because, the baby's foot having been in the outside world, infection of the mother's womb was certain.

"So Tucker brought that mother a nice live baby," said Benaron.

### VIII

If doctors, if mothers, had time to wait, then all but five percent of all childbirth would be natural, would be spontaneous, so says De Lee, the master. And of all the desperate measures that have to be taken in that five percent of childbirth that must be ended by operation, the only one that is not attempted in their poor women's homes by the Center's doctors is the Caesarean operation. Mothers needing this operation are taken to the Chicago Lying-in, the Cook County, and other co-operating hospitals. For the successful outcome of this spectacular, dangerous way of bringing new life these hospitals get the high praise of the birth-helpers of the Center.

Yet here again Tucker, Benaron, and their youngster doctors and nurses play their part by their alertness—before the baby comes—to find danger signals of eclamptic poisoning, of threatened hemorrhage, of deformed pelvis, of failing heart that may demand the child be brought by the knife.

Expert obstetricians know that tragedy, for mother or baby or for both, is too often due to this: that the need for the Caesarean operation wasn't found beforehand. So that the mother was brought under the knife, exhausted, often infected, and on the verge of dying. It is well to remember that the mortality of mothers from Caesarean operations in our hospitals runs close to ten out of every hundred women whose babes are brought by the knife. It is in general more dangerous to have a Caesarean than to have typhoid fever. And so far, not one of the Center's patients—now nearly a hundred in all—who have been sent to hospital for this operation has died.

What is the secret behind this situation that it is so much safer for the poverty-stricken women of Chicago's wasteland to have babies than it is for their more fortunate sisters the country over? It's no great secret. It's vigilance that explains it. If it's too much to say that any woman has one foot in the grave while she's having a baby, it's no exaggeration to say that she has one foot over a precipice. This is at the roots of all the birth-helping art and science of De Lee. That's the reason for the vigilance of his young birth-helpers at the Chicago Maternity Center. They concentrate enormously more time and care upon Chicago's pauper mothers than your average physician can give to the average childbearing woman in our country. Yes, and more than the expensive obstetrician can give to those ladies of the rich who still bear children.

You protest that the remedy should be simple. There should be more birth-helping doctors, more nurses, available to all. Yes. But we must never forget to be practical. The rank and file of our physicians, already working for a too meager profit, if they had to spend so much more time on one mother, then how would they, the doctors, be able to feed and clothe their own wives and babies?

## CHAPTER FOUR

# THE BLOOD IS THE LIFE

IT is only human life and never profit that is the concern of the workers at the Chicago Maternity Center.
Its life-bringing business is run on a shoestring; from one
year to another it is not even sure that its existence can continue, but that does not prevent it—as of today—from being
a college teaching one fundamental: vigilance. Nothing
could be more uncollegiate, in the sense of today's hand-
some piles of brick and mortar, than this drab ancient building at the corner of Maxwell Street and Newberry Avenue.
Yet here more than three hundred medical students and
doctors are yearly inoculated with a virus of mother-saving
alertness. Here the laws of our moneyocracy are suspended.
In our stingy world this is a fantastic oasis, for, while these
youngsters learn their birth-helping here, they are taught
to act as if human lives were of the utmost value. Here is
the preparation for disillusion: because from this teaching
they will be forced to go out into a world where life is cheap.
While these young students and doctors are bringing babies
to the mothers of Chicago's wasteland, during those days
of ordeal, it is as if the life of every one of these women
were as precious as that of a queen, a banker's lady. Here
again is irony: once the child is safely born, the Center's
doctors must forget mother and baby, now consigned to take
their chances in our life of laissez faire— After a few tender
days during which it seemed as if those lives mattered to our
civilization to which the prodigality of life seems now the
chief embarrassment.

When you go to watch the art and science that are so

superbly taught at the Chicago Maternity Center, you climb
worn stone steps, and at once you see something not-worldly
about this old mouse-colored house of hope. Its battered
green outside doors swing in-and-outward and have no lock
on them at all. So for forty-one years—since the house was
built for De Lee—these doors have yielded to the touch of
thousands of women, nauseated, pain-racked, in fear of hemorrhage, of convulsions. None has ever been denied. And
this is in contrast to modern hospitals where they have to
see the color of your money before they'll minister to you
even though you're in danger of dying. These doors have
swung outward before countless mothers going home to wait
their time of travail, knowing that theirs will be the utmost
care that obstetric art and science can give them.

You pass through these lockless doors to face the telephone
switchboard to which is flashed to the Center's directing
doctors every happening of their fight for life's beginning
from every mean street in Chicago. You understand no babies
are born at the Center. It is a sort of GHQ of the life fight
that goes on in thousands of cottages, tenements, hovels,
every year. You turn from this switchboard to face the big
green bulletin board that is the staff map of these fights with
death. On it—hieroglyphic to you if you're no nurse or doctor—there is posted the hour to hour record of all these far-
flung struggles to bring new life. Here's the latest news—
hopeful or ominous—flashed from the young doctors and
nurses who are the front line fighters in every part of this
slum that calls itself America's second city.

This big green board dominates the lives of Beatrice
Tucker and Harry Benaron who are the directing brains of
this art and science. This board is the battle. From its rows
and columns of figures they get the good news of a new life's
safe entry to the light of day. Or they're told of the threat
of mortal danger. When word is flashed from any part of

Chicago of a mother's pains telling her that her time has come, it is a never-broken rule that the Center's doctors go right now. Not pretty soon. The moment one of these routine delivery crews—intern, medical graduate, nurse—get to the bedside, there is quick examination of the mother. Then the details of her situation are telephoned from the nearest corner grocery, saloon, or cigarstore to the green board for the scrutiny of Tucker or Benaron or the reigning resident physician. If, in the judgment of one of these three, there is the faintest danger to the woman now in the hands of the crew of medical fledglings who attend her, then there's fire-department excitement, then one of the supervising experts hurries there by motor in defiance of the laws of traffic.

Such is the essence of the Chicago Maternity Center's birth-helping practice.

During the bitter months of the record cold 1936 winter your chronicler watched them working. This above all other impressions was burned into his memory: that for these fighters for life nothing was ever too much trouble. He has seen a crew of these youngsters come back from twenty-four hours of vigil and action at a bedside. Before they'd got out of their overcoats in the gray of the sub-zero morning there was a buzz at the switchboard. Yes, all the other delivery crews were busy at the bedsides of nine mothers having babies. Sorry. So they departed again, on a nine mile streetcar ride to another woman reporting her pain's beginning. Two hours later they came back. Their eyes were redder-rimmed, their faces fagged and gray. Hard luck. It wasn't labor pains the woman was having, but just a bad toothache. Of course they groused about it to Tucker and Benaron. Of course they were told to laugh it off. You never know. When the switchboard tells you to, you go. This is the discipline of the Chicago Maternity Center.

## II

It is the most fundamental of all the laws of the Center that when, upon arrival in any home, the delivery crew find the mother to be truly in labor, they stay by her till her babe is born, or till it's certain her labor will be so dangerous that she must be taken to a hospital. They watch every mother from beginning to end of her ordeal. To this law there are no exceptions, no matter how long or seemingly uneventful the travail. For this rule there are no evasions, no matter how horrible the home, how child-becluttered, stinking, or dingy. So our young medicos and nurses have an unparalleled chance to learn the natural history of childbirth. They learn every step of the unfolding of that terrible power by which a mother's body must force new life from her.

This is what is most galling to them, children as they all are of our modern life of rush and hurry, that the basis of the birth-helping art and science of the Center is summed up in the four little words of Beatrice Tucker. When you ask that tall fighter the secret of her institution's low death rate, she smiles and says: We sit and wait.

They sit and wait, with a most curious long-drawn-out alertness—and how can humans be alert for long?—but they must sit and wait, so long as there's no sign of danger to mother or child. They have it burned into them that childbirth must march to its outcome with the very least possible scientific (and so often dangerous) meddling. For there is now a highly developed science of meddling with what, till not so many years ago, had been a process of nature. Not so many years ago it was discovered by the English chemist Henry Dale that extracts of the pituitary gland had a curious stimulating power to the muscles of the wombs of female creatures. And this womb-contracting energy stoked up by this magic drug pituitrin has indeed saved thousands of mothers from death from hemorrhage—*after their babies have been born.* But, in the lives of today's practicing doctors, and even of obstetricians, who to make their livings must rush from one childbed to the next one, this powerful pituitrin has been put to another use, the result of which is sometimes sinister. Among hundreds of thousands of American mothers pituitrin is now used *to bring on their labor.* And here its inexpert use has consequences that are awful. This pituitrin stirring the womb's muscles to an unnatural power may cause them to contract so violently that the babe is locked in the mother, and dies. The womb may rupture, with fatal hemorrhage. Or it may be lacerated with the mother left invalid. Or the tissues of the womb may die —with fatal infection following. Or the violence of the womb's contractions, beating the babe's head upon the pelvic bones of its mother, may so damage the child's brain that it is born alive maybe, but forever imbecile.

So dangerous seemed this two-edged sword, pituitrin, when given not to stop hemorrhage after the baby's birth, but to induce the baby's coming, that the French birth-helper, Cotret, sent out a world-wide questionnaire about it. The answer from the world's best obstetricians was this: that pituitrin so used is dangerous, maybe deadly to mother and to child. It is widely used to hasten childbirth in America.

Now if the peril of the mother or the child demands that labor must be started, milder means—or else the Caesarean operation—are used by the doctors of the Center. And the use of the drug pituitrin for this purpose is absolutely prohibited by the directing doctors of this house of life. It is notable in the Center's practice that its young doctors get to every mother's bedside—and stay there—long before this would be considered necessary by many expert obstetricians. Watching here, these interns, medical students, nurses, learn the unforeseen development of sudden obstructions that so many babies have to meet while they try to be born. The examinations these fledglings are premitted to make upon the mother are safe and simple ones. Tyros, their grave conclusions as to when and how the baby is to come, are often grotesquely mistaken. Tucker, Benaron, or the resident physician do not allow themselves to be annoyed by such blunders. Nor are the medical youngsters ever scolded for false alarms that they so often flash to the green bulletin board at the Center—

"We never bawl them out for calling us when it turned out not to be necessary. Only when they fail to call us when they should have." So says Benaron. This is the candor that makes Beatrice Tucker and Harry Benaron the teachers that they are: they freely tell their students that they themselves could have made like mistakes in judgment, and that in fact they have done so. This honesty Benaron says they have learned from De Lee, their master. "When we're humiliated by one of our mistakes, De Lee always tells us—in his forty-five years' experience—he's made nearly every blunder possible in obstetrics!"

III

So the life-guarding science they learn is that arduous science of we-sit-and-wait. Yet at any moment this doldrum may be ended by the hurricane of disaster. At four on a bitter January morning a call comes to the big green bulletin board from the home of a twenty-eight-year-old Negro woman. At seven good news is chalked up: the baby's position in its mother is what it should be, for an easy, natural childbirth. Its heart tones are strong and good. The mother's pains are powerful, coming every two or three minutes. No need at all to worry, for the directing doctors. Only another experience of conducting a natural childbirth for the young intern, medical student, and nurse.

Now in this Negro home that child has come, with no notable loss of its mother's life-blood. Now there is a little trouble, but nothing uncommon. The baby refuses to breathe. The intern and his medical student are admirably taught the simple science for such emergency. They hurry from the bedroom to the kitchen with this dusky little one in their arms. Deftly the intern slips a thin rubber tube into the babe's mouth and down his windpipe, first to suck possible foreign matter from the child's lungs, then gently to blow his own breath into the baby's lungs, even as Elisha did in the Bible story.

For five, ten, fifteen minutes the intern breathes into the baby, and it is no go. And now, presto, a tiny gasp, and then another, and then in a moment a lusty cry, and the baby is living, breathing. His dusky blue changes to his natural pickaninny color and it is another triumph. They have obeyed the Center's motto: to bring a living mother a live baby—

—At this moment the nurse hurries from the mother into the kitchen. Her face is anxious. She whispers to our two proud young birth-helpers. Going about her duty, routine, of making the Negro mother comfortable, she finds her lying in a pool of blood—

They do everything they've been taught to do in this emergency and the mother goes on bleeding. Telephone! And in five minutes Tucker and Benaron are running through red traffic lights—without the official privilege accorded ambulances—to arrive at the tenement where a moment ago a nine-and-a-half pound pickaninny has been brought by the young learners. Our hemorrhage crew stumble up dark stairs. They grope and hesitate among mops, buckets, piles of children's dirty clothes outside the door. They pound at it. They push it open. They stop to introduce themselves—no matter what the hurry they're punctilious about this—to the distracted Negro father. They hurry from him to the now disordered room where the mother's life is leaving her. Quick examination tells Tucker and Benaron they must now use every trick of their death-fighting science. The mother's blood pressure is already very low. Her pulse is thready. Now action. While the nurse warms up the glucose solution, Benaron—Benny to you—has a syringe needle into the arm vein of the panicky husband. Then he's off running more traffic lights to a nearby hospital's laboratory to make the quick test to see if the father's blood will match the dying mother's.

Minutes are hours, but by the clock it is not actually long before victory on that bloody battlefield seems certain. No, they won't need the transfusion! Tucker has injected the glucose solution into the mother's veins. And salt solution, a whole quart of it under her dark skin. Her blood pressure quickly rises. Her pulse beats stronger. And here's Benny back from the laboratory and good news. Here's the ace-in-the-hole of their game with death. Yes, the father's blood matches the mother's. There is poetry here: this wife can now be saved by her husband. But maybe she won't need to be. The transfusion apparatus gleams, unlimbered and ready, but now they won't have to use it. Examination of the mother, quick, gentle. Then packing of gauze into the source of the bleeding. Okay. Good news. She isn't bleeding now—

How's the baby? Listen how it's bawling. They are all happy now. They've brought a husky baby to a mother who's now going to live.

Tucker bends over the mother just to make sure everything's all right, and wait, her lips are pale. The pupils of her eyes are wide, staring. Her pulse? Suddenly it's almost nothing.

Now the crew of them snap into the extreme of action. First: adrenalin injection to stoke up her just beating heart. Now quick the transfusion. This is the last word in science. This will save her. It can't be too late. No. Now they look for the vein at the crook of the mother's elbow. Alas, the mother's blood pressure has sunk so low there is not a sign of it. For a moment even Tucker is desperate. "God! I can't find that vein!" But there's this that's left in their bag of scientific tricks. Are the instruments boiled up? Yes. All ready. Here's the scalpel—

Tucker bends over, cutting down upon where the vein should be and now quickly she exposes it. It is not too late. The mother is living, yes. Now the dark blood gushes into the transfusion apparatus from the husband's arm and the mother still is breathing and with the blood connection made to her from her husband, her eyes are open. The blood is the life. So says the Book of Deuteronomy and so De Lee keeps telling them. Now the life-guarding blood flows from this man to his mate and science is powerful—

Now they hear the mother talking, calling to them in a low voice as if from very far away— "Doctor! Save me! Save me for my babies!" And then, more faintly: "Doctor, you won't let me die?"

These are the last words of this Negro woman who fought hanging on to harder and harder breathing, hoping her man's blood might save her.

Remembering her last words, Benaron told this present chronicler: "When you hear a woman say that, you die too. Yes, she died. When we realized she was finally dead, Tucker and I dropped our apparatus and began crying. The intern and the medical student and the nurse couldn't keep their eyes dry, either. We all just sat there and couldn't stop our crying."

### IV

It is not simply that they cared so much that they all wept over this defeat by death, that's not the point, no, the point is that Tucker and Benaron aren't ashamed to remember and acknowledge their breakdown after this disaster. They are simple people in our world of intellectuals and cynics. They are ashamed of one thing only. They are ashamed of death. "When you look back on any death, and go over everything you might have done but didn't, you'll begin to believe that mighty nearly every maternal death could have been prevented," says Beatrice Tucker.

One of the scientific wonders of the Chicago Maternity Center is the series of detailed records kept of the more than fourteen thousand women who have had their babies under the Center's care. Toward the bottom of the last page of each record you find these words—

*"Tell what you might have done better and what to do next time."*

This is the sharp focus of all their teaching. Here every last student, intern, nurse, the resident physician, and Tucker and Benaron put themselves upon the spot. Here, when these rare deaths happen, they must take their part of the responsibility. Here in the particular case of this Negro mother, those two youngsters, the intern and the medical student, had to take the rap. Save blood! Take alarm early! Procrastinate for nothing! Immediately institute anti-shock measures! These stern hemorrhage-fighting words of De Lee's had not been heeded while those two boys were so busy trying to breathe life into that woman's baby in the kitchen. Yet we must remember the intense responsibilities of those two youngsters trying to save two lives at the same time. They had left the mother alone too long, yes, but only to save her baby. And now this conference—tell-what-you-might-have-done-better!—this will burn their blunder into them. How can they ever forget—if in our hard world they can make shift to remain human?

Isn't this too grim a laboratory in which to learn safeguarding mothers against the peril of fatal bleeding? Must all the Center's young birth-helpers go through this experience? That's the point. They do not have to. Such is the power of their death-fearing emotion that Tucker and Benaron succeed better and better in communicating this fear of loss of mothers' blood to all the young doctors and nurses who come to the Center. What, after all is the glory of teaching, if it is not to make us strong beforehand, to break down the ages-old tragedy of learning only by fatal experience? It is nearly three and a half years, now, since any woman having her baby under care of the Chicago Maternity Center has lost her life from hemorrhage! Of all the now more than 14,500 mothers who've been brought their babies by these young doctors—only two in all have died from loss of blood.

This record is ten times better than the national average—

Both their hemorrhage deaths occurred in the first two years of the Center's existence. Since then more than 9,000 mothers in succession have had their babies with not one dead by bleeding. Yet the more remarkable their record becomes, the greater is their terror of this danger. When you congratulate Tucker or Benaron on their record, their eyes light up but only for a moment and then they mutter that maybe after all they've been lucky and then they knock on wood—remembering eight, ten, a dozen mothers having their babies, this moment, at the hands of these tyro birth-helpers in every part of Chicago. And if their hemorrhage-fighting record is an all time high, then there are other preventable deaths they ought to conquer—

After all, out of their more than 14,000 women delivered, three have died from tuberculosis. But, you protest, this is not an obstetric cause of death. It is not so listed, among deaths due to the childbearing state, in the International List of Causes of Death. It would not be fair to blame our Center's doctors for these TB deaths. Wouldn't it be like accusing them of responsibility for an earthquake that might kill a woman in childbed? No. Tucker does not take refuge in such arguments. There is now available the x-ray's magic eye—that can detect the presence of even minimal tuberculosis in a pregnant woman. There is the great new surgical treatment of tuberculosis, so powerful that pregnancies no longer have to be terminated in women found tuberculous. Then why didn't these mothers—needlessly dead —have the benefit of these scientific weapons? Why isn't every expectant mother coming to the Center before her baby is born, x-rayed as a routine? Why can't they all be given this added chance for life?

Tucker's answer is simple and bitter. For the x-ray apparatus, the films, the salary of a roentgenologist, the Chicago Maternity Center has not got the wherewithal.

## CHAPTER FIVE

# FOR LIFE, NOT PROFIT

IT is lucky for Chicago's poverty-stricken mothers that the science to guard them from the most formidable of all threats of childbed death can still be afforded by the doctors of the Chicago Maternity Center. Childbed fever is still the chief enemy of American women who are going to have babies. Of all the mothers who lose their lives to give the world new life, forty out of every hundred die from infection during childbirth. Of American mothers who bear children, close to one out of every four hundred dies this death—now needless. To this nationwide butchery the record of the Center's birth-helpers makes a devastating contrast.

It is a curious fact that the spreading abroad of outstandingly low death rate records made by any one institution or group of doctors and nurses is disliked by some physicians. "Let sleeping dogs lie. We're doing the best we can to remedy these scandals within our profession. These records—good or bad—are not the public's business." It is with such objections that the reporting of your chronicler is sometimes met, by some high-ranking doctors. It is not that the brilliantly low maternal death rate record made by the young obstetricians of the Chicago Maternity Center is a lie. It is only that the comparison between it and the national maternal death rate (which stinks to high heaven) is invidious. Or by some it is so considered.

This is a measure of the backwardness of medical practice compared to that of certain other professions. Railroad experts are proud of records of all trains speeding millions of miles without death of passengers. The white flame of scientific investigation is turned upon airline disasters, and these are placed under scrutiny of the people. Each new scientific trick or wrinkle to checkmate death is broadcast with exultation. This is the secret of the progress of men who fight for a life that is faster yet safer. People in general do not stop riding in airliners because of their spectacular accidents. They show faith in science fighting for more safety. Now, in medical practice, a most amusing smokescreen is laid down to cover childbed fever's scandal. It is the pious fear that mothers, told of childbed fever's threat, will dread to have children and actually stop having them! This is nothing but contempt for women's intelligence. And further, to allay women's fears, childbed fever's danger is belittled. Now it's admitted that good administration and technique have reduced infection's terror almost to the vanishing point in many modern maternity, and some general hospitals. But in which ones? And many a husband can be reassured when his wife's physician tells him that his own low death rate promises the baby will be born safely. Yet for the mass of American fathers and mothers there is this enigma—

That, while our general death rate has dropped one-third since the beginning of the century, while the baby death rate has been cut in half, childbed fever has gone down little if any. It remains the chief killer of childbearing women. Now since this present story of the fight for life means the fight for life for all, then it cannot be indiscreet, or against the public interest to report the battle fought against motherhood's most terrible danger by the birth-helpers of the Chicago Maternity Center.

Their low death rate record in the first two years of the Center's history was an excellent one. Their record of the past three years is one of the major achievements of mankind's death-fight. Against childbed fever death it is—in your chronicler's knowledge—unprecedented.

## II

It is no startling new discovery these birth-helping young-sters have made. You already understand all of the basic facts of this science; and every physician in America has been exposed to them. It is a scientific chestnut how Ignaz Sem-melweis pointed out that every childbearing mother is a gravely wounded woman, and how childbed fever death can be washed off the hands of those who bring the baby. It is high school text-book platitude how Pasteur discovered the most terrible of the childbed fever mother-killer to be the streptococcus. Few doctors are ignorant of the death-fighting science of our famous Surgeon William S. Halsted—who proved how you could still further guard the life of wounded people by wearing thin rubber gloves—boiled free from deadly microbes.

It is all old stuff now, commonplace to the non-medical masses, how this scrubbing of hands, boiling of instruments, dousing of germicides, wearing of sterile masks and gloves, how all these simple tricks—conscientiously and invariably performed—alone guard the lives of myriads of human beings necessarily wounded by surgical operations. Why then isn't every last mother, wounded as she must be when her baby leaves her, likewise guarded?

Why are our young birth-helpers smiled at—as fanatics—when they apply De Lee's fanatical cleanliness to poor mothers in those so often filthy tenements and hovels of Chicago's shadows?

Is it that the wound made inside the mother by the coming of her child is not dramatic to the doctor, not obviously open like the gaping wound of a surgical operation? Is it that the threat of the invisible streptococcus that he may carry on his hands or instruments is made to a wound likewise not visible? Partly and maybe that's a reason.

But how can it be that, by their very dirtiness, these poor

Chicago homes are safer than many hospitals seemingly microbe-proof, what with their white tile and gleaming paraphernalia of germ-fighting science? This is the story. This is one of the secrets discovered by De Lee and practiced—as a ritual, a religion—by his birth-helping followers at the Center. This religion is the explanation of their glorious record against childbed fever; this, and their honesty in their white hot hatred of all death.

Of course, among the 14,500 women to whom the Center's doctors have brought babies in the past five years, there have been a few who've died of childbed fever. There have been a number infected, and luckily not fatally. Yet, for each one of these rare deaths, when you probe the details of each tragedy, the Center's birth-helpers could have dodged responsibility. And at the beginning of their work, in 1932, it did not seem as if their record was going to be anything to write home about. They had safely delivered their first 369 mothers in succession, when a routine delivery crew, rushing to the dilapidated home of a nineteen-year-old wife, found she'd borne her first baby before they could get there—

Already a little fever. Nine days later—death. Autopsy. Death due to the breaking of an abscess, caused by gonorrhea, that had occurred long before the Center's doctors so much as knew this girl existed.

"Yes, we count her as our death, just the same," said Beatrice Tucker to your protesting chronicler. With a deplorable disregard of scientific reasoning Tucker said: "If you start selecting, if you start eliminating in your statistics, you can eliminate yourself out of any death at all!"

Now months went by. Tucker urged the interns, the medical students, the nurses to a fury of cleanliness by scrubbing. She was everywhere in these homes "on the district"—which is all over Chicago—lynx-eyed about the boiling of instruments. It was ruled next door to criminal for any birth-helping neophyte to introduce his hand—even though gloved and sterile—into the passage toward a mother's womb to examine her, unless some disaster in her labor made this absolutely unavoidable. All routine examinations of the progress of the childbirth were rectal. Now by De Lee's safe and sane system of we-sit-and-wait, by not using instruments to bring any baby if nature could bring it without detriment to the mother—under Tucker's stern yet strangely democratic dictatorship, 1,832 mothers were brought babies in succession— Without one dying from septic death.

This was really excellent! One out of more than two thousand—as against one out of every four hundred odd mothers bearing children dying from childbed infection the country over. Then, alas, a second mother, after an easy labor, went into an unaccountable, lingering attack of fever, seemed to be getting better, then, against the explicit instructions of the Center's doctors, this woman douched herself internally. And died. There was evidence here, too, that this second dying mother had harbored gonorrheal infection before her baby came, that this was stirred up to peritonitis by her child's arrival—

Your reporter protested to Beatrice Tucker that, by the rules of The International Classification of Causes of Death, this death need not be called maternal. Tucker's look was a severe one. "She's our death. We *may* have slipped. I couldn't testify that the intern or nurse or medical crew didn't put some other infection in there."

By now Harry Benaron had joined the staff of the Center and Tucker and Benaron—the tall woman so effervescent and the young man so cool and laconic—have this in common. They incessantly engage in analytical self-accusing postmortems of their blunders. Of course Tucker and Benaron couldn't be everywhere all over the district spotting every flagging of the vigilance of all their young intern, medical student, and nurse-apprentices. Yet the fury and honesty of their teaching deserved a better reward than it now got.

For now less than a month passed. Only 172 additiona
babies had been born since that second mother's dying. Now
here happened a childbirth that certainly needed no exper
supervision by Tucker or Benaron. Here was the bringing o
a healthy baby to a seemingly healthy mother by a routine
delivery crew of youngsters who'd arrived at the home shortly
after the first labor pains began. There was plenty of time
for them to be deliberate, scrupulous, in the aseptic, anti
septic ritual of preparation of themselves and the mother
No labor could have progressed more serenely. It was nor
mal. It was easy. As the baby came into the world, the young
doctor had only to bend its head gently forward with his
sterile gloved hand. No instruments. No internal examination—

Six days later this mother was dead, of explosive child
bed fever, in the hospital to which they'd had to take her
when her fever flared two days after her babe had been so
safely born.

When she had first got ominously sick, Tucker had of
course hurried to this mother's home, had gently questioned
her. "Yes, Doctor, I've got a bad sore throat— I had a little
sore throat the day before the baby came," said the mother.

But again this was not the fault of our apprentice birth
helpers! Hadn't this mother suffered from "auto-infection"
—from that self-infection from virulent germs already in a
woman's body? It is to this possible chain of events that it
is now the fashion to ascribe many deaths from childbed
fever. Surely, if the evil streptococcus was in this mother's
throat, it might have sneaked into her blood, and then down
to her womb, and so from there to its deviltry of a fatal
peritonitis! This was science. This was logical. But was it
true?

Not necessarily, said Tucker. Wasn't it possible one of the
young doctor's hands had been infected by spray from the
woman's coughing? Yes. And had they watched every slight

movement of the mother's own possibly infected hands, during her ordeal? No. Could they swear that her own hands, infected from her throat, had not strayed down to infect her, one moment when they weren't watching? No, they could not swear it.

"After all, we did miss one trick," said Benaron. "We should have noticed that woman's sore throat before her baby came. She is our death. That sore throat's no alibi."

Yet their record was a respectable one as of this date. Three deaths out of three thousand and four cases. Better than twice as good as the national average for childbed fever. And now a year passed. So sharply did Tucker and Benaron keep this one issue of life-and-death in focus before their apprentices that the Center's records now boasted 2,756 of Chicago's mothers, delivered of their babies in succession— Without a fatal case of childbed fever.

They were surely justifying the science of tragic Semmelweis, of fiery Pasteur, of death-hating De Lee, their master. They were giving the lie to the comfortable buck-passing pseudo-science that childbed fever is often auto-infection. Yes, death comes from outside. You can keep death out. If you're super-clean, super-careful, if you're conscientious.

Then a colored mother died, from infection, fourteen days after the Center's doctors had brought her baby. They had not been called to the shack where this woman lived, till an old crone of a Mississippi Auntee midwife had made an internal examination of the mother with her dirty, ungloved hand. Worse yet, the next day after the baby had come, that same granny had anointed the entrance to the passage to the young mother's womb with a salve of vaseline and sugar!

"Just the same," said Beatrice Tucker, "if we had been on our toes, if we'd *taught* that mother properly, she would not have allowed that old midwife anywhere near her. She's our death."

### III

Such was their fourth death from childbed fever—four deaths out of 5,130 mothers delivered of children. Now their record was more than respectable, it was excellent—one out of 1,282. Three times better than the national childbed fever death rate. And this death happened three and a half years ago. Since then they've lived a taut battle, twenty-four hours of every day and night. It is a struggle to guard against every conceivable ambush of this subvisible death, these murderers whose subtlety, whose very tininess, is what makes them so formidable. Tucker and Benaron keep saying they are lucky. They work with their fingers crossed.

None can foresee, nobody dares say, to what peak this record will go. But it is already remarkable enough to make the shades of Ignaz Semmelweis, of Louis Pasteur, of Joseph Lister, bless these youngsters' final proof of this fundamental of mother-saving science—

That, in the enormous majority of cases of fatal childbed fever, death sneaks into a mother from outside. These disciples of Joseph B. De Lee have at last and to the hilt confirmed the theory, the great conjecture, of those three pioneering searchers. They have built a landmark in the fight for the lives of mothers. When you talk or argue with Tucker and Benaron—as this chronicler has done far into the night of many nights—these two are, strangely, of different opinion as to the chief cause of their present run of successive confinements in which there has been no childbed fever death at all.

On the ground of his own microbe-hunting experience your reporter argued it must be simply the terrific cleanliness they teach their birth-helping youngsters.

"All right, admitted we're clean. We're the cleanest I've ever seen," answered Benaron. "But even so, I've shown you bad slips in technique with every mother you've seen us deliver."

Tucker bridled. "But we're not filthy, Benny!"

"No, but we're far from perfect. No, it's the fact we deliver women in their homes that's at the bottom of it. They're probably immune to their own bugs in their own homes."

—This was sound microbe-hunting science as well as honesty on the part of Benaron—

Yes, in the excitement and the rough-house science of a difficult delivery of a baby they perforce make many a slip that would contaminate and wreck a laboratory experiment in microbe-hunting. Your chronicler has observed it. But, God, they're on their toes and cleanly! This reporter best of all remembers that night in a desolate two room flat where he lived what seemed a lifetime from midnight till the dirty gray of the February dawn. Here Benaron guided the fight of a crew of student birth-helpers in the ticklish business of the bringing of her baby girl to a colored mother. Her home was dirty and forlorn. Her husband had just deserted her, leaving her with two pickaninnies and now this new one coming. A few minutes before this midnight, the routine delivery crew from the Center had taken alarm. The mother's blood pressure was rising, her head was aching something awful, so she said, and then her labor pains had died away.

What your chronicler now saw was a supreme example of the Center's "luck" as certain envious physicians will describe it. The intern, at this moment, knew that here was not only the threat of eclampsia. He knew that eclampsia—unchained—is potent to lower a mother's resistance to infection. He knew here was the time for drastic action. So now, ominous figures chalked up on the Center's bulletin board brought us there pellmell.

The birthroom in this home served as kitchen-dining-living-room, and it was half-heated by a rickety cookstove in which used dry-batteries, paper boxes, miscellaneous rubble from the floor were trying to burn but only succeeded in filling the den with an acrid smoke. The drain of the kitchen sink emptied into a dirty pail. Above it was a shelf that was the family larder—holding one egg obviously ancient, and a quart milk bottle in which powdered milk had been shaken. In every corner of the room were heaps of dubious rubbish. Now Benaron called to this reporter from a little room in which he was donning his immaculate white birthroom uniform.

"Come and see the star's dressing-room," he said, smiling. He was adjusting his garb in a dim-lit combination lavatory and toilet room, of which this bitter winter had some days ago stopped up the plumbing. He pointed through the door to the strange scene in the center of the kitchen. Here were gowned, rubber-gloved, masked, yellow-aproned Resident Physician Hy Reitman and his intern assistant, wielding long-needled syringes to give the mother the local anesthetic the Center demands for operative deliveries. Long ago they've found that this keeps down the pneumonia deaths that are wont to follow ether. Close by, super-competent Nurse Norling directs student nurses in the laying out of trays of instruments, sponges, basins of disinfectant, gauzes —on a newspaper-covered ironing board supported on two backless objects that served the family for chairs—

The whole crew of them were not hurrying or jostling. Speaking low monosyllables they were taut at their work of fashioning a microbeless island of safety for the mother's ordeal in this dirty hell that she called home. They prepared a clean portal through which the baby would make its entrance into a world where it certainly was not needed.

"Look at it," whispered Benaron. "The best hospital's no safer. You see, the dirt's dramatized here. You've got no sense of false security. In this damned hole you get your sterile-gloved hands within a foot of anybody, anything, and you just assume you've got contaminated. It's not like a hospital where everything *looks* sterile. There are just three things those kids are keeping clean. Their hands, their instruments, and the exit from that woman. It's *concentrated* cleanliness!"

The baby wants to come and now the forceps begin their life-bringing assistance, under an incessant drenching, by Nurse Norling, of the genitals of the mother. The baby is being born. There is a cry from the mother. "Sorry, mother, it won't hurt long," says Benaron. "I'se sorry, too, Doctor," she says, and laughs a little.

Now the baby, not drugged as it would have been had its mother been given ether, grotesquely begins to bawl before it has completely left its mother. Immediately there is a letdown in the tenseness of the whole crew of the birth-helpers. The carriage of their bodies shows pride in this forceps delivery cleanly, well, and safely done. Then—it could not have been more unexpected—hemorrhage. Now, for maybe fifteen minutes they worked, and couldn't stop it; in spite of massage of the mother's body, in spite of injections of pituitrin, of ergoklonin, of all Benaron—now in command—was doing with cool desperation—

Your chronicler couldn't stand the cascade of blood, and went out into the ice-covered passageway, and though godless, he began a silly desperate praying for all of them inside there. Coming in at last from the dark and rain he was reassured by Benaron's smile. That hombre—on what had once been a green iron chair—was squatting before the mother, expertly finishing his packing of gauze into her, gently inserting the last of six yards of gauze—

Tended by one of the medical students, the new baby girl was waving her arms and legs and crying— Now the mother was back in her sheetless bed, and quiet under ragged blankets. In the kitchen all was cheerful action. Nurse

Norling who that night had been everywhere and had never been asked for anything now directed the packing away of dirty instruments. They all were gay now, till Benaron came out the bedroom door—

He glanced at the stove whose feeble fire wouldn't have boiled water in an hour. "Get back to the Center, quick. Bring the emergency hemorrhage kit. She's bleeding. She's spotted through the packing."

A half hour later Resident Physician Reitman and Nurse Norling, white-tired, came back lugging the heavy bag of sterile instruments; at Benaron's direction the medical students carried the mother back on to the kitchen table—

## IV

"Guess I must be getting to be a fussy old granny to have worried about that little spot of blood that showed through that first pack," said Benaron. We were walking back to the Center, stumbling and skidding over piles of dirty ice, wading through pools of sooty water in the gray of dawn. "If we'd left her that first time, and gone home, I wouldn't have slept. Blood is a woman's resistance. Blood fights infection. That little trickle of blood wasn't dangerous in itself. But she'll need all her blood if she's going to have fever," he said.

Your chronicler was too let-down, too dog-tired, to discuss it or to argue, but that night of February, 1936, is now today as if it were only yesterday. It was just that little extra carefulness, that added hour of work that maybe wasn't after all needed, it was just this that might not have been done by a good doctor who perforce was working for his own profit not for life alone. The night was memorable, too, because of the concentration in that dingy kitchen of the power of eighty years of science—against eclampsia, hemorrhage, childbed fever—of all this science working in the still slightly unsure yet safe hands of all these birth-helping youngsters who were learning. But most notable and unforgettable is the picture of Benny Benaron just before the crew of them left this home without a father. According to the ritual of the Chicago Maternity Center, he had gone into the mother's bedroom to bid her good-by. The mother lay there very quiet, very tired under her ragged covers. Benny smiled down at her. She looked up at him. Then she turned a little, stretched out her hand, and touched the baby now sleeping beside her. Benny reached down and patted the Negro mother's shoulder.

"You're going to be all right now, mother, good-by," he said.

She looked back up at him and only said, "Thank you, doctor, good-by," and what she felt was plain in her dark eyes following him as he turned to go.

These events were observed in February of 1936. Now, at present, this is the record of the doctors of the Chicago Maternity Center—

For more than three and a half years no mother has died from childbed fever in the service of the Chicago Maternity Center. Many have had fevers, yes, but not from microbes savage enough to kill them. As this is written, *9,370 mothers have been delivered in succession without one mother dying from childbed fever.*

As against our national average of one mother out of four hundred who bear children, only to perish from infection.

## CHAPTER SIX

# WHAT THEN SHALL WE DO?

IT is time now to comfort timid souls—who fear, like our wealthy northern businessman in the case of the lowering of the pellagra death rate, that here is only another triumph of science. Admitted that the Chicago Maternity Center's fight for life's beginning is only the story of little lives, not needed, brought to Chicago mothers in too safe profusion. Granted too that these mothers have been saved, but only to the end that they may produce more not-wanted life. Yet our timid souls need not—as of today—take too much alarm. After all, examples of low death rate obstetrics are not so many in our nation. The Frontier Nursing Service has a wonderful record, it is true. But here, again, it hardly affects the national average, it's only a matter of their saving a few thousand hill-billy mothers yearly. Of course there are excellent maternity hospitals, and a goodly number of physicians who bring babies to mothers so safely as to send shivers down the spines of those believing that of human life there is already far too much. Even so such frightened folk may—for the time being—rest easy. There seems to be no immediate danger of the rapid spread of this super-safe birth-helping science and art. Then too, the news of just which maternity services, hospitals, and physicians are the unsafe ones, is not persistently or very widely broadcast to America's endangered mothers. Better yet—for those to whom life's increase is a cause for jitters—this is encouraging: the very existence of the Chicago Maternity Center is precarious! All this brings it about that the death rate among our childbearing women is, in general, still a fairly satisfactorily high one—

For all who believe it socially and economically sound to check the upsurge of life among the human mass.

But here is comforting counsel best of all to quiet the heebie-jeebies of those to whom the glut of human low life is a source of worry. More and more, among the owners of the lives of the people, the belief spreads that too much human life is what ails us. Now the mass of the people do not own their science. The owners of the lives of the people are also the ones who own the science of the fight for life. Today they can turn it off and on like water from a spigot. Then what can be simpler than for them to withhold that wherewithal without which mass life-saving science must languish? With only this precaution, that to maintain the social *status quo,* the mass of the people must be kept in ignorance of such deadly statesmanship. Yet this is less and less easy, since they begin to doubt the bookkeeping of our budget-balancers befuddling them by a maze of figures to prove that life-saving wherewithal is, alas, less and less available.

There are mutterings among the people that the balancing of the human budget comes before the balancing of the budget in terms of money.

Of course, to all who have followed thus far this present story of the fight for life, it is plain that your chronicler is not of the life-fearing or life-denying persuasion. This should not alarm our timid souls unduly. Only a few thousands among the lower myriads will be able to read this chronicle of the adventures (and frustrations) of the men and women who fight for life for all.

Then why go on to tell the deeds of death-fighters like De Lee, Tucker, Benaron? The answer is a plain one. Your chronicler keeps at it because it is his hunch, his intuition— or call it what you will—that today's denial of life is not a permanent one. It is only a symptom of the mortal sickness of an economic order now dying. Some day—the date not here predicted—a new order will arise. In it human life will be the one wealth sought for. Then mankind will begin marching, singing the democratic marching song of poet Schiller's *Ode to Joy* to the stirring music of the *Ninth Symphony* of democratic Beethoven. But your chronicler does not fool himself, knowing that today's partial denial of life-saving science is perhaps only a first hint of mass-murder that may come. He hopes, himself, to gather enough courage to stand firm against this terror. Things must maybe get much worse, in the people's fight for life for all, before they can get better—

Yet from the downfall of our old civilization now looming, there is a chance that some good fragments may survive. These cannot help being of use and encouragement to the fighters for life who are already arising to build the new better order, beginning with such sound science as can be salvaged from the old. This story of the now frustrated fight for life is worth the telling because De Lee, Tucker, Benaron—and all those whose deeds will be told herein-after—are forerunners. They are only prophets of what can and will be.

## II

Tucker and Benaron who work among the families of Chicago's lower five know that the overwhelming majority of those mothers to whom they bring new life are unspoiled and strong, even if poor and simple people. Tucker and Benaron have this advantage over today's despisers of human mass life: they live with the fathers and the mothers of the mass during the deepest of all life's experiences. They know that these women—with few exceptions—have the same longing to live, the same tender joy at their babies' birth, as that exhibited by the refined and educated ladies of our bon ton —intellectual or financial. It's good to listen to Beatrice

Tucker when some confused person of the upper brackets congratulates her upon the Center's fine work in birth control—

"Birth control! Why, we don't try to keep babies from coming. We're not interested in that. We *bring* them babies!" Tucker says it, with indignation, defiance.

There is biologic science to defend her devoted bringing of new life to Chicago's nether myriads. Refined folk—convinced of their own biologic superiority—may protest that while it may be all right for Tucker and Benaron to bring babies safely, yet they're bringing them to the wrong class of people. Then our two birth-helpers really do become indignant. For what, after all, is there to this pseudo-scientific claim that it is now the people who ought not to have them who today have the most babies?

Admitted that birth control is practiced more regularly and effectively by the socially and economically more *fortunate* classes of mankind than by the less fortunate. This fact is so stated by famed Biologist Raymond Pearl but the italics are your chronicler's. What makes this statement startling is Pearl's use of the word "fortunate." Is the vanishing fecundity of prosperous people, of college graduates, a peril to the human race? Will it end by dragging all humanity down to the economic and social level of those nether myriads to whom Tucker and Benaron bring new and (allegedly) not-needed life? Biologist Pearl doubts it. He questions it not on the ground of his prejudices (which are aristocratic ones) but on the ground of science. He explodes the prevailing nonsense that worldly success is in general an indication of the biologic superiority of today's succeeders. Have our more *fortunate* classes got that way because they are composed of people who are actually superior—mentally, morally, physically, and by heredity? And will their children likewise be superior?

Or—asks Biologist Pearl—are the more fortunate classes

where they are simply because they have been more fortunate? Bluntly, is it because most of them have been lucky? Pearl says that this may be alleged with at least equal truth. He points out that, when an animal breeder believes he has a superior horse or cow or chicken, the one scientific test of his hunch is the quality of the colts or calves or chicks produced by his experimental matings. But humans? Alas—

"In absolute numbers," says Biologist Pearl, "the vast majority of the most superior people in the world have in fact been produced by mediocre forebears; and furthermore, admittedly superior folk have in the main been singularly unfortunate in their progeny, again in absolute numbers."

Yes. Ludwig van Beethoven—whose "van" is not aristocratic but means only that his forebears were peasants of the beet field—was the son of a drunken tenor who might have been sterilized by today's Nazi myrmidons. Beethoven's mother, illiterate, was exactly the humble kind of woman to whom Tucker believes she is justified in bringing babies. And, on the other hand, would the music of Bach's sons be remembered, were it not for their father? And where are the scientific geniuses among the progeny of Galileo, Newton, Faraday, and Pasteur?

In short there'll never be a chance to breed human superiority till mankind transcends its present morals, inbreeds itself deliberately, as the animal breeders now inbreed to get faster horses, higher milk-producing cows. Till that great change happens—if ever—it will continue to take millions of plain folk, mating, to produce a few superior people who in turn cannot hope to pass on their own superiority. The present science of race and family superiority, inherited, is poppy-cock and balderdash.

So Tucker and Benaron can sleep easy. They are not menaces to humanity. They do not have to apologize for bringing babies safely to the wives of steel-puddlers, taxi-drivers, and day laborers (even those on WPA). A healthy human mass is the only matrix for its able people, its geniuses, its leaders.

### III

When then shall we do? Why then should not the mass of American babies be well born, and why should not all American mothers have the benefit of all the now existing science and art to see to it that they bear their babies safely?

And what is more bitter than this fact today, that the mass of American mothers do not in general know where to go to have their babies at the hands of those who know and wield this safe birth-helping science? Why is this knowledge kept from them? Let us say that you, a woman, were faced with the possibility of dying, and knew it. Or that you, a man, knew that your wife—within nine months—faced six chances out of a thousand that she might die.

—This, in round numbers, is the American obstetric death rate—

Now it is a fact that science and art exist to give prospective mothers six times better chance than this to live. The obstetric death rate among the more than fourteen thousand mothers brought babies by the Chicago Maternity Center is less than one in every thousand. Why then does not this magnificent birth-helping art and science, of the Chicago Maternity Center, of the Frontier Nursing Service, of certain excellent maternity hospitals and skilled physicians, spread to all doctors and hospitals? Why do not our doctors, as a body, learn right now to practice this life-guarding science and art?

This answer is simple and the doctors are not primarily to blame. The mass of the people, the mass of wives and their husbands, have not demanded that their doctors learn to use it. Here today we whirl in a vicious circle, because there are many physicians who do not believe that the mass of mothers should be soldiers in this fight for life, or should even know of the existence of this safe science so that they could then rise up to demand it. Medicine is a proud and ancient profession, still more than half priesthood, and it does not easily admit the plain people to knowledge of its mysteries. With a determination that would be grotesque if it were not so deadly, some physicians maintain that the having of a baby should be a matter between the individual woman and her individual doctor! Yet this is not the belief of the majority. And this is not the basic reason of the failure of the science to spread.

### IV

It is the mothers who have to do the dying—not rarely, not inexorably, but in numbers which, if all the truth were known, would far exceed the fifteen odd thousand recorded as dead from childbirth by our Bureau of the Census. Hundreds of thousands more of them are grievously, and many permanently, invalided, while the number of their babies who die a-borning is more than four-score thousand. What is this massacre then, if it is not a public health question? It is so held to be by Surgeon General Thomas Parran, of the U. S. Public Health Service. Parran has put this shrewd query to the lay women of the New York Maternity Center Association—

If an epidemic disease, if a new wave of influenza arose to sweep away fifteen thousand of our grown-ups, and eighty thousand babies, would there be any limit to the public measures to combat it, or to the public spirit aroused? Would this be anything but a public health question?

But against this preventable death of mothers and babies it appears that our public healthmen—federal, state, county, or municipal—have no power, or if they have, then it is not generally exercised.

For otherwise, in this first and gravest of all public health questions, could not wives and their husbands band together, to demand that their healthmen take action, to ask their health authorities these questions—

Have you, our healthman, the records, in respect to the life and death of mothers having babies, of all doctors who are licensed to bring babies? Have you the life and death records of the hospitals where we have our babies? And, if you have these records, why do you not publish them for our information?

—After all it is we, the people, who give you your bread and butter, and it is we, the people, who want to live, and it is we who are now doing the dying—

Why, healthman, do you not see to it that every one of us who has been determined pregnant is reported by the attending doctor, by number, to your health department? Exactly as every case of measles, scarlet fever, diphtheria, is now reported?

Why isn't this number then placed upon the birth certificate of the baby born, and on the death certificate of its mother if she should die?

And shouldn't this information be available to you, whether the baby is born at home, or in hospital? And shouldn't the name of the doctor delivering the baby go along with this number in your files, healthman?

Now remember that we, the people, know that we ourselves are not competent to determine whether any given woman has died needlessly, or whether any baby has been butchered by bad obstetrics. But why can't you, healthman, see to it that all the facts of every case of childbirth, with happy or tragic outcome, are available to a board of expert birth-helpers?

Why shouldn't every death, every disaster, be thus analyzed by obstetric experts, in respect to its preventability or unavoidability? And, analyzed, why shouldn't the record of the doctor and the hospital involved in it be open to the scrutiny of ourselves, the mothers, and of our husbands?

We hold you, healthman, accountable for the prevention of epidemics of diphtheria or smallpox. Then why shouldn't you give us a like accounting in the now much more serious question of the needless dying of childbearing women?

This is the plan for the joining of the people in the fight for life's beginning, advanced by Beatrice Tucker. Who has a better right to put forward this practical but devastating proposal? That's the catch, it's devastating. That's the bug in this noble scheme of making mothers co-fighters in this fight for life's beginning: administered honestly by our healthmen, what would be this plan's immediate result? What would have to be done, for the protection of our childbearing women, about the doctors, the hospitals, whose high obstetric death rates showed them to be incompetent to bring mothers their babies safely? Would not these doctors have to be taken out of circulation—at least as birth-helpers —till they had learned obstetric judgment, learned when it was safe for them to attempt delivery of a mother and when best to turn the dangerous job over to an obstetrical specialist? Would not the hospitals—at least their maternity divisions—have to be closed down until they build strictly separated maternities, or made cross infection into their present maternity wards impossible?

But if our healthmen, freed from the meshes of lay and medical politics that entangle them now, could take these drastic steps, if they proceeded now to take unsafe doctors and hospitals out of circulation, who would bring our mothers their babies, and where would they be brought? In short, would there be enough doctors truly skilled in obstetrics, and enough hospitals where it is safe for mothers to go?

Hasn't Beatrice Tucker—good as her stern plan is—got the cart before the horse?

Isn't it best for the people to begin their fight for life's safe beginning by demanding the immediate training of competent doctors, the immediate building of safe hospitals —before the incompetents and the dangerous hospitals where they practice are taken out of circulation?

The immense majority of physicians—just give them the economic chance to—would be glad to take time off to learn the latest obstetric art and science. Hospital superintendents, too, if they had the wherewithal, would be proud to build safe maternities.

## V

Here is the plain ten-point death-fighting platform—it could be a manifesto for the lives of the nation's mothers— that Tucker and Benaron have perfected on the basis of the art and science of De Lee, their old master—

Supervision by the Center's expert obstetricians is ready for every childbirth.

The poor homes, in which nineteen out of every twenty of the Center's babes are born, are made as safe as the safest maternity hospital.

No instruments are used to bring a baby unless the life and health of mother and babe demand it.

There is a doctor, nurse, and medical student present at every childbirth.

Should danger threaten that cannot be coped with in the home, then the mother is rushed to any one of the four finest hospitals in Chicago.

The pre-natal care given to all women registered is alert, fanatic.

The cleanliness organized in the dirtiest homes is before godliness.

There is a doctor and a nurse at every mother's bedside from the moment she reports herself in labor till at least two hours after her baby is born.

General anesthetics are used in only fifteen mothers out

of every hundred, yet the relief of their pain is skillful and sufficient.

Finally—excepting in the most remote rural regions, it would be hard to find a smaller number of the so-often deadly Caesarean operations done than the Center does among its mothers.

## VI

How many obstetric training centers at all comparable to this one can be found in this country? How many doctors are financially able—if they want it—to take time off from their practices to gain this birth-helping knowledge? To ask these questions is to answer them. Yet our skilled obstetricians could prepare a justification, on the basis of the book-keeping of today's economics, for the national allocation of wherewithal to found ample facilities for the teaching of this art and science, and money to pay our rank-and-file physicians to learn it.

To finance such obstetric teaching centers and to train the doctors a certain number of millions of dollars would be needed yearly. There is no doubt that the figures for such a budget could be arrived at by a council of our leading birth-helpers. At the same time let them embark on a second computation. Let them cast up the figures of the cost of mothers, babies, needlessly dying in our country. Let them estimate the millions our communities now waste and throw away—

Upon the funerals of the thousands of mothers who now die needlessly. For the hundreds of thousands of babies who die a-borning or who never see the light of day at all. For the myriads of women who have to pay for operations, for hospital care that is the aftermath of their bungled childbirth. For the treatment and care of babies injured at birth and later crippled, or feeble-minded.

What would be the national saving, in hard cash to taxpayers, if this preventable death, invalidism, and maiming were actually prevented?

This true economy has never yet been audited, estimated.

Must our taxpayers have their saving *right now?* Or is our economic order still strong enough to plan to budget its fight for life in terms of, let's say, a generation?

The savings, to our entire nation, brought about by safe obstetrics would be formidable. And intelligent taxpayers know that their own children will have to pay taxes after the present taxpayers, themselves, are gone.

Your chronicler does not here maintain, along with Joseph B. De Lee—idealist!—that human life is the only wealth. Putting that philosophy into practice generally, would gravely upset our present economic order. He only asks what flaw is to be found in this bookkeeping proving that we are financially a nation of wasters—so long as we go on allowing mothers and their babies needlessly to die.

Meanwhile, though government and private philanthropic agencies know of this low death rate record of the Chicago Maternity Center and its power for obstetric teaching, this house of life may have to close its doors for lack of financial support.

*Part Two*

MEN AGAINST THE MAIMING DEATH

## CHAPTER SEVEN

# OF TRAIL-BLAZERS

THE story of the fight for life's beginning is simple, seems pollyanna-ish compared to the hardly started war against the death and maiming that lie in wait for children not long after life's begun. The science of the fight for life for mothers is established; but to every scientific fact known about infantile paralysis you can still oppose some enigma to put the usefulness of that fact in question. Victory in the war to save mothers waits only for the banding together of all the people to demand and then to see to it that the known science is used. To fight infantile paralysis—because of its terror and tragedy—the people are now ready to organize themselves. But what weapons will their fighters for life place in the people's hands?

That's why the war against the paralytic death can be truly said to be hardly more than started. The existence of this horror has been known for nearly a hundred years now. The groping of microbe hunters and healthmen into this maiming mystery has been going on for just half a century. The universality of the menace makes it a social leveler. For between the haves and the have-nots of our economic order the subvisible virus of infantile paralysis makes no distinction, plays no favorites. It is not—like tuberculosis and other deaths of children—the penalty of poverty. Once this paralytic terror begins stalking, wealth can't buy immunity. The well-fed babies of the boulevards are no safer than gamins in the gutter once this crippling, killing midget-microbe's on the rampage. Before it the coupon-clipper's lady and the worker's wife are equals. The more fortunate people of the upper brackets may ask in vain where they shall take their children to safeguard them. All realize that for their own to be protected, the pestilence must be kept from all people. This is the merit of the paralytic plague that's otherwise so damnable.

It would be wrong to say that against it there is utter lack of science. At the very moment this is written fathers and mothers are in a fever of fear in Chicago, in Toronto, and a possibly hopeful scientific sortie against its siege may be organized by healthmen and physicians. Yes, possibly hopeful, that's the trouble. For hopes against this crippling death have been raised before and then disappointed. And in councils of men against the maiming death at which your chronicler has been privileged to be present, this has been outstanding: that our fighters for life stand in awe of the wee microbe's trickery and resourcefulness. They may have in their hands—as they do have right now—experimental science that should give mankind at least a slight edge in the fight against this particular microbe. Yet in these councils your reporter has always had the feeling of being present in the training camp of a challenger—already half-beaten before he steps into the ring because the champion he is going to fight is so undeniably redoubtable.

This brings it about that in the present infantile paralysis outbreak of 1937 there is no hope of a fight to a decision. Indeed the challenger may hardly dare to climb into the ring. Yet it begins to appear as if the microbe author of this worst tragedy of childhood does have a weakness, an Achilles' heel. A few bold microbe hunters have spotted this weakness, are more and more sure of it. A few—but very few!—healthmen are at this moment hot to take advantage of it. They are opposed by a greater number of healthmen and physicians who raise objections to the joining of the battle. Some of the obstacles they point out are serious ones, and real. Others are phantoms, are only fears raised by the precedent that in this death-fight the infantile paralysis microbe has always been victorious.

Such is the justification for the telling of the story of this fight for life, even though its present outcome is in question. Yet the final victory of our fighters for life is possible— If, faithful to the leadership of more and more powerful scientific facts, they will only all fight together. The terror inspired by the sickness is their best ally. Its awful impartiality makes infantile paralysis the one plague against which our death-fighters may be sure of backing by all levels of the people.

II

Infantile paralysis was a no-account sickness when old German bone-setter, Dr. Jacob Heine, first accurately reported it in 1840. It was not feared then as it now is. It was unheard of for it to sweep through communities, leaving behind it a shambles of the maimed and dying. In Heine's day it only pounced upon a few babies here and there, and there was no indication that it was contagious. It struck them down at their loveliest, when they were just learning to toddle, but Heine took a crumb of comfort from this: that he'd never seen or heard of its killing any child. (Though death for some he saw would have ben preferable.) It is curious that Heine never saw a victim of this sickness till years after it had done its paralytic mischief, but remember he was a bone-setter and it was in this capacity that he saw them. To him, over a long term of years, there had come maybe a dozen or two children, all told. With one or both legs thin and blue. Or with calves of their legs doubled back on their thighs. Or with thighs pulled up close to their bodies. Or with one or both arms hanging limp like flails. Some pulled themselves pitifully about in little wagons. Others hitched themselves along upon their bottoms. Or went on all fours like dogs. He could not cure them. Yet the kind-hearted old physician took a simple joy in exercising them, mud-bathing them, bracing them, operating them out of part of their hideous deformities, so that some of them could walk partly upright almost like humans, though grotesquely, with a hint of the robot, the automaton, about them.

Heine made no conjecture as to the cause of their awful maiming, excepting that it might be due to difficult teething. He guessed—shrewdly—that the mischief had been made in the nerve stuff of their spines. But he knew nothing of the plague's treacherous onset, beyond reports, by various parents, that it had started in the instance of their particular children with a little fever.

You see, these maimed German toddlers were personal, not communal tragedies. And so the disease remained, till forty years after Heine's classic first report of it. Then, mysteriously, a sinister change in character came over the demon of this paralytic sickness, for what otherwise could you then call it, but a demon? Now, 1881, Latitude 64 degrees North, under the northern lights just south of the Arctic Circle, infantile paralysis took up new man-plaguing tactics. Now in the little town of Umea, Sweden, instead of picking out a random child here and there, the sickness paralyzed twenty children in quick succession. The ominous event was observed by Swedish Doctor Bergenholtz, yet it caused no excitement among death-fighters, and why should it have done so? Umea was remote from civilization.

### III

Now it seemed as if the demons of the paralytic plague were not sure of their epidemic genius; and the sickness skulked for six years with no one reporting it as a contagion. Then, in 1887, a nasty little epidemic of it exploded in Stockholm, Sweden, and now at last the sickness began to try its strength in what's called civilization. The Swedish physician Medin immortalized himself by first observing and widely reporting it as epidemic. It no longer began with little no-account fever. "I was astonished at the terribleness of the acute symptoms of it," reported Medin. Healthy children came down with it, suddenly, with high fever, restlessness, pains in their heads, stupors, upset digestions, and then in two, three, four days—paralysis. Medin watched this palsy strike the legs of a three-year-old girl baby, then creep up and up her body, till at last it paralyzed her muscles of breathing, till at last it strangled her, so that she died. Medin saw it choke an eighteen-month-old boy and a five-month-old baby girl to death. Yes. Heine was wrong, the sickness could be fatal. And, this 1887 summer from June till November, forty-four children were stricken in Stockholm.

Three dead little ones played their own part in the fight against infantile paralysis. They were autopsied. The signs of the sickness were found in the motor nerve cells of their spinal cords and the lower part of their brains. These cells were wrecked and blasted. By infection. By what must be a microbe, unknown, but a microbe no doubt of it.

Now again the terror went into hiding, flaring up only in little epidemics in France, and then curiously in Vermont in 1894. So till 1905 and this was the sinister summer of the first great infantile paralysis epidemic in human record. Again the demons did their damage in Scandinavia, and that summer more than a thousand children were paralyzed, and hundreds of youngsters did not live. Mankind was fortunate this 1905 summer that there was, in Sweden, a physician who may be called the Sherlock Holmes of infantile paralysis. This was Ivar Wickman. He was everywhere that summer, taking nobody's word for anything, going into every Swedish home stricken with the new pestilence, and in many more homes that mysteriously escaped its horror. Ivar Wickman was exact in his observations. He was fussily painstaking with his records. And he must have been goggle-eyed at the caprices, the weird habits, of this completely unaccountable contagion—

He named the sickness the Heine-Medin disease. It was called infantile paralysis, yes. But Wickman watched it strike down the forty-six-year-old father of nine children only to pass all the rest of the family by, leave all the children healthy, and walking! And, just as infantile paralysis paralyzed those no longer infants, he saw it sicken infants, not paralyzing them. In one thatch-roofed Swedish cottage Wickman found a little girl with dead, cold limbs. It had all begun with fever, nausea, stiff neck and back. Her little brother had had the same symptoms at the same time. But here he was running round playing with no sign of palsy. And another brother—living right in the same room—had not been sick at all.

The plague played strange and devilish tricks, no doubt of it. In the rural parish of Trästena our medical Sherlock Holmes trailed the unseen paralytic death to its lair. It had first broken out in the parish school where it had smitten the schoolmaster's own children. But what mystery was this? A school-going brother and sister—who'd suffered never a sign of the sickness at all!—had brought it home to paralyze their baby brother. This was outlandish, yet certain: that youngsters more often caught the terror from playmates who didn't have it, than from those who were actually suffering. It seemed as if those not having it, who had been in contact with those sick, *were the carriers,* the truly dangerous spreaders of the evil.

But how spot these unwittingly dangerous people? There was no scientific answer. (And there is yet no answer today in 1937.)

Mankind can't live without hope and here was a bright side of the disaster that terrorized Scandinavian fathers and mothers that 1905 summer. Wickman observed that the disease did tend toward recovery. Youngsters might be limp as rags, absolutely powerless all over their bodies, just barely able to breathe, not able to swallow, not able to talk or even cry at their terrible pain, and then they'd up and slowly but surely get stronger, get better, and walk again at last. Yet, when the physician was called to the bedside of any child in the first feverish stages of his danger, there was no known way to prophesy the outcome. The mildness or the severity of the acute first stage meant nothing. A mild fever might leave a horrible paralysis that was permanent, might even kill a child if the mischief extended to the nerve cells that controlled the child's breathing. On the contrary the first stage might be alarming, with the baby given up for lost, yet that youngster might recover completely—

And Wickman in his honest Swedish manner admitted that there was no drug, no remedy, that could be said in any way to influence the outcome. (It is a pity that all physicians today are not similarly remorseless in their self-criticism when they try some drug or serum.)

But, if you couldn't cure the sickness, could you maybe stop its spreading? Here again Ivar Wickman had to admit his utter powerlessness. He'd made a basic discovery finding it could only spread by personal contact, but how could you keep it from going from child to child? By quarantine? Maybe. But healthy people spread it more than sick ones! Then which ones would you quarantine? The whole population? Exactly. Idiotic. Hopeless. And what was the scientific explanation of this caprice of the gods of chance that made the very great majority of both children and grown-ups proof against the sickness, resistant to it? While at the same time they could give it to others who were susceptible?

To this there was no answer. (To it there is no answer today after thirty-two years longer searching.)

### IV

This is another grotesquerie of this mysterious human malady: that it doesn't pick out weakly, ill-favored children; no, there are those who swear it smites the strongest ones.

What kind of fantastic microbe—there *must* be a microbe since the disease is contagious!—but what sort of fantastic germ was this that could be carried by unscathed weaklings to strike down other people in their strength and vigor? Wickman and his Swedish co-workers could find no microbe of any sort whatever. But now quickly—1909—there followed a truly fundamental find to light the unknown in which the Swedish death-fighters had been groping. The sickness was spreading now, epidemic, over Europe, over America, too, summer after summer. And now, from Vienna good news flashed telegraphically to every corner of a world worried by this terror against which it was so helpless.

Now big, slow-speaking Viennese Karl Landsteiner took the terror from man to monkey. Here on the autopsy table in the dead house lay the paralyzed dead body of Viennese gamin, Fritz. (Ivar Wickman had always said if your child only weathered that bad fourth day his chances got better and better.) But here was a bit of the nerve tissue of the spinal cord of this youngster, who'd died on the fourth day of his sickness. Now this bit of the wrecked nervous tissue of urchin Fritz was out of the syringe in Landsteiner's sure hands and into the body of the baboon—*C. hamadryas*. And into the capering carcase of his lowly monkey cousin, *Macacus rhesus*. This was a day full of foreboding for simians. For in Landsteiner's laboratory a few days later lay the luckless remains of *C. hamadryas,* baboon, dead of experimental infantile paralysis. And close by in his cage the hitherto gay and irresponsible *Macacus rhesus* now was no longer mischievous and merry but sick and sad, and dragged totally paralyzed legs after him. Yes. Infantile paralysis. No question.

Yet Landsteiner, keenest of squinters through highest-powered of microscope lenses, could spot no microbe in these sick or dead simians. (Even today no experimenter has spied it, though some have thought to have, only to be proved in error.) By shrewd combinations of measurements of what they cannot see plus guesses, experimenters believe the size of this subvisible midget to be less than a millionth of an inch. And the latest science has it that this unseeable fleck of so deadly poisonous almost-nothingness is hardly alive. Or that its only living quality is its gruesome one of being able to multiply itself, *ad infinitum,* in the bodies of its myriads of human (and monkey) victims. And that it is a mere sub-microscopic speck of protein on that mysterious borderland of matter that separates non-living stuff from the tiniest living beings—

But here we verge near philosophy, which does not concern us in the fight for life. Here was scientific fact, solid, hopeful, not disputable: *Landsteiner had trapped the sickness in the laboratory!* He could keep it going in his laboratory, just give him the macaques and the baboons who must be the martyrs. All that was necessary was for Landsteiner, with proper bacteriologic precautions, to take a bit of the wrecked nerve tissue of the spine of a dying paralytic monkey. Make a soup of it. Suck it up into a syringe. Drill a hole in a healthy monkey's skull. Shoot a bit of the deadly soup into that monkey's brain. And presto. And so on. From monkey spine to monkey brain to monkey spine to brain again—till he could have killed or paralyzed mighty near all the monkeys in the world if you had passed them through his laboratory.

Even in the beginning of this unquestionable triumph there were forebodings that it might not mean the plague's immediate conquest. The disease Landsteiner had passed from poor Fritz to his simian relatives was infantile paralysis, yes. Undoubtedly. But the sickness in monkeys was not quite the same. It was much more fatal than it was for children. Nine out of ten macaques died when Landsteiner shot this subvisible death into their brains. In the worst epidemics hardly more than fifteen out a hundred children died among all those stricken. In children the disease was contagious.

But in monkeys it wasn't at all. Monkeys live very dirtily among themselves, as German searcher Römer put it. Yet, healthy monkeys could be caged with sick and dying ones with absolute impunity. So this must be faced: that the brilliant monkey science could not after all explain the mysteriousness of the contagion—for children.

Landsteiner's find set laboratories all over Europe and America—that is to say those laboratories whose budgets allowed money for monkeys—into searching. Out of the sickness, palsy, and death of uncounted thousands of monkeys and baboons came this gleam of hope—

That, let a simian suffer an attack of infantile paralysis, yet not die, then, try as you might to infect him, in the great majority of cases he was resistant to a second attack. He was immune. He could go on living to enjoy lifelong paralysis. So, after all, the plague did have a weakness. Its weakness against monkeys held true for children too, for searcher Wickman had never seen it strike twice in one child. That way it was like other, conquerable infections, like typhoid fever, like diphtheria. Wasn't there hope, then, to turn its weakness against the paralytic microbe? Wasn't there the chance for some sleight-of-hand of science, like Jenner's against smallpox, like Pasteur's against hydrophobia?

## V

Maybe yes, and laboratories were a-buzz with plans for experiment. But in another way infantile paralysis was the opposite of diphtheria and typhoid fever. These latter plagues were on the way to being conquered, for one reason, because the microbes causing them could be seen through microscopes. You could spot those microbes in folk dangerously spreading them about, even when those people themselves were healthy. But infantile paralysis? How could you spot what you could never see?

Nevertheless, thanks to the monkey science of pioneer Karl

Landsteiner, 1909 saw the laboratories of the world in a taut fury of searching. Now a fireworks of new facts shot up out of those laboratories rich enough to afford the absolutely necessary experimental monkeys. Our own famed Simon Flexner and his helper, Paul Lewis, at the Rockefeller Institute in New York; Paul H. Römer who was Principal of the Hygienic Institute in Marburg, Germany; searcher C. Leiner and his aristocratic assistant, R. von Wiesner, in Vienna; the strange Constantin Levaditi toiling in the Pasteur Institute in Paris—all these now followed the lead of Karl Landsteiner the trail-blazer, all making discoveries so fast, so simultaneously, that it was hard to say who should have the honor of priority, who deserved the basic credit. Now these fighters for children's lives began to learn curious traits of this midget microbe even if it was too small for the strongest microscope to uncover. The death was found to be so tiny that it could pass through the finest porcelain filters that held back all visible microbes. The death was so hardy that it would stay living for months in strong glycerine. It was very resistant to drying. The death was a peculiar one; it was strangely choosey; from examination of the dead bodies of children and God knows how many thousands of dead monkeys it became plain that the midget microbe's mischief was made mainly—maybe exclusively?—in the nervous tissues of the spinal cord and the lower part of the brain.

But how did it, then, sneak into children to do its damage? What was its point of entry into a threatened child or baby? Here in these first furious days of searching microbe hunters groped on the verge of deep discovery. Searchers Flexner and Lewis rubbed a little swab—it was soaked with this paralytic death—high up inside monkeys' noses. They died from infantile paralysis. Then he went that experiment one better; he threw that experiment into reverse. He shot the death direct into other monkeys' brains. A few days later, as they began to sicken, he found the death had already made its way to the outside world: he found it had leaked out of the brain into those monkeys' noses!

Could this be the explanation of the way it sneaked from child to child? Could it be that here was the one gateway—in and out of humans—for the paralyzing midget microbe?

Alas, this little hint of another one of the paralytic death's weaknesses was lost in a hub-bub of a hundred other experiments, and some of them seemed hopeful. Even in the early 1909 days there seemed hope that some sort of life-guarding vaccine might be found. Every once in a while, when one of our pioneering searchers shot death into monkeys' brains, one of such monkeys might strangely fail to develop the deadly sickness. Then they'd inoculate him again, and sometimes then he'd sicken and die, but other times he'd turn out to be solidly immune, resistant. Was it that first inoculation of deadly stuff that had mysteriously guarded him instead of killing him? Yes. But so what? What price this science? What folly to think of shooting dangerous virus into a child on the chance that it might protect instead of kill him!

But again there was a gleam of hope here. For hadn't Pasteur turned the deadly, rabies-soaked spinal cords of rabbits into life-guarding vaccines just by drying them? Hadn't that old English genius, Jenner, turned virulent smallpox virus into something gentle and protective just by passing it through cows. Unquestionably. And now a dozen tricks were tried by our pioneers in New York, Paris, Vienna, and Marburg, Germany. They took the dangerous spinal cord nervous tissues of dying paralyzed monkeys; they dried them, heated them, mixed them with chemicals, with serums, to try to abate their deadliness and turn them into life-saving vaccines.

They had small successes—saving monkeys. More often they failed. What was strong enough to set up immunity in your monkey was too often strong enough to paralyze and kill him. It was a terrible tight-rope walking. It was altogether too dangerous to try on babies. There was something gallant yet pathetic in our searchers' fumblings because of the profound impracticability of any vaccine—even if they'd chance to find one that was at the same time safe and powerful. Here were the fatal obstacles and who could climb over them? Their one source of infantile paralysis microbes needed for all experiments was the spinal cord of sick and dying monkeys. Where would you get the money for enough monkeys to go round to furnish vaccine to guard hundreds of thousands of children, say you did find out how to make a vaccine? And, too, in any epidemic of the sickness, only a small percentage of youngsters out of all exposed ever came down with it. Any inoculation was bound to be formidable, even dangerous. And would parents allow it—seeing the chance of their child's sickening was hardly more than one out of a hundred in the worst epidemic?

—Remember in these early days the sickness was only beginning to become the terror that it is now: there were not yet hundreds of thousands of children on crutches, and tens of thousands dead, as there are now—

Yet the statistics of America's and Europe's healthmen brought disquieting news of the spread and increase of the maiming death, and our searchers were working under the pressure of popular panics that grew worse, summer after summer. If they could find no practical vaccine to *prevent* the death and maiming, might there not exist some trick to cure it?

After all, stricken children were feverish, headachey, nauseated, stiff-necked, for two or three days before the paralysis hit them. Didn't that mean that the sickness, in its first days, was spread throughout their little bodies before it concentrated its deadliness upon their nervous tissues? Our American searcher, Flexner, for one, thought he'd found evidence that this was true. All right then, wasn't there some way to head off the midget microbes before they began their blasting at the small victims' brain and spinal nerve cells?

Karl Landsteiner in Vienna, Levaditi in Paris, found a fact that again seemed hopeful. You remember if a monkey perchance recovered from the paralysis you gave him, he was immune. The same held good for children who, though paralyzed, yet remained alive. Now our searchers discovered that the blood serum of such recovered children and monkeys had in it a power to kill the paralytic microbes when you mixed a brew of them with such serum in a glass bottle. They knew this because such mixtures failed to paralyze and kill healthy monkeys when shot into their brains—

All right. Excellent. Now if the serum of a recovered victim will knock out the microbes in a test-tube, why shouldn't it kill them in a child's body as well?

This reasoning was according to the rules of logic that, alas, misleads our searchers as often as it helps them.

But to hell with the pitfalls of logic, here was a straw to grasp at. If you injected this immune blood serum into a baby in the first days of its sickness, *before* the paralyzing microbes had sneaked inside the brain and nerve cells of a child's spine to make their mischief—

Why shouldn't you shoot this serum into the blood or even right into the spine of a threatened baby while it was in the first feverish stage of its sickness, so that the power of that serum would be ready to meet the paralyzing microbes before they accomplished their paralytic invasion?

Distinguished nerve doctor A. Netter tried this trick in Paris in 1910. News flashed that here was a triumph at last. Certain children, undoubtedly sick, surely threatened, seemed to become less severely paralyzed after injection of this serum! There was excitement on both sides of the Atlantic, though even in these early days of the serum-hope certain monkey experiments—made by hard-boiled searchers!—threw cold water on this scheme that seemed so logical—

Searcher Leiner in Vienna made an experiment that should
have been enough to call this hope in the gravest question.
He inoculated monkeys—direct into their living brains—with
infantile paralysis virus. It would take some seven days before he would begin to show signs of sickening. But now, on
the very same day that Leiner shot in this death, he injected
quantities of this supposedly life-guarding serum into half of
these monkeys—

Alas, these serum-treated ones became paralyzed and died,
exactly as quickly as their pals who'd got the inoculation of
the paralytic virus only.

## VI

Such were the hopes and doubts raised by our poliomyelitis pioneers in those prosperous days just before the World
War, when many laboratories still had money for monkeys,
when science was encouraged. The hopes and doubts raised
by their experiments had not yet greatly touched the people.
The searchers themselves—though some of them foresaw that
one day this too was going to have to become a people's
death-fight—still worked comfortably in the ivory towers of
their laboratories. So far as useful infantile paralysis-fighting
science went, our healthmen who were the front line fighters
for children's limbs and lives had only Ivar Wickman's epidemic science to go by—

As a natural consequence of Medin and Wickman's proof
that the sickness was contagious, healthmen and fathers and
mothers could only do what was done for other infectious
illnesses: quarantining of the sick one, disinfection of his
surroundings.

But what terrible difficulties there were in regard to such
quarantining and disinfection! You'd have to include all
people who carried this death: the paralyzed children, those
who'd got sick without paralysis, those who carried the danger, though neither paralyzed nor sick.

But who were those last ones? How could you find them? You have no microbe-hunting means to spot them as you had in case of diphtheria or meningitis.

How then could you carry out an exact quarantine? You couldn't. In an epidemic you'd have to be absolutely crude about it. About all you could do was to close the schools: forbid school-age children school during the time of epidemic. You could forbid children to gather in meetings, theaters, playgrounds, swimming-holes, in the time of danger. You could keep them from doing everything they wanted to do, as children—

And what would you disinfect? Could you knock out the subvisible murderous midget microbes as they left any human body—sick or healthy—to sneak out to try to get into the body of a still healthy child? Would you disinfect handkerchiefs? Would you counsel the wearing of masks as in influenza? Would you disinfect all intestinal discharges?

—There was already the beginning of a scientific scuffle as to whether the death entered or left the human body by way of the digestive system—

These vague recommendations sound strangely modern, don't they? Yet they were made by Ivar Wickman way back in 1911. And what better have our healthmen to offer frightened fathers and mothers today—when it comes to quarantining to guard children this 1937 September? What do our healthmen mean when they say they "have the situation well in hand"?

How do the great modern epidemics arise? Why does the maiming death begin to stalk in mid and late summer and early autumn, when children are at their healthiest? Why is it that the great majority of children—in any epidemic—catch immunity instead of paralysis and death?

"None of the deductions drawn can be considered conclusive; in the natural sciences it is rare to find a certainty."

These are the words of infantile paralysis-fighter Paul H.

Römer. And his despair is not expressed today but was written a generation ago; yet his words are modern. And all honest gropers against this awful death and maiming know that Römer's words are true ones, and that they are as good now as they were twenty-five years ago.

But Römer brought his great treatise on infantile paralysis to a close with other very modern words that were whole generations ahead of their time. Will they be heeded by the owners and rulers of the people? Römer—candid about all the scientific hopes that had already failed—gave out a battle-cry, told the true, humane reasons why experiments to prevent the terror should go on, why they should be multiplied in spite of all discouragement. Experiments in prevention, no matter how far-fetched and hopeless they might seem, must go on, first of all because there was no way to curb or cure the terror in a child once it had started. And special preventive measures, chemicals, vaccines, serums, must continue to be looked for—

*"Not only for humane reasons caused by the miserable spectacle of the paralyzed children themselves . . ."*

Not for mere humanity, for altruism only, no. Here Römer peered into the future. He looked the cruelest characteristic of the maiming death in the face. He saw this: that for every child that this death kills (mercifully) it maims, cripples, makes pitiful wrecks of ten to twenty others. He foresaw the slow, terrible accumulation of a population of human flotsam bereft of strength that should be the birthright of all human beings. He looked forward to a situation that exists in our own country now—where, if they could be gathered together for our edification!—we, as citizens, might view a sad parade, in wheel-chairs, on crutches, or dragging themselves along by the aid of braces and metallic contraptions, of an unknown number, but of many thousands of children and grownups. No, said Römer, it was not for humane reasons caused by this miserable spectacle that our fighters for life should go on fighting, searching. Not for those reasons—

*"But for economic ones.* For the majority of those surviving remain paralyzed and therefore economically ruined."

Römer had talked to many a mother. They had often told him they'd rather have their children suffer from a sickness more dangerous to life, yes, they'd rather have them die, and this strange fear of infantile paralysis was based on a sure and instinctive appreciation of its economic consequences.

Then, in the midst of the World War, the first great American epidemic spread its terror among fathers and mothers. Now our fighters for life had to come out of their ivory-tower laboratories and try—with what dubious weapons they had—to guard the limbs and lives of the little ones among the people. Now out of the very disappointment of their hardly justified expectations emerged new science. And it was not hopeless.

CHAPTER EIGHT

# HOPE OUT OF DISASTER

THE New York infantile paralysis epidemic—1916—was the worst up till then recorded, world-wide, and even to this day it remains so. It was disastrous to the lives and limbs of thousands of children. It was ruinous to the science of those who fought for life, as well. Out of this terrible summer came bad science, from that summer's death-fight came false hopes that even to this day, twenty-one years after, you find entertained by parents, by many physicians, though for these hopes there is now no longer scientific foundation. That hot summer in New York and its surroundings one child out of eighty was stricken with the paralytic peril, and now of course the struggle against it had to become the people's death-fight. It did so with a vengeance. But neither fathers and mothers nor their physicians were ready for this stern battle. Yet nobody can blame them, any of them, lay or medical. At the beginning of that awful summer, first in a few homes, next week in dozens, then rapidly in hundreds, then in thousands, fathers and mothers had heartrending experience in common. A youngster in a family had for a few days been upset, irritable, feverish, drowsy, headachy. Then one morning the mother would go into the room of her baby who'd been suffering from "summer complaint"—or so said the doctor—to find the child couldn't move its legs, or arm, or couldn't raise its head, or couldn't talk or even swallow, and maybe was having a fight to breathe. Now millions of fathers and mothers became frantic—no matter whether their children's sickness actually did remain "summer complaint" or ended in paralysis or death. This, then, was how parents

joined the death-fight: with tears they begged physicians to
do something, anything, no matter how drastic, to guard their
feverish, not yet paralyzed babies from the terror that had
already maimed or killed their neighbor's child.

What then did physicians do? What could they offer? They
did have monkey science that was not debatable. It was true
that the blood of monkeys (and humans too) who'd been
paralyzed but not killed by the midget microbe had in it a
strange virtue. Such convalescent blood serum—so it was
called—actually could kill the infantile paralysis virus when
mixed with it in a test-tube. But in the living bodies of
children? What kind of science was this that had been reported by the famed French nerve doctor? He'd shot such
convalescent serum into the sick spines of a few children already paralyzed. It seemed their weakened muscles had become stronger, not completely strong again, but not quite so
powerless—

Alas, if this French Doctor Netter had only stopped to
think, if he'd gone back into the archives of the Swedish
fighters of the sickness, he'd have found the same thing happened in many children who'd got no serum whatever. But
now this 1916 summer, who could stop to think? Now there
began a buzzing about, even of the cool-headed, comfortable
searchers in the Rockefeller Institute. There now began a
day and night searching for crippled alumni of infantile
paralysis of other years, a pleading with them, then drawing
of possibly paralysis-fighting blood out of their veins—

That 1916 summer in New York and its suburbs there was
action, not science. Everywhere you saw physicians, nurses,
crews of microbe hunters, specialists, rushing from motor cars
into houses where babies and children lay, feverish, vomiting, *not yet paralyzed,* yet many of them with pain-racked
bodies shrinking from any touch, many of them stiff-necked
and yes, this was going to be infantile paralysis surely! Or was
it really? Well anyway.

So now without waiting—waiting might be fatal, mightn't
t, if it *did* turn out to be infantile paralysis!—now immedi-
tely these physicians gently turned such children on their
ides for the delicate operation of the spinal puncture. Before
hey shot in the convalescent serum they must withdraw an
mount of the child's spinal fluid equal to the amount of
erum they were going to inject.

Wait a moment! Weren't there already reports that simply
rawing out a certain amount of children's spinal fluid, sim-
ly that, not giving serum, seemed to heal certain cases of
aralysis?

But we must not, we cannot wait. This is the time for
ction. Waiting might be fatal. This is our responsibility. So,
ito thousands of New York children that 1916 summer went
ntold quarts of the blood serum of other children who had
-unfortunately?—survived the paralytic death. So mercy
hased the hunt for truth out the window in many homes.

Now there were huzzahs and enthusiastic reports from
iany physicians and among these were some who had been
roud of their devotion to cold science. There were happy
eports of how marvelously this very sick but not yet para-
zed baby had not become paralyzed at all; of how that one,
iough very sick, had yet survived, and was not paralyzed
adly; of the next one who'd become paralyzed immediately
fter the serum injection but had then recovered to such a
emarkable extent that you'd have to look sharp to notice
s one leg just a wee bit thinner, weaker, shorter, than the
ther!

Who can possibly blame these New York physicians for
ow forgetting that exactly parallel observations had been
iade by Scandinavian physicians long before a convalescent
rum was even dreamed of? Dr. George Draper was a leader
nong those who shouted hoorah for serum. He was ex-
erienced in the subtleties of the sickness observed at hun-
reds of babies' bedsides. The illness, said Draper, in its

early hours is like any acute infection of childhood. "Ever
in the midst of an epidemic it is hard at first to realize tha
the patient is in the grip of the insidious disease that ma·
cripple for life if it does not kill."

Draper knew well the sinister sneaking trait of the midge
microbe that could paralyze an only slightly sick child, with
out warning, so that the babe itself would wake up on·
morning not knowing its power to move was gone. Ther·
was macabre poetry to Draper's impressions of the fight fo·
life put up by children when the sickness hit the nerve cell
that controlled their muscles of breathing. At bedsides wher·
he watched these struggles it was burned into Draper how
after fast advancing paralysis of a youngster's legs, up and u·
its body to its arms, at last embarrassment of breathing mad·
its terrible appearance.

Though it was remarkable that some children, sai·
Draper, might have serious trouble with their breathing, an·
yet recover. Such were the caprices of these infernal midge·
microbes, sometimes, nobody knew why, not completing thei·
blasting of the nerve cells that controlled the breath of life
Now some of these he saw recover, had done so, maybe, afte·
he had given them—in desperation!—the convalescent serun·
injection.

Had they recovered because of the serum? What brair·
could remain cold, skeptical, in the midst of such dreadfu·
drama? Draper was honest. He admitted that he had seer·
many maybe-going-to-be cases of true infantile paralysis wh·
never did get paralyzed, though no serum had been give·
them. But he'd seen a lot, too, whose possible paralysis ha·
seemed to be prevented by big shots of serum. Yes. Excellent
Many of each kind. But how many of each kind?

Draper admitted he had no figures that clearly told th·
story. He had the *impression* that the serum prevented pa·
ralysis, "and this cannot be transmitted adequately in words."

But the figures, the cold figures? Based on accurate ob·

ervation made by critical men, such figures could be trusted,
uch figures would not lie. Draper went back to those origi-
al reports of serum cure by the French Doctor Netter who
irst raised hopes of the life-guarding power of convalescent
erum. "It is to be questioned," admitted honest Draper,
whether [Netter's] protocols bear out his contention since
vith him *as with us* the statistical proof rather fails to bring
onviction."

Yes, that was the tragedy of the New York 1916 epidemic.
o much of that fight for life was impressionistic. Impressions
re powerful to begin a hunt for truth. Impressions alone
an never bring your truth hunter to his trail's end.

II

Just the same—it was lucky for fathers and mothers and
hildren of the future—there were hard-boiled truth hunters
vorking and observing. New York's Dr. H. Schwarz gave
his supposedly curative serum to twenty-one children sick
out not yet paralyzed—

Nine of these escaped paralysis.

Schwarz gave no serum to a parallel series of twenty-one
other sick children—

Seventeen of these got better without any paralysis whatever.

Dr. Josephine Neal was a distinguished fighter in that epidemic. She observed 202 not-serum-treated children from the
irst beginning to the end of their sickness—

Of these, 173 recovered, not paralytic!

This beyond doubt would have been considered excellent
evidence of the serum's power, by those enthusiastic for
erum—if to these 202 serum had been given.

Physicians of the staff of the Queensboro Hospital be-
ieved they'd seen more rapid recovery in youngsters from
whose spines they'd **simply** drained spinal fluid, than in

children into whom—after such draining—the serum had been injected.

What was the aftermath of this tragic 1916 summer? The result was undoubtedly that the impressionists, the enthusiasts, triumphed over the skeptics. The truth hunter's discouraging figures were forgotten, were drowned out in the chorus of hosannahs of physicians who had shot serum into every threatened baby, child, even grownup whom they thought might have infantile paralysis—

They gave the serum to all without leaving equal numbers—not serum-treated—to bear witness.

It is easy to jeer at this failure of physicians to live up to what would be the A B C of science practiced in laboratories where the test animals are monkeys instead of children. Your chronicler has sat far into the night in many an argument over this question. And this must be acknowledged: that for fifteen years since that New York epidemic the impressionists—tender-minded—had the better of the battle. It is easy to jeer if you're not the doctor at the bedside. But if you are then how can you deny the serum—who knows, it *may* be curative!—to fathers and mothers, in tears, pleading: Doctor save our baby!

How can you take the responsibility of withholding the serum from any?

Yes, but you do not really know, the serum may really be powerless, and, giving it to all, don't you set up feeling of false security, don't you hold back science? If science once knows that serum's a flop, a failure, it will then search on a new trail, for something really powerful!

To such argument by your chronicler the answer has been made that frantic fathers and mothers would not stand for such experimentation upon their children. Panic-stricken fathers and mothers do not understand a scientific maybe, a skeptical we-do-not-know.

But in 1931—again in New York—fathers and mothers did

stand for it. Now at last the people truly did join the death-fight, not as blind graspers after straws of hope, not as un-critical supporters of pseudo-scientific folly, but as truth hunters, no less. This 1931 summer the people confounded the underestimators of the people's intelligence. That sum-mer New York's august Academy of Medicine sponsored a giant, epoch-making experiment to settle this question. It was directed by Dr. William Hallock Park. Now every other child—instead of every one—in that feverish stage before paralysis, was given convalescent serum. There might be parental tears. There might be pleadings. But alternate chil-dren were left without the serum.

The Manhattan experiment was made simultaneously with similar ones in Brooklyn, and in Hartford, Connecticut. And the Hartford experiment was portentous, because it was directed by famed infantile paralysis authority, W. Lloyd Aycock, of Harvard University. He himself had previously published observations making it seem as if the serum really did save human lives. And the results of these experiments?

They were identical. Between serum-treated and not treated children there was no significant difference in the numbers paralyzed or dying.

Now true fighters for life had every right to be discour-aged. It would seem as if the fight against the paralytic plague had slipped back twenty years, back to those first hopeful days when Karl Landsteiner had first brought the sickness from man to monkey.

III

Now the fight against infantile paralysis retreated again, for a time, to the remote unsentimental austerity of the labora-tories. Granted that the blood of recovered monkeys, of children too, did have a power to blast the infantile paralysis virus in test-tubes. But what of it? So asked a new generation of hard-boiled hunters for the truth. Doubts now arose about this virus-killing power of convalescent blood having any significance at all. You found that same power in the blood of many children, and of a still greater proportion of grown-ups who had never had the disease at all. You often found a higher virus-killing power in the blood of people who had *not* had infantile paralysis than in the blood of those who had suffered from it. You could find this power in the blood of children at the moment they came down with infantile paralysis—and why hadn't it protected them from being attacked?

Now there arose in California a new champion against the paralytic menace. He was a wrecker of the old science that had failed to conquer it. This was microbe hunter Edwin W. Schultz, a slender, bespectacled, studious-looking man. Externally he was every inch the college professor you see portrayed in the movies. Internally, mentally, he was hard as steel. He began his searching by driving nails into the lid of the coffin that held the old hope for convalescent serum. Experimenting with monkeys, Schultz imitated the manner in which the midget microbe was thought to sneak into children. He did not shoot the sickness direct into the monkey's brains. He dropped the deadly infantile paralysis virus into their noses. Now, one day, two days, three days later—long before these simians showed the slightest sign of paralytic sickness—he gave them enormous doses of convalescent human serum. Better yet, he gave other infected monkeys the serum of a horse whose blood he had made super-powerful—in test-tubes!—against the paralyzing microbe. He soaked the systems of those monkeys with various powerful serums—

But a few days later they all went limp. They all died of infantile paralysis.

Now, in the 1935 summer, in New York there arose a famous man against death to take the death-fight to the people again, to give a new hope to fathers and mothers

sleepless during epidemic threat to their young ones. This
new champion was William Hallock Park—the very man who
had exposed the serum folly in the human experiment of
1931. If serum couldn't cure the sickness, mightn't there
yet be hope of a vaccine to prevent it? Your chronicler must
here admit that he himself was influenced by Park's hope of
it, and that he fought hard—against scientific skeptics—to
make experimental test of this vaccine upon children possible.

It is deplorable that Park did not himself make or at
least repeat the monkey experiments that seemed to hold
out hope for guarding children. He left the doing of them
to his assistant, optimistic, hard-working Dr. Maurice Brodie,
who had the hunch to make the deadly virus gentle by treating the spinal cords of monkeys dead of infantile paralysis
with formaldehyde. So to turn the deadly microbes into a
vaccine—or so he fooled himself and Park, his master, into
thinking—that could protect monkeys against the paralytic
infection. So then to deceive himself—and Park and others,
your chronicler included—into believing this vaccine, guarding monkeys, might likewise make children immune.

The result of the human test of this vaccine is not a
happy story. Again our hope-wrecker, Edwin Schultz, was
busy in California, to make monkey science that should have
blasted all hope for the success of the human experiment
before ever it was started. Schultz carefully vaccinated many
monkeys with this vaccine brewed *à la* Park and Brodie. But
when he dropped a little of the dangerous virus into the
noses of these allegedly vaccinated simians, they all went limp
and died as promptly as their not-vaccinated monkey comrades—

Park and Brodie grabbed for a straw of hope. They believed they'd proved their vaccine set up some little virus-
killing power in the blood of children they'd vaccinated.
Now this too was dashed, when parents of North Carolina

joined the death-fight. They allowed their children—every other child—to be vaccinated by experts of the U. S. Public Health Service, leaving alternate not-vaccinated children to bear witness—

Again what good mere blood immunity? And if good, it did not result from this vaccine. Searchers Aycock of Harvard and Kramer of Brooklyn probed into the bloods of these two sets of North Carolina youngsters. They found that, during the 1935 epidemic, the blood of not-vaccinated children became immune, spontaneously, in the same proportion as the blood of those to whom the vaccine had been given! And, what was worse, this vaccine was not harmless. Some little ones were made alarmingly sick by it. And, worst of all, another searcher—John Kolmer—came forward with his own vaccine that was, for monkeys, somewhat more powerful than the useless vaccine of Park and Brodie. But it contained living, undeniably dangerous infantile paralysis virus—

Paralysis and, yes, death of children followed the injection of Kolmer's hoped-for preventive, and this even in communities where there was no sign of an infantile paralysis epidemic.

Yet it's darkest just before the dawn, so the old saw has it, and now, in the midst of these disappointments and disasters, a new, a revolutionary monkey science began to be heard of in the laboratories of searchers disillusioned of hopes for serums or vaccines to fight infantile paralysis.

### IV

This new monkey science was most upsetting and pessimistic. It came to America with no hoorahs or any publicity at all. It sneaked into our laboratories in highbrow scientific journals published in England. It brought with it no ballyhoo of hope for fathers and mothers already too often disappointed. Yet our Englishmen—their names were Hurst and

Fairbrother—told exactly why those tragic serum and vaccine failures had got to happen. For years these Englishmen had been training their microscopes upon thin bits of the nervous tissues of the brains and spinal cords of monkeys put out of their monkey misery at every stage of the sickness. From its beginning, just after those monkeys had been infected, to the awful last day when they had collapsed into helpless sprawling bags of bones and muscles. Till they were about to die.

Now this was the grim—on the surface hopeless—story their microscopic squintings told them—

Infantile paralysis is a brain, a spinal cord sickness. Nearly exclusively. Almost entirely. Maybe absolutely. In its very beginning, at the very first stage of a monkey's sudden sadness, of his feverish, trembling, frightened restlessness, if you killed him then, if you examined every tissue of his body, his blood, his muscles, glands, every bit of him, it was only inside his brain cells that you saw any sign at all of the microbe's devastation. Now day after day they could trace the sneaking, the dangerous march of death across the lower part of their monkeys' brains. Inside the nerve fibers and nerve cells the midget microbe multiplied, burrowed its evil way downward to the nerve cells of the monkey's spinal cord. Now, if you put a monkey out of his misery at the moment of his sudden, explosive powerlessness, it was only these nerve cells that you found wrecked and blasted by the subvisible terror. There was no sign whatever of its havoc in any other part of the monkey's body!

All right then, if it's the same in human beings, why then try—by serum—to keep the paralyzing midget microbe from sneaking from a child's blood into his brain, when the microbe was not in the blood in the first place, when it's the brain that is first of all invaded? And why be in any way excited about any mere microbe-killing power a vaccine might set up in a child's blood? Why, indeed, when this unseen death, in some way, by some mysterious path, through some hidden door, stole direct from the outside world into the child's brain to begin its microbe mischief?

Now this very strength of the unseen paralytic death was seen to be its weakness. Again in the California laboratory of our old hope-wrecker, Edwin Schultz, there appeared the first hint—it was the remotest kind of hope—of the real weakness, of a most curious limitation of the terrible power of this maimer and killer of children. Now the pieces of the grim jigsaw puzzle that this sickness had been, began to fall into their places. Now Schultz, destroyer of error, began to ask a series of embarrassing questions of the well-meaning perpetrators of mistaken science. It didn't matter to Schultz that these were distinguished men of science, and famous—he now asked—

Who had ever found the paralyzing microbe in the blood of any child in the feverish beginning of that child's sickness? Nobody.

Couldn't every one of a child's early symptoms be accounted for by mischief the microbe might make in the bottom of the child's brain? Yes.

Why had all attempts made to infect monkeys by feeding them virus failed? And if a couple of little epidemics were known to have followed milk routes, was it the milk that had infected the children, or was it the milk-man who had been the carrier, the spreader of the contagion? Why did monkeys sicken so seldom when you shot the virus under their skins? Why could they laugh off enormous doses of the death shot direct into their blood?

These riddles were answered now.

The paralyzing death must have the insides of nerves along which to travel to begin its deviltry inside the skulls and spines of men and monkeys.

It is nerve tissue, and nerve tissue only, that the paralyzing

midget must feed upon. Without nerve tissue it must die. It
is powerless.

And now, you recall that old experiment made by our
poliomyelitis-fighter, Simon Flexner, twenty years ago. You
recall how easy it had been for him to sicken monkeys simply by swabbing dangerous virus into the upper part of the
inside of their noses? You remember that, a few days after
he shot the virus into their brains, he could recover it from
the inside of their noses. Ah—

Now Schultz pounced on these old neglected experiments
and shook them back to life. Schultz saw their life-or-death
importance. Now he had it. Inside the upper part of the nose
of your monkey, and yes, of your human being, too, there is
a curious doorway by which the death can enter. Naturally.
So you don't have to inject it. Right from the outside world
there's a natural pathway. By it our nerve-loving midget
microbe can travel up into the brains of monkeys. And children. And by that one pathway only. Up there inside the
nose lie the tiny, hairlike endings of the nerves of smell.
They are unique among all the nerves of our bodies. Of all
nerves they alone lie absolutely naked to the outside breezes.
Through little holes in the bottom of the skull these nerves
pass directly to the brain.

By a succession of experiments Schultz and his comrades
proved that here was the Achilles' heel of the maiming death.
By washing out a monkey's nose with a solution just faintly
acid, you could give a monkey the paralytic death—ninety-
five times out of every hundred—just by dropping virus into
the nose of a monkey you'd turned bottom side up. You
didn't have to inject it.

Infecting monkeys this natural way, Schultz's young helper
Louis Gebhardt and baby-doctor Harold Faber now traced
the crawling of the death—

Up the nerves of smell, across the monkey's midbrain,
down into the monkey's spinal cord where, with a sudden

devastating fierceness, the infinitely tiny flecks of deadly life wrecked the nerve cells controlling the monkey's muscles, blew them up completely, sent the poor beasts into heaps of limpness, killed them.

Now Schultz—though credit for first doing it must be given to Maurice Brodie—made a curious experiment, and it is likely to be associated with Schultz's name, because he, rather than Brodie, saw its hopeful significance. With a bone-drill Schultz now buzzed his way into the inside of six monkeys' skulls down through their foreheads. Now with an electric knife Schultz and Louis Gebhardt burned, ruined, cauterized, those six monkeys' nerves of smell, right where they bulged out into little bulbs, just under their brains—it was a pernickety business. But it must have been done with skill, because those six monkeys recovered perfectly. They were gay, vicious, dirtily frolicksome. Now Schultz and Gebhardt waited for fifteen days and excepting for the little scars on their foreheads you couldn't tell them from any monkey in the world—

Excepting that those monkeys couldn't smell anything at all; and never would smell anything again.

Now our searchers dropped fatal doses, overwhelmingly enormous deadly doses of infantile paralysis death into the noses of three monkeys who had never been thus tinkered with, who still had their sense of smell.

And into the six noses of six operated monkeys who would never smell anything again.

And, within ten days, the first three went limp, then died. But the six others? Into their brains this death could now not find a way to go.

## V

You grin at the monumental impracticality of this barbaric experiment and ask, Isn't that just like a professor? You can picture mobs of worried parents. They will hurry their broods of little girls and boys to hospitals when maiming epidemic threatens. They will implore brain surgeons to guard their young hopefuls by amputation of their sense of smell. You may visualize whole cities happily free of the fear of lifelong crippling or the strangling death. But at the price of having their children robbed forever of knowing the fragrance of roses or the reek of slums. You can go on and buffoon Schultz's experiment as an example of the silliness of pure science, for pure science it was, no doubt of it. You admit that here's death's pathway into a child. It's known now, granted. You acknowledge that if the human race had no sense of smell, it would never have been plagued by poliomyelitis. Here's the death's gateway, yes.

But how block it? Barring Schultz's impractical operation, there is no imaginable way to block the death. You assert it with confidence; and so doing you reckon without the indomitable ingenuity of our men against the maiming death. You fail to take into account the puckish quirks of microbe-hunting, or the irrationality of this so imperfect science where searchers most often find what they did not at all set out to discover, where for years they fail to discover a fact for the reason that they want so very much to find it. Long before our so purely scientific Professor Schultz had given life to monkeys by forever robbing them of smelling, Charles Armstrong of the U. S. Public Health Service was fumbling toward a weird way of closing death's doorway against infantile paralysis.

Nobody could have been further, in 1931, from being called an expert in infantile paralysis than this same Charles Armstrong. His scientific aim was then merely the modest one of trying to find a trick to make the "take" of smallpox vaccinations not quite so ferocious. In his laboratory he nursed a smallpox vaccine virus that was vicious. It actually blinded rabbits when you dropped a bit of it into their eyes. Now—it was accident—he tripped over a funny little fact. If you slightly inflame the eyes of rabbits with the poison of the diphtheria microbe, then for a long time after that those eyes are curiously proof against the blinding devastation of smallpox virus. And you could search microbe-hunting archives in vain for a fact more remote from infantile paralysis.

Now Charles Armstrong is a scientifically unorthodox man, not traditional, not bookish, thinking left-handed thoughts, getting wayward hunches. And now this belief—it was unprecedented and not scientifically respectable—stewed in Armstrong's brain: maybe anything that irritates, inflames, then toughens, *tans*, any kind of mucous membrane may make any such tanned membrane tougher for any midget microbe to sneak into.

But you ask with reason what had this hunch—if true—to do with hopes to keep the infantile paralysis murder out of children? It was not the mucous membranes of children's (and monkeys') noses that the microbic assassin had to penetrate, no, it was the endings of the nerves of smell, nervous tissue, that it must fasten itself onto. So what of this heretical hunch of Charles Armstrong's?

Now the gods of luck look in upon this battle; and Armstrong, handy-man of the National Institute of the Public Health Service, the coolest kind of microbe hunter in epidemic emergency, was hurried out to the St. Louis sleeping sickness epidemic of 1933. About this sleeping sickness he knew absolutely nothing; and all the other microbe hunters and healthmen of America knew even less. But within a few weeks of this blistering summer Armstrong—along with microbe hunter Ralph Muckenfuss—had the virus of that very deadly ill trapped in monkeys. Then searcher Webster of the Rockefeller Institute carried it from expensive monkeys to ten cent mice. But again, this sleepy death was a far cry from infantile paralysis—

But wait, was it? Epidemiologist James P. Leake, Armstrong's comrade in the Health Service, saw this: that our old paralytic plague and this new St. Louis sleepy death are like as two peas in the way they sneak from one human being to another. And wait: just as you can paralyze and kill monkeys by dropping infantile paralysis virus into their noses, just so, by dripping a soup of the brain of a mouse dying the sleepy death into the noses of his healthy mouse comrades, if you kept at it, you could exterminate mighty near all the white mice in the world!

Now here was Armstrong back in Washington intent upon mass mouse-murder in order to find a way to guard future mice from the St. Louis sleepy death. And if they did die from it, what of it? Here again was the purest kind of pure science. He could try that heretic hunch now. It was outlandish reasoning. If diphtheria poison toughens the mucous membranes of the eyes of rabbits so that they can't be blinded by vicious smallpox virus, then if you toughen the inside of the nose of a mouse, won't he laugh off the sleepy death?

To look at Armstrong, stocky, blue-eyed, red-haired, matter-of-fact—learned old Dr. S. P. Kramer says he would have made a very successful midwest businessman or banker—you could hardly imagine him at such hare-brained woolgathering. But now he has passed from such fantastic dreaming to action. Now at the very start he's stymied. The mice, curse them! The insides of mouse noses refuse to be inflamed by diphtheria poison. Does that stop Armstrong? No, if his ideas are slightly daft, you've got to mark him one hundred for perseverance. He puts down his little phial of diphtheria microbe poison and turns to the bottle of the venom of cobras. Ah, now he has it. Wouldn't it be droll if the poison of this dreadful serpent—killing thirty thousand Hindus yearly—would irritate the noses of possible candidates for the St. Louis sleepy death so that healthy people would resist it? Armstrong is baulked again.

The cobra poison irritates the mice, don't worry. It swells up the insides of their little noses so that they cannot breathe through them. And for the mice this is unlucky. For—in Armstrong's words—with nose plugged up a mouse hadn't sense enough to breath through his mouth and so he ups and dies.

Let us not for one moment be discouraged. Not if we are Armstrong. Let's give these next mice just a little less cobra venom. Yes, now they survive, though they are somewhat sneezy. Now into their let-us-hope toughened noses goes the sleepy death virus. Do they resist it? On the contrary. They go into the sleepy death's convulsive tailspins in the regulation six days after the virus has been inoculated into their nostrils.

Well, let's see, ho-hum, what else is irritating? Armstrong fishes round his own room, round all the laboratories of the Institute for that notorious itch-producing stuff—the subject of indelicate jokes—called Spanish fly. He can't find any. Look. Here's a bottle of alum. Anybody knows how alum has an irritating, puckering action. This is a last fling at the hunch he was silly to have nursed in the first place. He mashes up the little brains of sundry mice who've gone West from the sleepy death. He gets ready delicate little syringes and with them drips sodium alum solutions into the nostrils of mice who do not like it but do, the majority of them, live through this annoyance.

Then, days later, he drips the brew of the brains of mice dead of the St. Louis sleeping sickness in to the noses of mice who've been sneezing from that alum—

The muggy 1934 Washington summer passes, and then the autumn and now it is two days before Christmas with Armstrong taut beneath his imperturbable exterior. Now Armstrong goes into a huddle with Surgeon W. T. Harrison, who is the infantile paralysis expert of the Institute. Then the two of them arrange nice clean monkey cages. They pick out healthy, obstreperous monkeys. They get ready to make serious, eight dollar science, to face the stern test to which the ten cent science of Armstrong's successful guarding of mice—by alum!—from the sleepy death has brought them.

## VI

Now the portentous experiment is ready, and what Chinaman's chance have they of succeeding? Just because the alum irritation and toughening of the insides of mouse noses will guard these little beasts from St. Louis sleeping sickness, why believe the same treatment of monkeys will protect them from infantile paralysis? Why dream that it will close the door of the maiming death, why should alum seal shut those delicate hair-like endings of a monkey's nerves of smell? It is true that news has just been published by searchers Sabin and Olitsky of the Rockefeller Institute. They are working with an obscure brain disease of horses—encephalomyelitis. They have dripped tannic acid into the noses of sundry mice. It makes them resist this horse-brain sickness.

Encouraging maybe? Maybe. But guinea-pigs take this horse-brain sickness too, when you drip it into their noses— And tannic acid is powerless to protect them. That's the devil of it— Nature is perverse. It is folly to reason from what happens in one sickness in one kind of animal to the same, or some other kind of sickness, in other animals. If you are sophisticated, as a searcher, you reason the opposite. You don't try to cross such rickety experimental bridges. Between different animals and different diseases the very opposite result is the one most likely to happen. So it is not too hopeful for Armstrong now.

So now Armstrong will try it.

It is the 22nd of January, 1935, and here in two cages romp four monkeys. One from each of these two cages, upon twelve different days these last four weeks, has been turned hind-end-up and has had his nose well douched with puckering, stinging, irritating, mucous membrane-toughening alum. One from each cage hasn't been manhandled that way at all. Now, this January morning, the Negro helper expertly snares these four monkeys, one after another in a burlap bag on the end of a long iron pole. Now head down he holds them, one after another, so that Charles Armstrong, steady, deliberate—superb bench-worker that he is!—can drop a dose, it is an enormous, a dangerous dose of the wrecked spinal cord of a monkey dead of infantile paralysis, into the noses of these four monkeys.

Now, to make triple sure that all these four shall have an equal chance to die the paralytic death, he repeats this attempt at paralytic murder three days in a row.

Nine days pass. In each of these two cages there lies one monkey who is limp and powerless. He is no longer full of monkey merriment. You only know he is alive by the look out of his baleful eyes, the sinister look that reminds you how monkeys hate you for being born slightly less monkeyish than they are. Beside each of these wrecked beasts, scampering, romping, screaming, chattering, sniffing at his paralytic cage mate, there is an absolutely healthy monkey—

Yes. In each of these two cages, the paralyzed, dying monkey is the one that Armstrong did not douche with his alum.

Now Armstrong and Harrison begin a taut check-testing, as reckless of monkeys as this eight dollar monkey science will let them be. And, after four months of trying to toughen the mucous membranes of the insides of monkey noses against the paralytic murder, here, for the first time in the up-till-now long losing battle against infantile paralysis, there is the first true gleam of hope for fathers and mothers who every summer must be worried for the limbs and lives of their children.

Here's the result. Let's tot up the figures with Charles Armstrong—

Out of nineteen monkeys who'd got no alum in their noses, only three had survived the maiming death.

Of twenty-three who'd had this alum irrigation in their nostrils, seventeen were active, screaming their monkey lingo, healthy.

But just how hopeful was this for fathers and mothers, for children of the future?

After all, in the worst epidemic, not one child out of eighty is stricken. After all, some of Armstrong's alum-douched monkeys had succumbed. Is it possible that, just as there were some monkeys Armstrong couldn't guard, so too alum might fail with certain children? Yet a child, in an epidemic, never faces the enormous doses of death that Armstrong and Harrison had poured into all their monkeys. But then here again is a more ominous objection to pouring alum into children's nostrils! Our searchers had doused alum—four times weaker than they'd used in their monkey experiments—into their own noses. It caused a most infernal tickling, stinging, sneezing, then a dryness for many hours. Armstrong was a practical man, knowing children. To your chronicler he said, at the end of these tantalizingly hopeful experiments: "No good. Kids would kick like hell if they had to have alum up their noses day after day during an epidemic!"

It was really hopeless. Now if Armstrong had had to search for something milder, yet just as powerful as alum, using those expensive eight dollar monkeys, he'd have thrown it up as useless. But here he was in luck. He had the cheap ten cent science of the sleepy death in mice to fall back upon. Yet he was silly to go on searching. According to his theory he should have thrown it up now. He believed that the more you inflamed, tanned, the inside of any beast's nose, the better you'd guard him. Okay. The more you'd irritate the inside of a baby's nose, the more impractical you'd make your science! Wouldn't doctors, nurses, and yes, mothers, give up in despair at their youngster's kicking and screaming?

Wouldn't they finally take a chance, hoping their babies would dodge the paralytic death this summer? The scheme wasn't reasonable.

So Armstrong went on with it.

He went back to his ten cent mouse science to look for something less stinging than alum, yet more powerful to block the St. Louis sleepy death. He used myriads of mice to search for this that was impossible. Now it is late summer, 1935. Park and Brodie's vaccine has been a failure. Children have died following the attempt to guard them by the vaccine of John Kolmer. Against infantile paralysis there is no hope whatever. As always the midget microbes are victorious against the best efforts of our fighters for the lives and limbs of children. Now it is late September of 1935 with Surgeons Charles Armstrong and W. T. Harrison alone in their monkey room at the National Institute in Washington.

This September morning reminds you of another famous day in science, that day at Pouilly-le-Fort, in France, when Louis Pasteur proved to the world he'd guarded sheep from anthrax. This 1935 day reminds you of that day more than fifty years ago because it is so different. Here this morning there are no dignitaries, big-shots, or newspaper correspondents, nor any French raptures over sheep saved from doom, nor any ballyhoo or fanfare whatever. Yet in these Washington monkey cages there is to be seen something portentous.

Here are four cages each holding two monkeys—eight simians in all.

Three days ago one monkey in each of these four cages had changed from merry to sad, had begun to cower in a corner with what seemed a restless fear. Its mate, in each cage, was happy.

Yesterday, in each of two cages, one of those scared monkeys had gone completely limp.

Now this morning, all four of these cages hold one beast

who's no more than a memory of what used to be a service-able monkey, now powerless, yes, dying.

While in all four cages there is a monkey comrade who you'd swear had never been near the paralytic death.

A couple of weeks before, into the noses of these healthy simians Armstrong had put a mild and rather inoffensive fluid. It was clear yellow. It did not seem to inflame, irritate or pucker as the alum had done. Armstrong had douched this yellow stuff down these monkeys' noses on six separate days. The last time had been just four days before he gave them the great doses of the paralyzing death that had now so completely wrecked their not-treated comrades.

Armstrong and Harrison had tried this yellow clear fluid on their own noses. It had stung a little. In their throats it had tasted bitter. That was all. So Armstrong's theory about the more irritating the more life-guarding was completely wrong.

But what matter, since this so mild, apparently harmless, six-tenths-percent solution of picric acid had so perfectly saved these four monkeys?

VII

Armstrong, first of all men, had found a way—experimentally in monkeys, remember—to shut the door against the maiming death.

Would Armstrong's still rough, imperfect science begin to lead the way to save children from the paralytic terror? Was the monkey science sure, substantial? Or would its human use again bring that disappointment that dogged every effort to fight the maiming death in human beings? The monkey science looked pretty solid. In California our hard-boiled mild man Edwin Schultz, without knowing of Armstrong's picric acid experiments, knowing only his partly successful experiments with that impractical alum, had made the same

tests with picric acid. They confirmed Armstrong's absolutely.

Could these two searchers now predict that what worked
so perfectly for monkeys would likewise work for man?

There were gleams of hope. It was nearly certain that the
maiming death could sneak into children only through that
one weak spot—only by way of the naked endings of their
nerves of smell high up inside their noses. And, if you could
guard monkeys against a death that killed ninety out of a
hundred of their untreated comrades, if you could only
douche children *sufficiently well* with this mild picric acid,
surely it would guard them? Surely, since the doses of the
subvisible death they'd have to meet in an epidemic would
be enormously less than Armstrong and Schultz had given
their monkeys?

Would the picric acid—proved absolutely safe for monkeys—be dangerous to some children? Armstrong and Harrison had douched their own noses with it twenty times inside a month. Result: a bitter taste in their mouths, that
was all. Children had been given, internally for other ail-
ments, two hundred times the dose of picric acid that would
have to be dropped into their noses. It is true that some
people seemed sensitive to picric acid, developed rashes from
it, but only from doses vastly greater than any that would
have to be used to block the paralytic death—

But how long would this picric acid guard children? It
was impossible to say. Monkeys were proof against the peril
for at least a week, said Armstrong.

How hard would it be to be sure you'd got the picric acid
thoroughly up there, so that all the delicate endings of the
nerves of smell would be well coated, guarded against the
attack of the vicious microbe midgets. Could mothers themselves apply this simple hoped-for safeguard to their children? Eventually maybe. But Armstrong knew that it was

of the gravest importance that, in its first human trial, the picric acid should be applied by competent doctors and healthmen.

Would it be possible that grownups, too, might be douched with his death-blocking chemical in the event of an epidemic? Yes, and here were a glimmer of another wild hope to smash the death forever—

The unseen microbe can only enter your susceptible child by way of his nerves of smell. But isn't it possible, isn't it almost certain, too, that these nerves of smell are also the *exit* of the death? The only way by which it can leave carriers of the death to go out to attack susceptible people? So, if you douched everybody, a whole population, you'd block the death going out of those people who are its unwitting spreaders, as well as into the children whom fate marked for its prospective victims!

It was a glorious stake to gamble for.

Was picric acid going to be the final answer? Maybe not. Schultz was already busy experimenting with other even simpler chemicals. In laboratories the country over there was a buzzing experimenting, and fiercely critical, too, with this new fantastic hope. Now at last the fight against infantile paralysis was going to be truly the people's fight for life. Would they respond to Armstrong's new-fangled science? After they'd been disappointed so often? It was very simple. It was very cheap. One cent a dose was all this yellow fluid would set parents back to try to guard the lives and limbs of their children! Was it too cheap and simple to be true?

The cheapness of the picric certainly had bizarre angles. Wouldn't it be fantastic if this yellow stuff that had killed and mangled so many millions of men in wartime should now turn out to be merciful? That was why picric acid was so cheap: it was the base for the high explosive, melinite. This demanded its mass production. Making it cheap enough to kill human myriads, had our chemical barons put it within the reach of all the people's children? And would it now guard the youngsters' limbs and lives from infantile paralysis —so that the high explosive melinite in turn would have its chance to kill them?

## CHAPTER NINE

## DEATH BLOCKADE?

CHARLES ARMSTRONG took the first test hop with his hoped-for life-guarding science from monkey to man in the summer of 1936. The experiment was grotesque, confused, inconclusive, unprecedented, and in a curious manner hopeful. An epidemic of infantile paralysis broke very suddenly that 1936 summer in a part of America supposed to be free from epidemic menace. When Armstrong arrived in Montgomery, Alabama, early afternoon of July 14th, newspapers reported business at a standstill. Public meetings were being banned in Mississippi. There was alarm in Tennessee. The disease popped up here, there and everywhere in these three states. Already one hundred and fifty-four children were stricken.

Armstrong went into a huddle with Alabama's healthmen and prominent physicians. With that understatement for which he is obscurely famous, he told them the lowdown, what to hope and what to fear about the hoped-for new preventive. That spring, for monkeys, he'd increased the already great protective power of picric acid, by mixing it with weak alum—half percent of alum and half percent of picric acid was what he proposed to spray up southern children's noses.

Could he say that what worked so well for monkeys would work as well for men? No, he couldn't prophesy.

Was he sure that the endings of the nerves of smell, up inside their noses, are the one door by which the paralytic death could enter human beings? No, it was not dead sure.

Yet Armstrong said that accumulating facts from laboratories the world over made it seem more and more as if this was the one possible way the virus could get into a victim. He told them a grim story of new evidence that it is only *inside* human nerves and nerve cells that the infantile paralysis virus can multiply. This scientific proof was tragic. Summer, 1935, certain children had developed infantile paralysis after they have been injected with a vaccine designed to guard them against the sickness. There was no epidemic in this region. It seemed almost certain the vaccine itself had infected them, and several of them had died. It was known that the alleged protective shots contained living infantile paralysis virus. When their paralysis had hit them, in all cases it began in the very arm that had been injected, exactly at the level of the spinal cord which supplied nerves to the injected spot. Absolutely the only way you could explain it was this: the injected virus must have sneaked up the nerves from their arms to their spinal cords.

Now if the virus *had* to grow and multiply inside human nerve cells, then it would have to attack a child by way of the nerves of smell. They're the only nerves with endings naked to the outside world.

So, therefore, he hoped Alabama's healthmen and doctors could see their way clear to recommend to parents to have their children's noses sprayed with picric-alum. Right now, while the epidemic was young. You had to hurry. Epidemics of infantile paralysis are here today and gone tomorrow. You had to spray the youngsters *before* any virus reached them. Once inside the nerves, no amount of spraying could possibly prevent disaster. It was chemical blockade, or it was nothing!

Now Armstrong became an emergency scientific missionary. To hear his possibly life-saving news emergency meetings of county medical societies showed unprecedented turnouts all over Alabama. He told the assembled docs he had nothing to sell them. Here were his lab experiments, he said, simply. Here's what the stuff does for monkeys. Will it do the same for babies? We do not know. He was only here to ask them, as physicians, to help him find out.

He begged that the doctors, and doctors only, apply the hoped-for preventive to Alabama's threatened hundreds of thousands of children. It seemed very simple to give. But, for this first test, surely it should not be allowed to get into the hands of the people. The doctors liked Armstrong's low-voiced, open-faced, sort of half-apologetic candor. They rained questions on him. No, it wasn't anything highly technical. Get the picric-alum solution now ready in all drugstores. Spray it, with three or four good squeezes on the bulb of an atomizer, every other day for three or four times, into each nostril. Then after that once a week so long as epidemic danger threatened.

The doctors liked Armstrong's common sense. He told them it was foolish to try to make a strictly scientific test of it. You couldn't dream of keeping half the people without the spray while you gave the rest the chance at the preventive. There'd be a riot. Frantic fathers and mothers would bootleg the picric alum into their own babies' noses should these be assigned to the not-sprayed, control group of children. No, the test must be voluntary. Those who would choose to have the spray, they'd be the test animals. Those choosing not to, well, they'd bear witness—

In the possible paralytic aftermath following your choosing not to spray, there you'd find the evidence.

Armstrong didn't kid the doctors. It was going to have to be an unheard-of, a giant, a mass experiment. So mighty few people came down with infantile paralysis even in bad epidemics, you'd have to spray hundreds of thousands to get any figures that would mean anything, scientifically, statistically.

But please, Armstrong kept repeating in his mild, unenthusiastic manner, please, wouldn't the doctors take full charge? The State of Alabama was broke. It hadn't a soo markee to finance the experiment. It is up to the doctors.

It is basic that the spraying must be done thoroughly. Would mere spraying really cover everybody's nerves of smell with the hoped-for preventive? Wouldn't it be more thorough to turn the children bottomside up and *pour* plenty of preventive into their noses?

Yes, probably, but Armstrong was practical, and wouldn't the babies kick like so many little steers at such man-handling? Wouldn't their bawling at being gagged with bitter picric-alum discourage fond mammas from bringing them back for the subsequent—absolutely necessary!—treatments?

That, you see, was the great point, Armstrong told the doctors. To be sure you blockaded monkeys against the death, you had to spray again and again, three times in a row. At least. And the protection didn't last long. Maybe a week? So they'd have to keep coming back, maybe every week after those first three sprays—till the epidemic faded.

It did look—again from monkey tests!—as if spraying would cover all the endangered area up inside children's noses. Monkey tests made under direction of Dr. Max M. Peet at the University of Michigan showed that three puffs from an atomizer did the trick for monkeys. Babies too? Well, it ought to work the same in children.

And, please, would the physicians keep most careful record of all children sprayed? Especially would they report all poisonous action? After all, spraying hundreds of thousands, you might find certain people super-sensitive to this ordinarily harmless picric-alum solution.

II

During the succeeding hot days the epidemic grew. Parents became frantic. The embattled southern doctors—your rank-and-file doc was never trained to be a healthman—were swamped by frightened mothers swarming into their offices to demand the spraying of Alabama's, Tennessee's, Mississippi's juvenile collective noses. The hoped-for orderly experiment turned into a series of little riots. The keeping of exact records was absolutely out of the question as mothers, desperate, invaded doctors' sedate offices with troops, whole regiments of moppets. Many doctors, harassed, undertook to show mothers how to spray their own little ones, told them to carry on the experiment at home. How could you conduct your practice with your office becluttered with mobs of bawling youngsters.

In no time at all the experiment had become a burlesque of what Armstrong had hoped for. Sinister rumors pervaded the southland. Certain nose specialists hinted that they couldn't be responsible for the harmful effect of this picric stuff on southern citizenry's sense of smell. And wasn't it bad public health practice, in time of epidemic, to collect these squirming hordes of kids together? Mightn't the all-pervading infantile paralysis virus spread amongst them before the preventive could be got up their noses to protect them?

The experiment by physicians turned out a flop, absolutely. What to Armstrong had seemed simple turned into chaos and now occurred a citizens' uprising unprecedented in scientific history; like a prairie fire the science spread to the fathers and mothers themselves. All right, if the doctors couldn't have their babies in their offices. All right, if some doctors were charging a dollar to do a spraying—a dollar means something to us! All right, so now southern folk, by hundreds of thousands, flocked to drugstores, bought gallons of the clear yellow picric-alum fluid and hundreds of thousands of atomizers. With Armstrong trying to be everywhere at once in the epidemic area in three states, the fathers and mothers turned themselves into scientific minutemen and minute-women.

To a laboratory bench-worker as precise as Armstrong, it must have been in the highest degree a shambles. In poor communities, in violation of all health rules dozens of families chipped in together to buy one atomizer which was passed from nose to nose among hundreds of children. Passing death that way? Who knew? Going from house to house among the people, Armstrong found that most of them had got their only instruction in this science from newspapers, or from neighbor ladies.

The way they sprayed was fearful and wonderful. The way they sprayed was every way that could be dictated by every human vagary, and with sublime disregard of science; Armstrong found himself confounded in the midst of a truly mass experiment, by the largely uninstructed masses, upon the masses—of the people, by the people, on the people. Now rumor spread and grew. Yes, the spray was stopping the epidemic. The spray was causing colds. The spray was curing colds. The spray helped hay fever. The spray was rotting off children's noses.

Yet this was fundamental, and more than a little pathetic: the people were so eager to do anything to try to guard their children. In eight hectic weeks—mid-July to mid-September— the yellowish mist was sprayed into nearly two millions of rich, poor, young, old, in those three states in the southland— Sprayed somehow, anyhow—

Now Charles Armstrong was not being neglected by that evil fate which seems to dog all fighters trying to take their infantile paralysis from monkeys to men. Now came news from Dr. Max Peet and his men at the University of Michigan. While spraying from an atomizer covered death's gateway in monkeys, it failed to cover the endangered area, surely thoroughly, in many children! This was fine news, alas, after the spraying technique of getting the picric-alum up there had been used in millions!

III

It is curious yet true that, in spite of its amateurish chaos, this mass death-fight cannot be said to have ended in total failure. After all infantile paralysis is peculiar, unique among all infections. This peculiarity gave Armstrong one great truth-finding advantage. After all, when infantile paralysis strikes a child, it leaves one sure sign that it has been there. You get infantile paralysis, and you don't simply die or get better right now. Your epidemic expert doesn't have to be on the ground right now to spot and record every acute attack of the sickness. No. Usually the disease leaves that telltale terrible wreckage, that aftermath—paralysis. So Armstrong, working slowly, precisely, examined the results of that wild spray experiment—after the epidemic was over.

In a mapped-out area in Birmingham and around it, where the spraying had been begun *before* the epidemic reached its peak in that region, our searcher now made an exact census. Visiting every family. Examining every child. Paralysis or no? Sprayed or not? How many sprayed had escaped the terror? How many sprayed were now despite it paralyzed or dead? When had they been sprayed? How often? And by whom? And how well? And had the spray done damage?

None that was serious. Headaches, yes, and some nausea, a certain proportion of pretty sore noses, and some said the spray had made them feverish, some that it had made them nervous; others—simply!—maintained it had made them feel bad all over. Five cases of severe hives and rash were reported. Two cases of kidney inflammation. But tracked down by Armstrong these turned out to be one of them bogus, and the other not necessarily connected with the spray at all. Armstrong was a hound tracking down reports, rumors, and found remarkable absence of harmfulness when you considered two million people had, the immense majority of them, sprayed themselves with the opposite of scientific precision or caution.

But here was the real nub question: Had this vast people's science had any effect whatever on the infantile paralysis epidemic that summer?

Had any children come down with infantile paralysis after they'd been sprayed with the preventive?

Yes. Here was a paralyzed two-year-old baby. Sprayed by its own mother. But with an atomizer, which, when Armstrong tested it, threw no spray whatever. And so on. But you must remember this about Armstrong: he belongs to that *élite* of searchers who first of all try to prove that their own science is mistaken. The epidemic terror had sneaked into certain children, though their mothers had sprayed them—apparently!—in strict accord with directions. But now, when Armstrong cast up his final figures, he included every last case, whether the child had been badly sprayed or well sprayed. He lumped them all together. The result—

The attack rate of the sickness in one limited, exactly studied area, was thirty-three percent lower among the children who'd been sprayed.

Doubters may say that this difference is not significant. Carpers may say this means nothing. These critics should be asked this question: if infantile paralysis had been thirty-three percent *higher* among children who'd been sprayed, wouldn't these same doubters have hinted that picric-alum had made the children more susceptible, instead of protecting them?

Let's face it: there are men of science who are so scientific that they seem not to want science to triumph.

When you take into consideration that merely spraying the picric-alum up there with a simple atomizer was by no means sure to cover the endings of the nerves of smell in the majority of children, then Armstrong's precise records were a long way from hopeless. But this was not by any means the most encouraging of the aftermaths of this wild strange experiment. At the end of his investigation Armstrong knew this: that, in face of an infantile paralysis epidemic, the people can be relied upon to employ any simple preventive that shows scientific promise. They'll let their doctors employ it

f their doctors have time to or care to. And, if not, then the
people themselves will try it.

"Yes, Doctor, I'm glad we used the spray," said one woman,
whose baby had died from infantile paralysis during the epidemic. "You see, Doctor," she told Armstrong, "we'd be
blaming ourselves now, if we hadn't tried everything to save
our baby."

In not one instance was Armstrong denounced by stricken
parents embittered by the spray's failure.

### IV

But now, in the 1936-'37 winter, while Armstrong was
weighing the gains and reverses of this first dubious battle,
came more hopeful news from California. And again, in its
own way, this news was thanks to the people's fight against
the maiming death. At least it was the people's nickels,
dimes, quarters, and dollars that had made this astounding new science possible. Armstrong himself had gone back
from this strange people's death-fight to his laboratory bench
in Washington. He'd root around for some new chemical
preventive, some magic stuff that wouldn't cause headaches,
nor hives, nor make people feel bad all over. If he had luck—
but who had luck with this infernal paralytic sickness?—he'd
dredge up some chemical whose death-blockading power
would keep paralytic pestilence out of all endangered children. Something the life-guarding power of which would not
be so transient!

"Yes, it's a big order," said Charles Armstrong, smiling, as
usual understating it, and vastly relieved to be back at his
lab bench, away from awful hurly-burly, so appallingly anti-
scientific, of the people's own fight for life.

Within two months from California came the first hint of
a new preventive. Its death-blocking power, for monkeys,
would be called formidable by your most conservative microbe hunter. How could its discovery have come so quickly

on the heels of Armstrong's only partly hopeful picric-alum
experiment, of the people, by the people, on the people? If
at this moment, the tragic history of the infantile paralysis
death-fight had been running true to form, Armstrong's experiment—ending as it did with results not striking—might
have faded into limbo. The whole death blockade might have
been just another one of those hopeful things—not quite sufficiently hopeful. Here, you see, was how infantile paralysis
had always bedeviled and baffled microbe hunters—

This particular midget microbe is extremely choice about
his victims, you remember. He disdains cheap, handy little
laboratory rodents like guinea-pigs, rabbits, or mice. He is
an aristocrat, this murderer, and must have men or monkeys.
So now, to test out possible new death-blocking chemicals
our searchers would have to have monkeys in companies,
regiments, armies, in such legions as any good searcher would
only dream to be available in that experimenting Valhalla to
which good microbe hunters go when at last they die. Now
such a plethora of monkeys seemed nothing if not millennial.
Because monkeys are expensive. Each monkey costs eight dollars! But we must be practical. A laboratory search for some
new chemical is feasible if it can be made in respect to a
disease that will afflict a mouse. All science is cut and try. All
searching is groping, means using up thousands of mice
failing, before you click on one life-guarding triumph
maybe. Yes, mouse science is practicable, economically.
Mice cost ten cents apiece. To make good science you need
not one mouse but many mice for each experiment. Being
cheap, ten cents, you can reach into a bin of mice and drag
them out by handfuls. But monkeys? Each one—eight dollars! So it had come about—this world being what it is—that
there are actually two kinds of death-fighting science. There
is ten cent science and eight dollar science. You can undertake adequate ten cent science against pneumonia. Truly
adequate eight dollar science to try to guard the limbs and

lives of our children from paralytic murder? Such expensive science freely at the command of our searchers was unthinkable!

In our world there is ten cent truth and eight dollar truth, and always will be—

But no.

Now there is a gleam of hope against this frustration of our men against the maiming death. Now suddenly there is money for monkeys. Monkeys in mouse-like profusion. Here, at last, in 1935 and 1936, our searchers have come into possession of what is—for them—outlandish money. January 30, 1935, the people of America have danced and made merry to keep the birthday of a man loved by the have-nots but not by the haves. He himself has been laid low by the maiming sickness and struggled up from it to lead our nation. So on this day have-nots and haves make common cause to celebrate our President's courage. And here is a sum of more than $240,000 placed into hands of searchers—our country over—who are qualified to join the desperate fight against the most resourceful, elusive of all midget microbes.

Among this far-flung band of microbe hunters—a little stunned at his own share of this lavish monkey money—is Edwin W. Schultz of Stanford University, California. Moneyless and therefore monkeyless, Schultz had given up hope of working any longer at the mystery of infantile paralysis. Now this 1936 winter he is hot back on the trail. His long low laboratory building resounds with the chattering and screaming of his monkey cohorts. Like Charles Armstrong, Schultz too finds the death-guarding power of picric acid. But that is only his jumping-off place into the chemical unknown. Now he begins to set up vast experiments—each one costing a hundred, two, three, yes, even four hundred dollars! He tests out chemical after chemical, more than forty different substances, and monkeys go limp and die in bevies, with Schultz and his fiercely toiling young co-worker, Louis Gebhardt, both of them working in a slight daze, a little incredulous at their monkey bonanza—

Now they've got it.

### V

This chemical that so powerfully guards their monkeys is old, is simple, is ordinary, is common as mud, in nature. The metal from which it is formed is in our drinking water, in cereals, milk, eggs, meats, and oysters. It exists in weighable amounts in our own bodies. It has been used by doctors for many years as an eyewash. In doses fifty times as strong as Schultz needs, to protect his monkeys against the maiming death, this chemical has been used to make children vomit when they have upset stomachs! So how can it be harmful?

It is common ordinary zinc sulphate in one percent solution.

The tests to which Schultz and Gebhardt now put this death-blocking chemical were in every sense severe ones. On five days in succession they turned batches of healthy monkeys bottomside up and with a power-spray shot the one percent zinc sulphate into each nostril of each monkey.

Then, four weeks in succession, five days a week each of those four weeks, they poured great doses—overwhelmingly fatal!—into those sprayed monkeys' noses.

Meanwhile they cut their sprays of zinc sulphate down to one time weekly. And alongside these sprayed creatures were equal numbers of monkeys not sprayed at all, but inoculated with the same overwhelming doses of the maiming death.

These last unfortunates were paralyzed and killed, without exception. Against such tremendous doses of the death at least one out of every four monkeys who've been sprayed with Armstrong's picric-alum fail to show resistance. It is too drastic. It is too much to ask of any monkey, or any death-blocking chemical.

But the zinc sulphate-sprayed monkeys? *All* of them survived this month-long bombardment with twenty doses of paralytic death, with not a sign of paralysis, without one sickening.

How long did this protection last? One of the practical objections to the spraying of children with picric-alum was this: you had to keep repeating the spraying. Armstrong thought the death blockade would hardly last more than a week— Now Schultz and Gebhardt flooded the insides of the noses of a batch of monkeys, held upside down, with their one percent zinc sulphate. Then they returned them to their cages. Did nothing to them for a whole month. Then, without any further zinc sulphate treatment at all, they assaulted these simians with successive overwhelming doses of infantile paralysis virus—

They survived it while all of their not-sprayed comrades became paralyzed, and died.

But, you ask—admitting that this experiment is academically marvelous—how in any community could you herd threatened children together to spray them five days in succession in time of epidemic threat? It's just not practical.

Schultz gathered together another band of sacrificial simians. Twelve of them. To these he gave just one thorough spray of his one percent zinc sulphate. He did nothing more to them for one week. Then he began to try to make experimental massacre. Now for seven weeks in succession he flooded them with paralytic death, dripped five times each week into their nostrils. It was a flood of the unseen paralytic death that no child would conceivably have to submit to, in nature, in any epidemic. During all these seven weeks of their five-times-weekly peril, Schultz gave these monkeys only two additional sprays of zinc sulphate—one at two weeks, the other at four weeks after the experiment began.

But that was all. And, after that last zinc sulphate spray,

our super-drastic searchers dropped additional death into their monkeys' nostrils for twenty-seven days—

Out of the twelve simians submitted to this dreadful ordeal by paralytic virus, ten survived without a sign of paralysis. All their not-sprayed comrades, the control monkeys, had long since gone limp to their monkey hereafter.

It seemed too good to be true, this peculiar galvanizing of the endings of the monkeys' nerves of smell—for a month—by this zinc sulphate. How could anything—apparently!—so harmless seal shut death's doorway for a whole month, or longer? Longer? Yes, for Schultz now discovered that a certain proportion of monkeys were proof against the death for two, and some for as long as three, months after they'd been treated three days in succession with this zinc sulphate. Of course the protection wasn't permanent. Keep them long enough and they all became as susceptible as any unsprayed monkey.

Schultz was conservative, claimed nothing except zinc sulphate's power to guard monkeys. June, 1937, Schultz wrote in the *Journal of the American Medical Association*—

"We may summarize the results very briefly by saying that two or three successive daily intranasal sprays with a one percent solution of zinc sulphate . . . will generally protect all, or nearly all of the animals so treated against virus administered one month after treatments have been applied."

Regarding the possible jump from monkey to man Schultz was cautious, as becomes your professor—

"The remarkable protection yielded by this simple and relatively nontoxic agent in animals suggests the desirability of carrying the investigation over to man," wrote Schultz.

Suggests it? No—for the people, the human test was now demanded. In the whole history of microbe-hunting, with due regard to all its triumphs in preventing death, its toxoids against diphtheria, its 606 against syphilis, its vaccine against smallpox, its sanitary engineering against typhoid fever—

never had any microbe hunter found a trick so simple, yet powerful, to prevent death so sure, so overwhelming.

For animals. In the laboratory.

To your chronicler Schultz wrote a letter permitting himself a gleam of hope, no more. "Somewhere the light must be shining for children threatened by infantile paralysis," Schultz said. "Will zinc sulphate be the answer?"

## CHAPTER TEN

# WE'VE JUST BEGUN THE BATTLE

OUR men against the maiming death were faced by this little enigma: is what's true for monkeys true for man? And what an enigma.

It did seem as if that question should now find a quick answer. What was now to hinder field tests of this super-powerful zinc sulphate preventive, in the epidemic of infantile paralysis that must surely break out, summer 1937?

Hadn't previous failures been due at least partly to this: that efforts to guard children had been improvised upon the spur of the moment? Hadn't they been planless? In the sense that there was no national, general death-fighting staff to organize the epidemic fight before the epidemic happened?

In the 1936-'37 winter your chronicler witnessed a first groping step toward the forming of such a battle plan. The monkey science of Schultz and Gebhardt had been made possible by the people's money. This had been administered by the President's Infantile Paralysis Research Commission. Now it was true that Schultz was only one of fourteen searchers sharing the Commission's $240,000. And, of course, with those searchers using the expensive monkeys freely—as if those monkeys were mere mice—it was natural that the Commission's funds were running low. Two hundred and forty thousand dollars is hardly more than chicken feed when more than a dozen laboratories are busy using it to make eight dollar science.

Yet a little wherewithal remained in the Commission's till. The Commission's Advisory Medical Committee—four able men of medical science—had pondered well this hopeful, powerful zinc sulphate monkey science. They had studied, too, the pros and cons that came out of Charles Armstrong's field test of the people, by the people, on the people, in the South in the 1936 summer. Did these facts taken together justify them in recommending to the President's Commission that it should support, with its remaining money, the momentous jump of this zinc sulphate science from monkey to man?

Three out of four of the Advisory Committee voted that this portentous step was feasible. Provided that certain little ifs could be answered. If this zinc sulphate can be applied to the insides of the collective noses of any threatened American community or communities—

So that the zinc sulphate shall completely cover the delicate endings of the nerves of smell, surely seal shut the door against the maiming death. If this can be done so that it shall not be harmful. And so that it will be sufficiently comfortable to insure parents bringing their children back for as many treatments as may be necessary while the threat of the maiming death is present.

The needed money for the answering of these ifs was allotted to experts at the University of Michigan Medical School at Ann Arbor, and at the start it seemed as if the answers would be quick and easy. Or so it appeared to your reporter, who must here confess that he is prone to be too enthusiastic in encouraging the always difficult jump of laboratory science from mice or monkeys to threatened mankind. Charles Armstrong's field test had proved that fathers and mothers—armed with atomizers—could not be depended upon to seal shut death's doorway high up inside children's noses. It was plain now that the preventive *must* be applied by experts. But how?

"The only way to get the stuff up there is to have it put up there by a man who knows how to put it there and knows when he's got it up there." This was the sententious comment of microbe hunter Edward Francis, of the U. S. Public Health Service. This super-skeptical, sagacious veteran hunter of truth had been the staunchest supporter of his comrade Charles Armstrong's southern human field test. Francis made it seem simple—to your chronicler.

But here was the rub: death's pathway into the human brain along the nerves of smell was way up high inside the human nose, hard to see, especially in the small noses of children, or in people who had bumped their noses and who had crooked partitions between their nostrils. There was no question you'd have to have trained specialists to look up inside there, to see to it that the zinc sulphate hit the spot.

—How many trained specialists, for how many hundreds of thousands of children, should epidemic threaten in some great city, say Chicago?—

And who would organize, and pay the specialists? Your chronicler did not bother to answer this question. First of all, how to get the zinc sulphate up there? In the early spring of 1937, it seemed to the Ann Arbor searchers as if this should be not too hard to do. A long-nozzled atomizer with a special spray tip was devised, inserted expertly, gently, past all obstructions to the top of sundry children's noses, then puff-puff-puff, the atomizer bulb was squeezed. Presto.

When x-ray opaque fluids were puffed up that way into various little human experimental guinea-pigs, it was beautiful, from the x-ray pictures then taken, how zinc sulphate high-sprayed up there would cover all death's doorway. So let's get ready, now, for the summer's coming battle.

There was one small difficulty. Surely this one percent zinc sulphate was harmless. But the six- to twelve-year-old kids who were having that long tip slid up their noses didn't like it. Definitely—and sometimes with embarrassing rumpus!— they fought it. You could bribe most of them to let you do it the second day, by bags of candy. They didn't make enough of a fracas to bother hard-boiled ear-nose-throat specialists and nurses. But their fond mammas? And just exactly where would you get to when you tried mass-production spraying on, say, five thousand fighting youngsters, chaperoned by their loving mothers, daily? In the excitement of an epidemic when you couldn't stop to argue?

That was a serious bug in this high-spray method and now an unexpected catch appeared in that harmless zinc sulphate. After all, it isn't only children who are threatened in a severe infantile paralysis epidemic, and, ominously, the sickness appears, as years go by, to tend to attack older age groups of human beings. Wouldn't it be wise to spray whole communities in time of epidemic threat, varnish the insides of all available noses with this life-guarding zinc sulphate?

—Doing that, you might prevent the unseen death from leaking *out* of the noses of carriers of the sickness, as well as keep it from sneaking into the noses of children susceptible. This was a dazzling possibility!—

So our Ann Arbor experimenters sprayed medical students, grownups, even themselves, with the high spray puffed out of the long tip atomizer and the results were terrible. Not dangerous, no. But contrary to the children, who got no serious after-effect to speak of, the grownups, most of them, developed terrific headaches. Some said they'd rather run the risk of being paralyzed for life than have another shot like that up their noses.

Here was what Armstrong and Schultz hadn't thought of. They hadn't consulted their monkeys about whether the spray gave them headaches.

Here was another headache—for the experimenters! When you really got the zinc sulphate up over the danger zone good and plenty, your human experimental guinea-pigs immediately lost all sense of smell. Now this doesn't matter with a monkey. And of course, with well-sprayed humans, you should expect it. If you varnished over those delicate nerve-endings that keep out death, what would you then have left to smell with?

And would it be too much to ask families to trade temporary loss of sense of smell for a chance to dodge the maiming death? Day by day our searchers made precise measurement of their sprayed victims' smell sense and in a week, ten days, two weeks, gradually it returned, finally to normal. And, looking on the bright side of it, wouldn't this very smell loss—during an epidemic—be a crude yet good indicator to the spraying doctors that they'd actually sealed shut death's gate in their sprayed children?

Now it was getting toward summer when the maiming death would begin to stalk somewhere in our country and now happened the worst of all disasters—disheartening to all who, confident in the power of Armstrong and Schultz's monkey science, were eager to see it tested out in human epidemic battle. Surgeon General Thomas Parran had expressed his willingness to throw the power of the Public Health Service into the hoped-for death-fight—provided Charles Armstrong approved the high spray as safe, as practicable.

## II

This reporter will never forget that hot 1937 June day at the University Hospital in Ann Arbor. Here were gathered famed brain surgeon Max M. Peet, of the President's Commission's Advisory Committee, and Henry Vaughan, the able Health Commissioner of Detroit, and Albert Furstenburg, one of the most distinguished of America's ear-nose-throat specialists. And Charles Armstrong, so genial, so mild, so absolutely hard-boiled about the distinction between theoretical and practical science.

And your chronicler, who, enthusiastic, had told millions of parents that this summer they'd have a real chance to join a people's death-fight. That the zinc sulphate would be ready for the crucial test—*this summer*—

It was Max Peet who had suggested getting the zinc sulphate up there by high spray from the long tip atomizer and if the kids kicked and raised hell, why, you'd have to pin them down and hold them, said good old Max. Was it hard to choose between a little squawking and paralysis, lifelong, or death? Henry Vaughan and his right-hand man, Don Gudakunst, were there, ready to offer thousands of Detroit's clinic children for the spray—so that Armstrong's public health doctors and nurses could perfect themselves in mass-production spraying. Dean Furstenburg acted in his capacity as nose expert and now began the battle.

Here sat young Dr. Jerry Hauser, formidable with his nose-expert's head mirror and long-tipped atomizer, and the first four little boys he sprayed set up a terrible squirming and bawling. Worse yet, the noses of three of them bled a little at the end of the simple operation—and what would anxious mammas say to that, when in epidemic time you got them together in thousands with thousands of their children?

Armstrong's face fell as he watched this minor shambles, and with it fell the spirits of your chronicler. Armstrong asked the Ann Arbor experts: "You've shown me how it goes with kids of seven years old and over, how do the little kids take it?"

They hadn't tried the high spray on children of seven years old and under.

"But that's where the incidence of infantile paralysis is highest!" said Armstrong.

So we all trooped to the hospital's nursery. And if the objections of the seven-year-olds were enough to discourage Charles Armstrong, they were nothing to the protests of the toddlers, who began to whimper before young Jerry Hauser even got near them with his atomizer. But when the long gleaming metal tip went up their noses the din they set up was appalling.

They fought and squirmed and twisted like embattled eels and again there was bloodshed, not serious at all, mind you, but blood did show on the gauze after the operation was over.

Armstrong's face was a study. After all, he was the father of this chemical blockade against death. He knew atomizers in the hands of mothers were no go. He knew that somehow, experts had to get the chemical way up there. Laboratory bench-worker that he was, maybe he exaggerated the importance of this juvenile and infant fighting and bawling which was everyday stuff to nose expert Octy Furstenburg and surgeon Max Peet. And yet what he saw that day was certainly no smooth-running demonstration of mass-production spraying that the Public Health Service could recommend to worried cities as a perfectly simple, entirely safe procedure—

Mightn't children injure themselves twisting their heads and fighting against the hard metal spray tip?—

Yes, that was possible. And yet Armstrong, in his quiet manner, as much as anybody in the world, wanted to see a real human field test of this hopeful science of which he was the father. His face was certainly a study with the chance of a real 1937 human death-fight with the powerful zinc sulphate going glimmering. It was the moment for somebody in our glum bunch to make an appropriate remark. Armstrong made it—

"I've got an idea," he said. "You might be able to hold those little kids still if you put each one of them in a plaster cast while you did the spraying!"

That let down the tension and we burst out laughing, louder than was seemly in hospitals where there's rarely laughter. The very ridiculousness of it made us all feel better. Armstrong's dismissal of their science put spunk into the searchers, too, by gosh they'd show him there was a safe simple way to do it!

Yet Armstrong had to go back to Washington, unable to

recommend the high spray method as something practical, with which the Public Health Service could supervise the getting of zinc sulphate into the endangered noses of many thousands of children this 1937 summer.

This is only another example of the hellish resourcefulness of the infantile paralysis virus. Zinc sulphate blocks it, yes. But why does the virus have to choose such an infernally un-get-at-able corner of the human anatomy for its path of entry? The virus has some satanic genius at foiling human experiments to block it. It seemed clear to most of us, that afternoon, that at best a team of doctors and nurses couldn't spray more than a dozen children an hour with this high spray. And since infantile paralysis—even in bad epidemics—attacks so few children, relatively, you'd have to test the zinc spray out on many thousands to get the answer whether it really blocked the death.

Such is the lowdown on why our healthmen did not in the summer of 1937 make a giant field test, conducted by experts, supervised by the U. S. Public Health Service.

Respect must here, too, be paid to the foresight of Dr. George W. McCoy, Chairman of the Advisory Committee of the President's Infantile Paralysis Research Commission. McCoy alone—though he granted the solidity of Armstrong's and Schultz's monkey science—did not believe a field test of zinc sulphate's death-blocking power was feasible. When the other three members of the Committee, all willing to try it, asked him why what worked so well on monkeys shouldn't also work with children, McCoy said—

"When you try to put it up their noses, they'll wiggle."

### III

Late the afternoon of that depressing day your chronicler drove home alone very fast into the setting sun. Altogether too fast but not caring because here was a defeat for one of his most deeply held hunches. It was his belief that what

foils science is lack of wherewithal. But here our searchers
had the wherewithal to discover the zinc sulphate, to find
ways to apply it. And what a failure.

The 1937 summer was a fairly bad one for infantile paralysis, with more than seven thousand children and grownups
stricken in various parts of our country. There is no doubt
that, if the Public Health Service had only been able to
recommend a spray trick, big field tests might have been
tried, and many of those poor children saved—*if what holds
for monkeys holds for men.*

But all is by no means lost, for life is short and science is
long. And real steps ahead were made this 1937 summer,
though haltingly, and in a sort of guerilla warfare against the
maiming pestilence. There is this that's good about the
paralytic sickness: it is so fearsome, for parents, doctors,
healthmen, for everybody, that it makes you do something
about it, makes people grab at any kind of straw of hope.
So it came about that Max Peet's alleged impracticable high
spray did get a field workout, even if you couldn't call it a
proper field experiment, in Toronto.

When the 1937 outbreak sent chills up and down the
spines of Toronto's fathers and mothers, that city's Board of
Health called its ear-nose-throat doctors together. Forty of
the best of them formed zinc-sulphate spray teams. Each
team had one doctor to do the spraying, two nurses to hold
the battling babies and youngsters, and one nurse to keep
accurate records of the name, address, and the date on which
the child was sprayed.

Children, three to ten years old, could come to these forty
clinics, with coupons their parents clipped out of the newspapers, entitling the kids to one free spray—till five thousand
should be sprayed in all. They came, in a rush, with a
vengeance. (As Armstrong had found, you don't have to
urge your scared fathers and mothers.) And in four days'
time, five thousand children had the insides of their noses

varnished by zinc sulphate against the maiming death—each spray team handling fifty kids per hour!

Then economics stopped the experiment—which went fairly well in the hands of those experts with no serious trouble or harm to the children. Yes. The doctors had volunteered for this public health work. But they were all of them privately practicing specialists. And, of course, no matter what the menace, you couldn't ask them to let their practices go untended. Not for the small *per diem* the city was able to pay them.

Now there were only two thousand or so cases among Toronto's maybe more than two hundred thousand children. So, what kind of information could the city's healthmen expect to get, out of those five thousand sprayed? It has been reported that the experiment failed to demonstrate protection; but it is known too, that a large proportion of the sprayed children did not lose their sense of smell. So the blockade had not been performed as it should have been.

Then, late August and early September, the Chicago epidemic broke, and, as more and more children came down sick, went limp, died each day, telegrams and long distance calls went in and out of the office of Chicago's fighting health commissioner, Dr. Herman Bundesen. The newspapers had been full of rumors of the spray's power and parents were bedeviling their doctors—many of whom, knowing nothing at all of Schultz's or Armstrong's monkey science, told the worried parents there was nothing to it and to forget it. But Bundesen called a conference, not of sublimely ignorant practitioners but of men who ought to know.

Here for the first time your chronicler saw a gleam of hope for the human test of the death-blocking zinc sulphate, so powerful for monkeys. Herman Bundesen had called together an able cohort of the top ear-nose-throat specialists of

the Mid-West, headed by Dr. William P. Wherry, Executive Secretary of the American Academy of Ophthalmologists
and Otolaryngologists. In a tense huddle that lasted more
than three hours, it was evident that these experts, putting
their great experience and brains to it, were agreed they
could devise a safe, simple, almost one hundred percent sure
way to get zinc sulphate up into children's noses. To try to
block the death.

There was enthusiasm and good news that morning. From
the University of Michigan's experts came the report that
very likely you'd not have to use that long-tipped atomizer
that caused the nosebleeds and the wiggling. No. To varnish
those delicate endings of the nerves of smell that are almost
surely the gate of paralysis and death, you simply laid the
child on a couch or table, head back over the end, so its
nostrils faced up. Then you proceeded to shrink the membranes insides its nose, to open the narrow passages, with a
little ephedrine. Then you poured a teaspoonful of the zinc
solution into each nostril—allowing it to stay up there for
a couple of minutes—

So, curiously, the experts had come back to the primitive
douching of the chemical by which Armstrong and Schultz
had first saved their monkeys' lives in their laboratories.

The majority of those present believed this simple trick
would seal death's doorway. This was hopeful, but what
most stirred your chronicler that morning was the enthusiasm
of Wherry and all the specialists present.

They caught the drama inherent in the situation, the
curious fact that suddenly, for the first time in medical history, it was up to the ear-nose-throat specialists to become
front-line public health fighters. Wherry is nothing if not a
man of action, and now, all over the nation, members of his
Academy of specialists began working, spraying thousands
of children, finding ways to ease the annoying headaches in
grownups, finding that, among thousands experimented

upon, there has been no permanent discomfort to anybody so far. They have no fear of the zinc sulphate.

But they know that they, the ear-nose-throat specialists, must lead the coming battle. "The only way to get the stuff up there is to have it put up there by a man who knows how to put it there and knows when he's got it up there," microbe hunter Edward Francis had told Armstrong in the beginning.

"It can do no harm," agreed expert Dr. Ralph A. Fenton, of the Academy of specialists. "But it must be done right by a doctor who is well acquainted with the nose."

"If someone in your family were exposed to infantile paralysis, or lived in a place where the disease prevailed, would *you* use the zinc sulphate drops in his nose?" expert Ralph A. Fenton was asked.

"Yes, sir! Right away. It causes a little headache sometimes— But running the risk of permanent paralysis because one is afraid of the slight discomfort is foolish. Better be safe than sorry," Fenton said.

So now at last Charles Armstrong and Edwin Schultz have comrades—men who know how to put it up there—to take the fight from monkey to man in the field test that their laboratory science without a doubt demands.

## IV

So now again, when the battle is joined, it is going to come down to a question—that old simple question—of where do we get the wherewithal? The sure, no longer questioned experimental science has been provided by Charles Armstrong and Edwin Schultz. The expert ear-nose-throat doctors to carry this science across from monkeys to mankind are ready, yes, raring to go. With a simple zinc sulphate nose wash now available, Surgeon General Thomas Parran will be ready to mobilize his epidemic experts of the Public Health Service, Charles Armstrong at their head, so to con-

duct the great field test that the portentous truth will be
found—

What will be the fateful number of the children stricken,
whose parents volunteer to have them treated? Compared
to the toll of paralysis and death among those whose parents
are unwilling?

The local healthmen of endangered cities will be willing
to furnish their facilities, if the U. S. Public Health Service
believes the attempt to test the new death-blockading weapon
is ready. In the event of great emergency, veteran death-
fighter William De Kleine—he of the pellagra battle—will be
eager to ask the American Red Cross to furnish personnel
of nurses, and its experience of organizing populations in
disasters.

Granted this is excellent. But what agency will have the
needed wherewithal, so that all battle plans can be laid beforehand? So that there will be entirely ample funds to re-
imburse the expert doctors who are going to have to head
the nose wash crews of doctors and nurses who will be the
front-line fighters? For this is certain, because of the sud-
denness with which epidemics of infantile paralysis explode,
the fighters must be ready for instant action at the first muttering of danger.

The answer is ready now. It is found in the new people's
fight for life, in the new Infantile Paralysis Foundation now
organized by President Roosevelt. With finally adequate
sinews of war, this new Foundation will fight the sickness on
every front—to finance the science of its prevention; to
broadcast to doctors knowledge of the modern treatment
that can now prevent the horrible deformities that visit
those maltreated when they are stricken; to help communities organize themselves to make self-supporting citizens of
those wrecked by the paralytic aftermath of the pestilence.

The battle will not be a helter-skelter one, as it now is in
the instance of every sickness that plagues us. It will be

planned, co-ordinated by the best scientific brains in our nation. And so, when epidemic looms, the Foundation will instantly pour in money needed to pay well the expert doctors, the community's physicians and healthmen, and its nurses to make the field test of the preventive upon all children whose parents demand it.

The people will not be misled by the raising of false hopes. They will know that Armstrong, that Schultz, that all the most dauntless of the men against the maiming death face the field test with crossed fingers. Subtle and damnable is the sneaking of this paralytic virus. How many days elapse from the moment the unseen virus is wafted up a child's nose to fasten its tiny deadliness upon the nerves of smell, until that child suddenly sickens, becomes paralyzed? This length of time is not exactly known. It may be ten days. And again instances of as long as twenty-nine days from time of sure contact to outbreak of paralysis have been reported.

And it is certain that the zinc sulphate nose wash must be applied, the chemical blockade must be effected, *before* the virus enters.

But what if—and there are scientists who maintain that it is possible—this devilish virus spreads itself through our population months before the onset of epidemic? What if it then sleeps in populations, only to be roused to its paralyzing fury by some subtle climatic influence not yet understood by our death-fighters?

If that should be true, then the most highly organized widespread nose washing campaign could not stem the epidemic fire. Granted. And such possible failure will be looked for. But what then is to prevent the next experiment? Why then should not the children of our communities be given this simple zinc sulphate nose wash in the springtime before the epidemic threatens? This possibility is a challenge to the determination and foresight of our healthmen, and of all of us.

Our men against the maiming death do not for one moment fool themselves that this chemical blockade is the final weapon in the fight against the paralytic death. At the very best it is a makeshift. Even though the damage is temporary, it is not good that the sense of smell should have to be suppressed to gain protection—also, alas, temporary—against the maiming terror. If this zinc sulphate varnishing of the delicate endings of nerves of smell must be repeated, month after month, summer after summer, among masses of our population—who knows the final outcome? Might it result in the mass misfortune of a population with permanently ruined noses?

Yet this is basic in this terrible death-fight: one sure proof —by lives saved—that, some way, you can block the entry of the paralyzing virus, such proof will give our fighters a great lift, will give them new courage. Thanks to the money provided the President's Infantile Paralysis Research Commission by our people who in 1935 danced and made merry, in many a laboratory the keenest virus-fighters in our country are looking for life-guarding tricks whose effect may be as powerful, but more permanent.

At Long Island Medical College in Brooklyn, veteran infantile paralysis-fighter Sidney D. Kramer is perfecting—upon monkeys—a strange new nasal vaccination. Yes, believe it or not, after all those vaccine failures, by a most peculiar stunt he can make many monkeys actually immune.

He sprays up into healthy monkeys' noses a curious mixture. It is made from extract of the pituitary gland, plus adrephine which has the power to shrink nose mucous membranes. This mixture is completely harmless—

Then, four hours after this spraying, he pours virulent infantile paralysis virus into the noses of these gland-sprayed, nose-shrunk simians—

This dose is invariably fatal to healthy, not-sprayed monkeys—

But now their gland-sprayed comrades—seven out of ten of them—are proof against the death.

And not for a week or month, but solidly immune, the way a vaccinated human being is immune to smallpox!

So Sidney Kramer is edging toward the solving of an old riddle regarding the paralytic sickness. Why is it that, when you pour the deadly virus into a monkey's nose, he nine times out of ten succumbs to the paralytic sickness? Why, during epidemics, do only one out of a thousand of all human beings, and never more than one out of eighty children contract infantile paralysis? What is the defense of the majority of human beings? Why do monkeys lack this natural immunity?

Now by his nose-shrinking, gland-spraying trick, Kramer, as he says, has made monkeys like men, has made—so far as infantile paralysis goes—a man out of a monkey.

Of course three out of ten of Kramer's experimental monkeys go paralyzed and die in spite of this gland spraying, when he pours the virus into their noses. And he does not advocate gland spraying our children and then pouring virulent virus into them to try to make them permanently immune. No.

But look. In times of epidemic danger the subvisible virus rampages through our communities, widespread, sneaking into the noses of the majority of our people. Now, what if you sprayed gland extract and adrephine into all of them? Then let the virus, as it does in nature, find its own way into the already sprayed noses of the entire community. Mightn't the susceptible people of the community then become naturally vaccinated, protected?

How does this shrinking of their mucous membranes and douching of their noses with pituitary gland extract protect monkeys who would otherwise surely succumb to this pouring of infantile paralysis virus into their noses?

Kramer cannot answer. He only knows that his peculiar

spraying trick sometimes calls white blood cells, phagocytes, to the scene of battle. They swarm in the mucous membranes around the endings of the nerves of smell. Do they gobble the invading virus? Who knows? The virus is too small to see. There is yet no rime or reason to this science. You only know that one monkey dies where three died before.

### V

But if all these hopes of blocking the death are dashed, yet in other laboratories other searchers are probing into other corners of this dark unknown. Where, in its human spreaders, does the subvisible terror breed? How can you spot such carriers? Can a test be discovered to pick out the relatively few children who are susceptible? What are the peculiarities of the anatomy, or the physiology of those children who are susceptible? Let's face it: there is no more formidable life-wrecking mystery than this of infantile paralysis. The fight to solve it is bound to be a long and stern one. But now, working with the sinews of war granted them by the President's Infantile Paralysis Research Commission, our searchers have had a chance to renew these fights which for fifty years have ended in failure.

Now it is the President's hope that the new Infantile Paralysis Foundation will make it possible for them to go on to the end of the struggle.

Where will they get the money for the monkeys, monkeys as many as mice, the millions of monkeys, maybe, that victory demands?

The people are going to be asked to give the money. And will it be possible for the President, and the organizers of the great new crusade, to show the people that their money is not being sought on a basis of begging? There is this defect of sweet charity. It assumes that the poor ye have always with you. There is this trouble about sentimental giving to aid our fighters for life: this altruism, emotional, is temporary, is fitful. But our death-fighters do not assume that we will have infantile paralysis with us always. Deep down in them, one and all they're working to wipe it out. But they know that this curse is not like some flood, earthquake, or any other spectacular disaster that calls out public generosity. This is not the nature of the maiming death. Year after year, every year, in small and great epidemics, it goes on stalking, and piling up its horrid aftermath. So for thirty years in our country it has been adding to a longer and longer parade— of young Americans condemned to hobble by the aid of canes, to go on crutches, to be wheeled about in chairs, to be bedridden and deformed for life and hidden from the world in shame by their families.

Now the fight to stem the growing of this mountain of human wreckage, of people to whom death would have been a kinder fate, this fight will be nothing if it is not unremitting.

The people must not, then, be asked to give their money only to honor our President for his conquest of his own life's wreck. Or because they can be stirred to sentiment by knowledge of the strangling of a child by this paralytic terror. Or because their eyes can be made wet by the sight of one youngster robbed, lifelong, of strength at life's beginning.

No, it is cold self-interest that demands the fight against the maiming death should be fought through to victory. Consider one child, twelve years old, deprived by infantile paralysis, for life, of his body's power. Then calculate, on the basis of what your average American earns from manhood till three score years and ten, the loss to the nation, in dollars, caused by that one citizen who cannot work. Add to this the cost of that citizen's medical care. Then ask out of whose pocket is this life-wrecked child—unless it belongs to the rich minority—going to be supported? Then multiply this cost, for one citizen, by the hundreds of thousands of victims made wholly or partially non-productive by the maiming plague.

Will the organizers of the new Infantile Paralysis Foundation have the courage to approach our people with such a cold-hearted request for money for the death-fight?

Do they dare to make the new Foundation an experiment in public health economics?

Can the long battle begin on a basis of business, not begging?

Nobody knows how much money will be needed to conquer the paralytic terror. Many millions, yes, hundreds of millions doubtless, before the fight is won.

Then can the whole people be made to understand this new bookkeeping: that, in the long run, the millions they will give are mere small change when you balance them against what this plague has already cost, is costing, and will continue to cost the taxpayers of our nation?

The answer depends upon the skill, the boldness, the lack of mawkishness, with which this grim matter of dollars and cents is placed before the people.

*Part Three*

IT COSTS US MONEY TO DIE

## CHAPTER ELEVEN

# DETROIT AGAINST
# TUBERCULOSIS

WHO truly understands the heart and the brain of the people? Are cynics right about the invincible boobery of the human mass? Will the people ever understand the collective self-interest of joining the fight for life? Or are they only to be stirred to fitful support of it by the tear-jerking technique of mob masters? And our rich men? To support science in the old stingy manner, are they only to be separated from driblets of their wealth by their uneasy consciences? And are the people of the middle levels only willing to bear the burden demanded by the death-fight after they've been told sob sister's sagas of mothers dying, children paralyzed, of babies shrieking in the torture of meningitis?

Are our armchair pseudo-psychologists correct in believing mankind incapable of foresight? Could the people understand the balance sheets of a new death-fighting bookkeeping that takes you into the red today to get you permanently into the black—not at the end of this year but within a generation?

Would the rulers and the owners of the people understand such new public health economics? Or what would their arguments be against it?

Up till now, conscience money, nuisance money, has feebly supported our men of science. Mawkish money—and little enough of it—has always furnished the sinews of the fight for life. Now if the human mass is asked to dry its tears and get perfectly hard-boiled about wiping out a given death, what will be its reaction?

If the need for this new economy were really rammed

home by every means of dramatizing it to the people, would a ho-hum be the answer? Or would the people turn in fury upon those who try to measure life and death in dollars?

And if this sacrilege aroused anger, who would be the victims of the rage of the people?

These strange questions are now finding their answer in Detroit's new fight against tuberculosis. Though maybe not yet appreciated as such, this people's death-fight is perhaps almost as momentous as the laboratory adventures of Pasteur and Koch of sixty years ago when these geniuses proved to men that microbes were their most murderous enemies. It has been the luck of your chronicler to have had a ringside seat at the very beginning of this new battle. And the band of pioneers there present hardly realized what they were plotting, that December night in 1934.

What the Detroit healthmen and TB experts then tried to plan was a new way, very novel, of saving Detroit's tax-payers' money. And as a by-product it was hinted that this might really start the wiping out of Detroit's tuberculosis. It was an unprecedented mixing of banking with bacteriology.

It is a widely held notion that the white plague is more than half-whipped already and that no severe effort is needed to speed its extinction. So why this hullabaloo about it? Such a belief is nothing but misinformation. In Detroit, where the new battle plans first were dreamed, TB is still murdering three times more young people of twenty and under than all other contagions put together. It is sending to cadaverous, coughing death more Detroiters in the prime of life—fifteen years old to forty—than any sickness whatsoever.

In this situation Detroit is not worse off than the average for our nation.

It is not the worst tragedy of consumption that—in spite of all our science—it is still such a formidable killer. In many places in America, TB's microbes, aided by their most powerful friend, poverty, are becoming more murderous. In a dozen of our great cities TB's death rate—which in past decades has made citizens complacent by its downtrend—has begun a sinister upsurge. One of Ohio's so-called prosperous industrial cities saw consumptive death shoot up twenty-nine percent from 1934 to 1935. Not only is tuberculosis still plenty formidable. But it could easily jump back to its old place of champion murderer of men.

## II

In that smoked-filled room in the Detroit Athletic Club, in December, 1934, did Detroit's TB fighters, sitting before their steins of beer, reveal some new serum, drug, to your reporter? Far from it. Their scientific weapons were not new. They could be made available to the physicians and health-men of every community—urban or rural—of every part of our nation. What this band of death-fighting plotters had to offer was an idea. It was as revolutionary as it was simple. It was powerful as it was plain and humdrum. Yet it was at first propounded as an impossibility by Detroit's health commissioner, Henry Vaughan. Then, who knows, maybe it was the bounteous beer being guzzled, the possibility of making that idea come true started buzzing in the heads of those plotters against death. They started building a beer-table utopia. That evening your chronicler, watching the faces of his five companions, felt a thrill at the life-giving possibilities of this notion, and pledged what help his typewriter might give.

You see this truth is burned into the brains of all who've been thrilled by the triumph of life-guarding science: our cities, counties, states, the nation, have always given the sinews of war to our death-fighters as a sort of dole; like crusts thrown to beggars; like coppers tossed to dry the tears of children. This is at the bottom of the frustration of science.

Hospitals, all their scientific apparatus, the pay of the scientists and doctors, all of these are financed on the ground of charity and they're never financed enough. Science is not supported because it can now build a new mankind, a universally strong humanity. The consciences of the rulers of the people keep clear by keeping the people half-alive. Let a hundred children live, it's okay that six others die. We're doing pretty good compared to what we used to, aren't we?

But now, this 1934 December evening, as our Detroit death-fighters translated their scientific facts and experience into figures scrawled on the backs of our menu cards, a challenge emerged. The wiping out of TB is not at all a humanitarian project. It is not to dry tears that it is demanded that we do it. No, it is to balance the city's budget. It is not to soothe mass heartbreak. It is to make the taxpayers happy. It is not philanthropy to rub out every last TB microbe. It is true economy. It was no pipe dream. There was no doubt that they could prove it.

### III

This was the vision of that band of death-haters this December evening and now weeks passed, and months stretched into a year, all of 1935, without any public move to bring this dazzling promise into action. Why this lethargy, when these men were so sure of the power of their science? Oh, well, who would believe it? Wouldn't the scheme sound too good to be true, wouldn't the city fathers say here's a scientific gold brick?

Yet, in respect to TB, these same men had got their city ready to make Pasteur's boldest dream come true. He had promised—if his science was correct and who dared deny its truth?—that it was within the power of men to make parasitic maladies disappear from the face of the globe. What prevented Detroit's men from right now going into action? They had the most fundamental grasp of tuberculosis-eradicating science to be found anywhere in America. To one of these five plotters, Dr. E. J. O'Brien,—Pat O'Brien to you—it was more than mere science, it was religion. Pat was no microbe hunter but only a chest surgeon, yet the fierceness of his understanding of this basic science gave him a death-fighting power beyond that of any bacteriologist of your chronicler's acquaintance.

At that first 1934 meeting, and every time he drank with your chronicler thereafter, Pat snarled and growled his TB science—

"TB's contagious. It's no act of God. It's caused by a dirty microbe. You don't get it unless from somebody who's already got it. The bug's spread only by sick folks spitting it out of open cavities in their lungs. Catch 'em in time, you can close all such cavities. By collapse treatment. By lung rest. When you close the holes, they can't spit the bugs out. Every hole you close is one less spreader of TB. And by God we could close 'em all if we caught 'em in time!"

This was all of O'Brien's science, and the ferocity with which he preached it made him not too popular among the more suave members of Detroit's medical faculty. Even some health experts thought O'Brien slightly bughouse. He was always saying: "To prevent TB, you've first got to cure it!"

Yet all respected O'Brien's superb chest surgery, his honesty, his emotion that came out of his own wife's twenty-years-long suffering from tuberculosis. And his basic TB-fighting science was vouched for, absolutely, by Dr. Bruce Douglas, TB-Controller of Detroit, who was one of our co-plotters that first beer-drinking evening. Sober, Quaker, teetotaler, Douglas backed up O'Brien's fiery science, quietly but entirely. They were a hard pair to beat, Pat and Bruce. Both fundamentalists. Pat threw the bombs and Bruce was the mopper-upper.

What sinister something tied the hands of these able death-fighters? They had a cheap good test—tuberculin—to spot the

lurking of TB microbes in the bodies of all Detroit's citizens.
But the trouble was that this reliable test was not enough to
spot the actual spreaders of the death. Many people not
sick at all, with the microbes absolutely dormant in them,
showed the red spot after tuberculin. To find the true death
spreaders, who were spraying the white death onto healthy
people out of holes in their rotting lungs (Pat's way of
putting it) the x-ray's magic eye is needed.

There was the rub. The x-ray films run into big money.
That was the catch. Henry Vaughan was a fighter as health
commissioner. Bruce Douglas in his quiet way was bold at
bedsides of the dying. Pat O'Brien for himself didn't give a
damn at operating tables where TB-riddled patients sprayed
death upon him. But the scientific boldness of all of them
was equaled by their curious timidity as citizens. Their plan
to wipe out TB was sound science. But the sums of money
they'd have to ask for, to train their x-ray's magic eye on all
the thousands needing it, to find all open tuberculosis, that
money sounded, to them, fantastic.

### IV

Yet it could not be said that, in the matter of TB hospitals,
of equipment for the modern lung-rest cure of consumption,
Detroit had skimped Henry Vaughan, Bruce Douglas, and
Pat O'Brien. In the number of TB-hospital beds available
Detroit had long led the nation. The city was fortunate, too,
in having a good number of surgeons and doctors who were
applying this lung-rest treatment. In Detroit, cavities were
being closed, death was being sealed up, on a scale greater
than in any other city in the world. The artificial pneumothorax treatment, the phrenic nerve operation, the last-ditch
operation of de-ribbing, weren't discovered in Detroit, no.
But, led by O'Brien and Douglas, a fairly large number of
Detroit's doctors realized that one or another of these means
of treatment—and not mere rest in bed—was the only sure

way of closing dangerous tuberculous cavities. So that now, while it is a major medical scandal how scores of thousands of Americans needlessly die every year for lack of lung-rest treatment, in Detroit in 1934, ninety out of every hundred known active consumptives were under one form or another of collapse therapy, had the benefit of this modern way of curing. But Douglas and O'Brien didn't stop to congratulate themselves on this record. They kept asking if lung-rest can cure so many consumptives already far gone, why wait till they've got to this advanced stage of their sickness? And they didn't think only about the individual consumptives. O'Brien was a nuisance in Detroit and Michigan medical and public health circles, insisting that every day any single consumptive lives with open cavities, he's spewing spit-bombs of death about him.

So why not close all cavities in their beginning? When tuberculosis was still early; minimal was the technical word for it.

Yes, but here was another serious rub. Of all the white plague's victims who came to Bruce Douglas at the Herman Kiefer Hospital, eighty percent were advanced cases when they got there!

But why? Why didn't they come earlier? But what *is* early, in this white death? Is it when you feel sick enough to see a doctor? A lot of doctors say that's when—when you just begin coughing, losing weight, feeling tired for no reason, having a little fever, sweating nights. They still believe that this is when TB's early. Then they tap your chest. They listen through their stethoscopes—

"So far as their spotting early TB goes, you might as well throw all the stethoscopes in the Detroit River," O'Brien says.

When there's any whispering of the white death so loud a doctor can hear it through his stethoscope, the sickness is no longer early, but advanced. That was the reason, said Pat

O'Brien and Bruce Douglas, that eighty out of every hundred were coming to the hospitals with advanced consumption—because the x-ray's magic eye hadn't been used to spot its unfelt beginning.

Vaughan had his plans all set to x-ray all people in Detroit who should be suspected to be minimals. If you could only do that, you might change Detroit's TB hospital population from eighty percent advanced cases to eighty percent minimal cases in a few years. You'd reverse the present figures!

Bruce Douglas could testify out of his enormous experience at the Herman Kiefer Hospital that, if you got hold of your consumptive, hospitalized him, began giving him collapse therapy while he was still minimal, you'd cure him twice as quickly, he'd only have to stay in hospital half as long as he would if he first came when his disease was advanced.

Pat kept repeating: "But we can't cure 'em till we find 'em. We've got to go out and get 'em. And how the hell are we going to get all of 'em till we've got the means to go out and look for 'em?"

You had to have x-rays to look for 'em.

But x-rays for everybody? For all known contacts, for all who could be proved endangered?

V

At our first beer-drinking scientific conference in December, 1934, Henry Vaughan put it down, black on white, that it takes an average of eighteen months for the city to cure an advanced case of TB, and only nine months to cure a minimal.

It was Henry's merit that night to become materialistic about tuberculosis, to reduce it heartlessly to a matter of dollars and cents. He said let's face it. TB is a poor man's sickness, and the poor families do not pay for their tuberculosis, or they pay only in their misery, their pain, their death, and heartache of bereavement, but let's forget all that —the ones who pay and pay and pay are Detroit's taxpayers.

Ditching all mawkish considerations Henry calculated that, if you could only fill the TB hospitals with minimals, eighty percent of minimals instead of eighty percent advanced cases, it would be wonderful for the taxpayers. So much per day to keep advanced cases eighteen months. Half that amount to keep the minimals nine months! Forget the TB's themselves or the happiness of their families but what convincing arithmetic for the tax-howlers!

It made you squirm a little but where was the argument against it?

It seemed the only way you might convince Detroit's budget-balancers. You had to show them it would be good business for them to shell out adequate money for unlimited x-rays, all the x-rays that Douglas, O'Brien, and Vaughan might deem necessary to find all early tuberculosis. This Detroit plan was now published, not in any solemn scientific journal but in that plain old farmer paper, *The Country Gentleman,* and then in a book called *Why Keep Them Alive?* The O'Brien-Vaughan-Douglas plan had no scientific name but was simply called "The People's Death Fight."

It must be here acknowledged that the story was written with no hope that it would really strike fire. It was written in despair because Vaughan, Douglas, and O'Brien, it was plain to your chronicler, had no hope that Detroit's people or its rulers would understand the simple arithmetic, the business sense, the economy of wiping out tuberculosis. The story taunted Detroit's people and jeered at them—

Detroit's TB-men are now all set to wipe out consumption but—

Detroit is too stingy.

The white plague can now be mopped up if—

Detroit's bookkeeping was not so cockeyed that the city couldn't spend a quarter—for x-rays—to save a dollar—for hospital costs.

Ho hum, who'd read the story? Who'd listen?

Well, William J. Scripps, of *The Detroit News,* read it. Young Bill got sore at this insult to Detroit. But who was young Bill? A director on *The Detroit News* board, yes. But only one director. And only a young director, only an aviating, hell-driving young Bill Scripps, who had wanted to be a scientist, or an engineer, not a newspaperman. Bill had fantastic ideas about the power of radio to move the human mass but he was a visionary, so don't take young Bill seriously.

But Bill was sore at this slur on Detroit's bookkeeping ability, mad enough to convene O'Brien, Douglas, Vaughan, Reporter A. M. Smith, and your chronicler at another dinner —beer was served—at the Detroit Athletic Club. Bill does not talk easily. Now he began to shoot slow, profane questions at us—

So wiping out TB ought to be a *people's* death-fight?— How the hell would Detroit's people ever know that, unless you got the news of it across to all of 'em? . . . And who could tell 'em? . . . Well, my frien's—this is young Bill, very earnest—my frien's, you can have the front page of *The Detroit News* to tell 'em . . . For as many days as you need it . . . You can have Detroit News Radio Station WWJ to tell 'em, for as many weeks as you want it!

Bill said he was ready to go the whole hog with us and that we could be as tough, telling the story, as we wanted to. It was all right with him if we shocked Detroit's people, jarred the people into seeing that here was no question of mercy, sweet charity. Here was no question of human lives. To hell with lives. No, it was costing the city good hard money to let its consumptives rot with tuberculosis! To take eighteen long months to cure them, or to let them slowly die.

It seemed too good to be true, and could young Bill get away with it, with the editors, with the other directors of the always decorous *Detroit News?* and what would happen to the paper's circulation when we began socking it into the customers that we didn't care about people's lives, to hell with their lives, but why were they such bookkeeping bunglers?

It must again be acknowledged that all of us lacked faith that such a sensational campaign would be feasible. All of us excepting young Bill, who in the months that followed, kept deviling Henry Vaughan to call another beer-table conference. It was only Bill who had faith in this wild plan, and so there developed, during the first ten months of 1936, as strange, as polyglot, a band of men against death as you've ever heard of. Health Commissioner Henry Vaughan, Tuberculosis Controller Bruce Douglas, Surgeon Pat O'Brien—those three were our captains, no question of it. We would faithfully follow their science. We would not exaggerate. We would not lie. But we would sensationalize, we would certainly set fire to the newspaper-readers' and the radio-listeners' shirttails!

The three TB experts now began working with young Bill Scripps, with Wynn Wright and Mel Wissman the radio men, with A. M. Smith and with your chronicler—none of us grave men of science, all of us mere publishers, actors, dramatists, reporters. Yet, at those nightlong beer-table sessions we writing-roustabouts were permitted as strong a voice as any. It is amazing that three serious men of science would now so completely accept our slogan: It's no question of mere life. To hell with mere life. What we demand is economy!

Since this proposed attack upon the white plague was to be put on a purely business basis, then we must have a solid businessman to keep our feet on the ground. So our Camorra became yet more polyglot when Herbert Trix, President of the Detroit Injector Company, became one of this unorthodox band of complotters against TB death.

## VI

We were all of us absolutely sure of the power of the science of our three leaders to do what it promised, but was there some bug in Henry Vaughan's new economics that it was costing Detroit money to let its citizens go on dying of tuberculosis? Now our little gang of nine—at one of our most enthusiastic evenings—were honored by the presence of a dozen of Detroit's most prominent citizens, bankers, lawyers, industrialists. Henry Vaughan was the suave and able *régisseur* calling upon each one of our gang to tell his own version of this new kind of science, this mating of bacteriology with banking to produce a powerful new, sound public health economy, to fight TB death—

The magnates were, one and all of them, amazed by the revelations here presented. They were flabbergasted at the millions that tuberculosis contributed to their awful burden of taxes. Vaughan told them that, as health commissioner, the city allowed him only 12¢ *per capita* to fight tuberculosis, to spot new death-spreading cases. He showed them that it cost the city $1.66 *per capita* to keep TB victims in its TB hospitals. He asked them would it be sense for the city to allow the TB-fighters, say, 30¢ *per capita,* for a term of years, so that this $1.66 *per capita* cost within, let's say, ten years, would be cut in half—

Because if you only could find the minimal, early cases, it'd take half as long to cure them, and cost the city only half as much to hospitalize them!

That night was memorable. When one of America's most prominent motor magnates heard the modest sum—$200,000— Vaughan would need to add to his annual budget to begin the wiping out of tuberculosis, or better to begin the easing of this tax burden, that great man wanted to go down to the City Council the very next morning. Why, he'd just spent twice that sum, he roared, to install machines in his plants to remove one quart of silica dust, to protect his workers!

The prominent citizens were unanimous about the soundness of this TB-fighting economy.

The nine complotters against tuberculosis overlooked no bets those months they prepared their newspaper and radio bombardment which was to be unleashed upon Detroit's citizens in November. Vaughan kept telling them that it is the doctor, the rank-and-file physician, who is the first line soldier. He should be in the attacking wave in this mass-fight against tuberculosis. He should be taught to find the early cases. This caused arguments round our beer-table—

"Tuberculosis wasn't created to put money into the pocket of the doctor!" roared Pat O'Brien.

Henry Vaughan kept coming back at Pat, admitting TB would never be wiped out if it remained a private matter between the doctor and his individual patients. This was like trying to put out a forest fire by pouring water on the individual trees. But why couldn't Detroit's physicians be turned into emergency healthmen? Why, examining patients coming into their office for this or that complaint, why shouldn't the doctors tuberculin-test all of them? And induce all positive tuberculin reactors to go to x-ray experts for a chest film? And why shouldn't the doctors be paid for this service?

What good would it do the coming fight to have the doctors, as a body, knocking it?

That was a tough one for any of us to answer. And now President Tom Gruber and other high officials of the Wayne County Medical Society were called to our beer-table. Good news. Yes, the doctors would become public healthmen. They saw no objection—if they were paid—to the wiping out of a sickness that weighed upon people, most of them so poor that they didn't mean much to the doctor's bread and butter.

Now at last in November, the drive timed so its zero-hour whistle would sound after the national election, the front page of *The Detroit News* began to tell Detroit's citizens that they were murderers. They were informed by black headlines that, once they knew the power of existing science to rub out tuberculosis, and knowing that, allowed the death to continue, then they themselves were co-guilty in the annual murder of a thousand of Detroit's people.

Now day after day the front page of this newspaper detailed a story of crime. Of the citizens' own crime of letting tuberculosis go on killing a thousand fathers, mothers, little ones, in their city. Through their smugness, lethargy, complacency. The arts of rousing fear were used shamelessly— but with no exaggeration.

So Detroit's citizens believed consumption wasn't so very contagious? No? Then they were regaled with true stories, each one taken from the files of Detroit's TB hospitals, ghastly examples of the white death's contagious terror. Of how a consumptive father, ignorant, refusing to be hospitalized and cured, had coughed three of his own children into tuberculous death, had infected two more of them, had paid for this homicide by his own consumptive dying.

He was a suicide, really, not going to the hospital for cure when his disease was first discovered.

Detroit's physicians were not spared. They were accused of this: that many of them were as ignorant as the lay people. For, if they weren't, then how had they missed spotting the tuberculosis of this other father who'd been treated for a stubborn cough, called bronchitis? Who, before he himself died of tuberculous pneumonia, had gravely infected his wife and five of his children?

Detroit's people were told how any citizen with open, active TB, not discovered, not followed by constant x-ray

checkup, not isolated, was more dangerous than any ma-
chine-gunning gangster. Here was the horrid history of a
deadly Aunty. In exchange for her keep she'd gone to live
with her married sister who had eight children. And so had
sprayed her own white death on all of them, infecting every
last one of them, killing the youngest—a six-month-old baby
who had just strangled in TB death.

If Detroit's people winced at such accusations, put down
their newspaper during those twelve days of our bombardment, and turned on the radio, they were likely as not to
shudder at a hollow, gurgling, tuberculous cough. Without
preliminary announcement or any warning that cough, three
times a day, came over the airwaves from Station WWJ.

The cough was followed by a sepulchral voice, intoning—
The—Cough—Of—Death!

These words had no sooner died away than they were
followed by a chorus of maniacal giggles, of sinister chortling
of "The Three Witches"—

"I am In*diff*erence. I just forget about the cough of death
—I suppose it's dangerous—but, oh, well—let it go on murdering thousands every year."

"I am *Se*crecy. I've heard about the cough of death—but I
don't think we should talk about such horrid things—I always hush up any discussion about it."

"I am *I*gnorance. I don't know very much about the cough
of death—so I just don't do anything about it."

You think, maybe, that this newspaper-radio bombardment would be ineffective because of its horror? No, there is
a fascination to the macabre. And, in every one of these tales
of terror and tragedy, there was a counterpoint of good news,
of the power of science, of the ability of Detroit's death-
fighters to stamp out consumption.

If Detroit's citizens would give them the means, the
weapons.

## VII

You have doubts of course. You ask if this isn't like other American ballyhoo? Hectic today. Forgotten tomorrow. Maybe no. Because at its climax, our death-fighters hit Detroit's people where they were most sensitive of all. They jarred the pocketbook nerve of the city. *The Detroit News* sent its last shot home with a simple devastating arithmetic. The front page told the authentic story of the simple cost of saving their fellow citizen, Sally. Nineteen years old, Sally had developed one of those "innocent" coughs that can spread so much death and desolation. When at last she came to the Herman Kiefer Hospital, the doctors found her consumption was already too far advanced to rest her sick lung by the air-injections called artificial pneumothorax.

Now for her life there began a battle. It is the same that has to be fought for every one of those forlorn thousands who—for the lack of x-ray's magic eye—have been allowed to drift from minimal, easily curable TB to far-advanced consumption.

By phrenic nerve operation Detroit's chest surgeons rested her lung enough to stem the tide of her sickness. They got her strong enough to stand the drastic, last-ditch ordeal of the thoracoplasty operation, the de-ribbing.

All who undergo this know that, without it, they are marked to die. Its use by Detroit's chest surgeons now brings nearly fifty out of every one hundred of consumption's doomed rearguard back from the grave. It now saved Sally.

Isn't science wonderful? Yes. But what was the money cost, to Detroit's taxpayers, of this triumph?

Because Sally's sickness had not been spotted early, she had had to stay two and a half years in hospital. Cost to the city—$3 a day. So, $3,000 to get Sally well.

While, if the x-ray's magic eye had found her sickness

when early, minimal, nine months in hospital would have cured her. Cost—$810.

And, aside from the $2,190 lost to the city because its death-fighters weren't allowed the few dollars they needed for adequate x-rays, how many other people did Sally's cough send to the hospital?

For one, we know that this innocent cough made Sally's sister, Henrietta, a burden to the city's taxpayers. It is true that Henrietta was examined by x-ray when Sally was found consumptive. At this time Henrietta's lungs were clear. But then, alas, there was no more money for the absolutely necessary x-ray follow-up.

Then, December, 1935, Henrietta caught a stubborn "cold." Her doctor to cure that cold took out her tonsils.

When Henrietta had gone downhill steadily and so far that the expensive x-ray could at last be afforded, the magic eye revealed her advanced consumption.

So now, in her turn, in the Herman Kiefer Hospital, she is costing Detroit $3 a day. To save her finally? Or to bury her? The doctors don't yet know. Her case is desperate.

Would it have been waste, would it have been municipal extravagance, would it have been scientific boondoggling, to have allowed Detroit's TB men, let's say, $50 for an amply adequate series of x-ray films for those two sisters in the first place?

Then next day the newspaper turned on a drum-fire of bitter denunciation of Detroit's false economy, its spendthrift folly. Stinginess of a few dollars kept Detroit's TB men from the chance to use their science for the early cure of those two girls, Sally and Henrietta. But what of the luckless thousands in Detroit, early tuberculous, undetected?

Today, Wayne County and the City of Detroit are hospitalizing 2,200 people sick with consumption. Eighty percent are advanced cases, like Sally. What are those 1,760 seriously sick people costing Detroit and Wayne County?

Because there wasn't the money for the x-rays and public health nurses to spot their peril early?

Let's be simple. Let's not go beyond third grade arithmetic. It costs $3 a day to hospitalize a patient with tuberculosis. Discovered early, this $3 charge shouldn't last more than nine months. On the other hand consumptives entering hospital, advanced, cost this $3 per day for eighteen months on the average.

To cure an early, minimal case—$810.

The cost for an advanced case—$1,620.

Now since $810 is lost on each advanced case and there are 1,760 of them in hospital in Detroit today, they are needlessly costing the city $1,400,000 more than they should.

For this waste there's a simple reason: Detroit's death-fighters haven't the money to discover these cases when they're early. Now for a moment *The Detroit News* let down in its castigation of money waste; and permitted itself the mention of the screams of babies dying from tuberculous meningitis—would the citizens like to be taken where they could hear them? There was lament for children left without fathers, for fathers without wives and without mothers for their children. Then the newspaper burst out—

"But to hell with death and tragedy. We ask economy, nothing more!"

But did this $1,400,000 poured down the rat-hole for needless hospitalization of Detroit's consumptive thousands represent the only loss to Detroit's people?

No. High actuarial authority proves that TB's the cause of from 30 to 50%—varying in different communities—of broken homes in large cities. There's no red ink for the heartbreak, the heartbreak is fine, but who pays the shot for the care of wives, babies, children, bereft of support by bread-winners now hospitalized with advanced tuberculosis? Who dares figure that cost in dollars?

It's known the hospital cost is $3 a day. It's also a fact

that this $3 a day is only 21% of the total burden such sick people constitute for their communities. The remaining 79% of the total cost of TB must be stood by the families, or taken up by charitable institutions.

So, again, to make it simple, to get closer to the real cost to the city, you multiply that $1,400,000 by 4.

But the worst is yet to come. Every advanced consumptive, for those months, sometimes for years during which such sick ones go the long road from early, unrecognized, minimal TB, every such human being is a spreader of further death to healthy people. Every such unrecognized sick one has been in contact with, and infected, how many other people?

You guess how many.

### VIII

Never has there been such an unanswerable attack upon any community's false economy. Would the city take up this challenge? There was good reason for the citizens to have confidence in their TB men. Did anybody dare to question the practical ability of the death-fighters—given the money—to wipe out the white death? It was mild-mannered, Quaker Bruce Douglas who gave the answer—

"Are we a bunch of hare-brained nincompoops, simply going off half-cocked, expecting to gain the moon in planning to eradicate TB?"

Even Bruce had been jarred out of his aloof scientific reserve by the totally unorthodox, let's admit it, medically unethical boldness of his comrades.

With the miserable funds—12¢ *per capita*—they'd had till now, said Douglas, they'd already given a proof of the power of their science—

With TB on the up in a dozen large American cities, and with jobless, half-starved human wreckage to work with during the desolate years of the financial collapse, Detroit's fighters had driven the city's TB death rate down by more than 33% in the past eight years!

And if now they could go out after all the early ones, the minimals?

Could they drive it down toward the vanishing point, toward zero? Could they make Pasteur's dream begin to come true? Vaughan, O'Brien, Douglas, did not hesitate to promise it. Now, immediately after the conclusion of the twelve day newspaper campaign, Henry Vaughan went to the Mayor and the City Council, with his proposed new TB-fighting budget. Up till now he had had to be content with $180,000 for the finding of hidden cases of the white death. Now he asked for $200,000 more than that, yearly. Such a sum to uncover hidden tuberculosis was unheard of in any city, any community in America. It was unheard of anywhere, excepting in the Soviet Union—but there the life of humanity is not figured in money.

Without a question, without one quibble, the Common Council of Detroit unanimously voted Henry Vaughan the money.

They further recommended similar appropriations, yearly, for as many years as might be necessary to reduce the white plague to the vanishing point. Specifically, for a trial period of five years the Council recommended the appropriation of the sum of $1,000,000.

They recommended this money not grudgingly as harassed budget-balancers but with a new strange emotion. One of the city's veteran councilmen couldn't keep the tears out of his eyes. To Henry Vaughan he told how the superb radio dramas of Mel Wissman and Wynn Wright had called up memories of his own bereavement by the white death.

"Henry, you fellows can have anything you ask," he said. "You can have a million dollars a year if you need it!"

What healthman had ever heard such generosity?

Vaughan thanked him, and smiled. "No, we're not looking

for money. We're no grafters. We're out to save you money. We think 200,000 will do the trick."

This then was our curious experience. These we now knew were the answers. If you appeal, in the matter of suffering and death, in mercenary terms to the people, they do become furious, yes. But it's their own ignorant penny-pinching they begin to hate. For the first time they begin to hate the TB microbe. You tell them to hell with all this misery and suffering, let's be frugal. That stirs them up to hatred of mass misery and death.

IX

Of course all honeymoons must end, the cynics say, and now the thrill of those twelve hectic days of the newspaper and radio drive was over; now Vaughan, Douglas, and Pat O'Brien had the actual money to spot the hidden death that was the cause of the white death's perpetuation; now it was up to Henry Vaughan to deliver. Now where do we go from here?

At the beginning of those great days of our ballyhoo, at a luncheon of distinguished citizens, Surgeon General Thomas Parran—who'd come from Washington for this purpose—gave the new fight his blessing.

"Detroit is pointing the way to the nation and to the world in such a fight against tuberculosis as has never before been undertaken," Parran told the citizens.

"My day here has convinced me that this campaign will succeed. There is no reason why it should not. This has been one of the most inspiring days of my life," Parran told the nine excited zealots who had organized the new death-fight.

What could be more heartening to them than this imprimatur of one of the world's leading healthmen, now given to these visionaries who had begun organizing their death-fighting dream not so many months before?

Could they now keep faith with Parran?

Could they now make this new fight live up to the praise
of it by one of Detroit's leading men of God? "You may call
this science," that reverend man said to Henry Vaughan.
"You call it economics. It isn't either of those. You know
what it is? It's really nothing but religion."

But could it be kept so?

In December, 1936, in the gray-light-of-the-morning-after
of this brilliant bombing of Detroit's people with the truth
that it was costing them money to die, the humdrum work
began.

Led by Henry Vaughan's epidemic experts, an army of
public health nurses got set to sleuth down every possible
contact to a known case of tuberculosis, to tuberculin-test
such people and to x-ray film them for early TB death that
might be lurking in their lungs. A thousand of Detroit's doctors began a systematic suspicioning of patients coming to
their offices, testing them and filming them if necessary—at
the city's expense if they hadn't the money. The public
health nurses—these are the shock troops of the death-fight—
got ready to wear out their shoe-leather, going from house to
house in Detroit's TB hot spots, already mapped, where the
white death is known to be most murderous—

By September, 1937, it was plain that you could find the
hidden death if you had the wherewithal to go out to look
for it. More than fifty thousand people, who never before
had given a thought to their possible tuberculosis, had gone
to the office of the doctor of their choice, had been tested
with tuberculin—and of these better than ten thousand had
been x-rayed.

Over three hundred new active, death-spraying cases of
tuberculosis had been found—which otherwise might not
for months, for years, have been discovered. Seventy percent
of these are already safe in hospital, on the way to cure, no
longer dangerous to the city.

In the old days, before the new death-fight with adequate

wherewithal was started, only thirteen out of every hundred people diagnosed tuberculous by Detroit's doctors were minimal, were early.

Now in this short time, forty-three out of every hundred were going to hospital in that early stage where it would take not more than nine months to cure them—

Excellent, yes, granted. But this was only part of the result of the new death-fight. It already showed other consequences, hopeful and ominous. We were, all of us, convinced that our newspaper and radio campaign had really reached down into the mass of the people, that it had really activated them to join the people's death-fight. But had it?

Alas. In those sinister, poverty-stricken regions of the city where tuberculosis raged most fiercely, what proportion of the endangered people there had gone—as a result of our warnings—to their doctors? Before the public health nurses began to visit them to urge them? Only one quarter of one percent of the white people of the TB hot spots were worried enough about themselves, their children, to go voluntarily for this free care to their doctors. Did it mean that, or did it mean that those poor people of the danger zones didn't read newspapers or listen to or own radios?

But here was something curious! Two percent of the Negroes of those very same regions—eight times as many Negroes as whites—responded before the nurses came to urge them—

Yet, what had our vaunted publicity meant, after all? It had only activated the upper brackets, the influential upper ten who could directly influence the city's rulers.

Then, in January, 1937, the public health nurses began their door-to-door search for death. These superb women showed us how feeble, after all, had been the results of our ballyhoo of November. By September, 1937, as a result of their earnest talking to, urging, cajoling—education!—of the white fathers and mothers of the TB hot spots, instead of the negligible one quarter of one percent, nineteen out of every hundred had gone to physicians for examination—

But the Negroes in those same danger zones? Forty-five percent, very nearly half the Negroes from the hot spots, had gone to Detroit's physicians, with their youngsters, to face the grim question of whether or no the white death was lurking in them. To face the stern possibility of their removal—for months or years—from active life, from their dear ones. Till their deadly cavities were closed. Till they'd no longer endanger the lives of others.

This news was certainly an eye-opener to all of us. It was humiliating in a way. And it was hopeful. When we'd got Henry Vaughan his needed money, those of us who'd manned the loudspeakers and typewriters thought that, for us, the fight was as good as over. We talked glibly of the people's death-fight, for which Detroit would now become famous. Now we saw that it would take more than twelve days of newspaper scare headlines and death-bellowing broadcasts to arouse the people, to educate the people. To help the public health nurses to bring the endangered people to our TB men who now had the wherewithal to give life to everybody, we realized that we would have to invent new ways, we'd have to begin our telling-it-to-the-people all over.

We who believed ourselves to be in the upper brackets of intelligence, had to face this—

That the humblest ones of the human mass were the most eager for help of this new great power of science to guard them.

How many of the nine of us who had organized this death-fight had publicly set the mass of Detroit's people an example? How many of us had gone to our physicians for the tuberculin test, and x-ray? Pat O'Brien and Bruce Douglas maybe, because, working in a rain of the white death every day, they had to take this precaution.

But had Health Commissioner Henry Vaughan faced the test? Had Bill Scripps, or A. M. Smith, or Mel Wissman, or Wynn Wright, or Herbert Trix? Yes, all of them had.

Or, to this moment, has your chronicler himself taken this precaution which should now be taken by all?

No. He has not done it. It is no good for us to say that we are lucky people of those upper economic brackets where TB is enormously less prevalent. TB does lurk among well-off people; and the outward huskiness of a man or woman does not mean that active, death-spreading tuberculosis is not present in that man or woman.

x

Of course this is the hopeful first discovery of Detroit's new death-fight: that our colored brothers and sisters—this is said advisedly!—have shown themselves to be the true leaders of the people's fight for life. It calls back memories of those old arguments with wealthy middle class people about pellagra. It calls back echoes of the wailing of that well-off white mother who complained (in regard to those pellagrous southern black folk) "but what *can* you do for such people?"

Now the cat is out of the bag. At last, given the chance for it, Negro fathers and mothers prove they are more eager to co-work with Detroit's TB men in the fight for life than are the fathers and mothers of the alleged superior white race. And why shouldn't they be more anxious? It is the Negro who is most terribly endangered by the TB assassin. And don't the dark fathers and mothers know it? They do not give a hoot about the arithmetical, the high economic questions around which we built the plea for money for Detroit's death-fight. They do not understand what it means when we say it costs Detroit money to let them rot for years with tuberculosis and to let them die. That is only the concern of the city's budget-balancers, of its property owners

who wail about high taxes, of its bankers who must worry
about the soundness of Detroit's bonds, its debt in which
they traffic. No, the Negro fathers and mothers of Detroit's
TB pest-holes and hot spots do not worry about the millions of dollars about which we had been preaching so glibly.
In their own fight for life, cogs as most of them are in our
industrial machine, they are lucky if they see a few hundreds of dollars a year. Momentarily—in its rapid transit from
their thin pay envelopes to the landlord, the grocer, the
butcher and baker. No, high finance is without doubt beyond their primitive understanding. But they are human,
don't mistake it. They are desperate at the horrible cry of
their baby in the last convulsions of tuberculous meningitis.
Best of all they understand it—because most of all of us they
live through it. A Negro worker father knows what it means
to be left to take care of his pickaninnies, now motherless
from TB's murder. And a Negro mother knows—better than
her betters—the grimness of facing the world, fighting for
her children's lives, after the father has been taken by the
white death. It is the people who suffer who want the power
of the science that can save them. That *should* be true.

And now we know it is true, with the facts of the magnificent co-working of Detroit's Negroes plain before us—
Half of all the Negroes of the danger zones coming for examination after hardly more than half a year of teaching by
Vaughan's public health nurses.

This is not said in especial praise of Negroes. It is said in
defense of mankind. Black or white or brown or yellow—
the eagerness for life is strongest where life is most endangered. The people will fight for life, let them know they at
last have the chance to.

This is a stern warning to Henry Vaughan, Bruce Douglas,
and Pat O'Brien, superb death-fighters that they are, in their
fight—now just begun—to wipe out the white plague of tuberculosis. They know full well that the Detroit Negroes

(and their white brothers and sisters of those hot spots) are
not the only reservoir of the hidden white death that must be
subjected to the tuberculin-test and x-ray dragnet. Given the
money, as they have been, they are under the grim obligation
to make good, within a few years to cut down the horrible
money cost of Detroit's tuberculosis. Where else will they
ply their dragnet to uncover the menace? And will all of
Detroit's citizens co-work with them as well as this nearly
fifty percent of the Negroes of the hot spots now are doing?

It is well known that tuberculous mortality bears heaviest
upon unskilled, low-paid workers. Will the industrialists of
Detroit co-work with Vaughan, to see to it that their men on
the production lines are tuberculin-tested and x-rayed? And,
if active, dangerous TB is found in many of them, will they
see to it—since these men needs must be hospitalized to cure
them—that their families are cared for while they are not
winning bread? Will half of the industrialists join this death-
fight? Will they show as much public spirit as the Negroes?

It is a fact, again, that mothers about to have babies are
especially threatened by the white death—just after their
babes are born. Will all the city's doctors, birth-helpers, join
Henry's fight, testing, x-raying all of Detroit's prospective
mothers? Or will half of them co-operate, in the same proportion as the aforesaid Negroes?

Physicians know, too, that people who are diabetic are
especially prone to be suffering the white death, and the
same is true of folk who are recovering from various acute
infections. Will half of Detroit's doctors faithfully look for
tuberculosis among all of their patients who may be death-
spreading menaces?

## XI

The man of God—on one of those exciting days of November, 1936—told Henry Vaughan that Detroit's TB-fight was
not science, nor economics, but religion. And in his emo-

tional state in those days of triumph your chronicler was inclined to agree. He thought that here was a new materialistic religion based on this: that the death-fight turned on full power is the soundest city banking. Your chronicler went on record, alleging that if Detroit begins to wipe out consumption's pain and death and heartbreak purely as a matter of economy, then what can stop the whole nation from following?

What valid religion, what faith strong and rich with hope for life for mankind, can help spreading like wildfire?

But will this new death-fighting religion spread in our nation? Again remembering Detroit's Negroes, will half of the owners and rulers of our people espouse it, act upon it?

The facts so far force your chronicler to doubt it. We have failed so far to induce our own State of Michigan to join this death-fight. Its hospital facilities to take care of all consumptives discovered are ample. It has doubled the millions needed for the state's counties to send its tuberculous sick to sanatoriums—more than eighty out of every hundred of them with advanced tuberculosis. But it has not got the money to allow the state's health forces to uncover early TB, to treat it, and so begin the wiping out of the sickness.

In San Francisco, prominent and powerful physicians praised Detroit's new death-fight to your chronicler. "But we couldn't even begin that here," said they, "because the city hasn't the hospital beds in which to treat the early cases if we found them."

In regions of the South you will find physicians without knowledge of the new collapse therapy that can close the dangerous death-spreading cavities of its tuberculous citizens.

In many a state, our country over, you will find long waiting lists of consumptives, already known, who—as Pat O'Brien puts it—are coughing spit-bombs of death upon their fellow citizens, their near and dear ones. Because there are not the sanatorium beds in which to hospitalize and cure them.

Areas of our country are devoid of access by their citizens to the x-ray's magic eye, and lack physicians who know that it alone can spot the lurking of early consumption.

Yes, the menace is a national one, and, so far there is no sign of the spreading of the unique power of Detroit's fight against it.

Death does not wait for the snail-like spread of Detroit's fight among leaders of individual communities, who may one by one wake up to face it that it is costing their city money to allow its people to go on dying from consumption. Death goes on, and so does its tax burden—a formidable part of that load about which there is now a nationwide complaint and wailing. Each year there are 70,000 deaths from tuberculosis in our country. For every death it is known there are five active cases of consumption. That means our nation is tolerating the existence of 350,000 tuberculous citizens.

What is their cost to the country? Able Dr. William Alfred Sawyer, Medical Director of the Eastman Kodak Company, has made a detailed analysis of what one hundred consumptives have cost—to industry, to themselves and their families, and to their community.

The tuberculosis of these one hundred people—from first to last—cost $406,162.

—And this does not and cannot enter Sawyer's calculations: that TB takes its heaviest toll in the early adult years when young people are establishing themselves in their life work. So that their disability is not only economically devastating at the time, but is likely to scar them, economically, for life—

All right then, if one case of tuberculosis—and this is conservative—costs our country $4,062, the money burden of the 350,000, when you make the simple calculation, becomes astronomical.

Is this then a waste that is worthy of the immediate attention, and action, of our President and Congress?

This cost is spread over more than one year, it's true, because it takes several years for consumptives to get better or to die. But the National Tuberculosis Association experts have calculated the annual cost of the white death for us— in loss of life and loss of wages. It is more than $600,000,000. To this must be added the yearly $76,000,000 that is expended upon these sufferers for their miserably inadequate sanatorium and hospital care.

Nationwide, only $115,000,000 is expended to prevent and treat the sickness, the great bulk of this is spent for mere treatment, and this includes all expenditures, local, state, and national.

Would it then be unsound national economy for our Government, through its public health service, to spend, let's say, $100,000,000 yearly for the uncovering of early tuberculosis? For aiding communities to mobilize their own physicians, nurses, x-ray men?

In order, within a generation, to drive the $600,000,000 of annual waste toward zero?

Could anybody call this boondoggling?

And if anybody asks the old question: "Where's the money to come from?" couldn't our President and the Congress turn to the country's bankers for an answer?

Couldn't they ask whether the underwriting of TB bonds would not be permissible? Bonds that our death-fighters and healthmen could promise them would be paid off within a generation? Plus the interest?

Is our present economic order capable of such foresight, such economy?

*Part Four*

**THE GHASTLY LUXURY**

## CHAPTER TWELVE

# MACHINE FEVER

THE microbes of tuberculosis and syphilis are not even cousins but the two sicknesses are ghastly twins among the ills that wreck and kill mankind. The scientific tests to spot every lurking of the tubercle bacillus and the syphilis spirochete are becoming more and more exact and accurate. The weapons to wipe out these tiny murderers grow more precise and powerful. Yet both plagues remain sappers of the strength of our people. Both strike down babies and kill men and women in life's prime. Ridding our people of them would cause a mass upsurge of human energy that would be astounding. The two plagues today are twin horrid luxuries that together cost our nation billions of dollars to maintain. The fight against both is basically a simple one. If there is any difference in the now practical plans of battle against them, it is that the contagiousness of syphilis is easier to put down; therefore syphilis should be easier to stamp out. Why then has TB, nationally, been for more than a generation on a downtrend while syphilis has seemed to continue on an unchecked rampage among us? The easiest answer is only partly true.

The general notion is that syphilis has gone apparently unconquered because up till a couple of years ago it has been so secret and shameful. Of course now it has been smoked out into the open to such a sensational extent that, if you know even a little about the syphilis scandal, you become a sought-for guest at polite dinner tables. In two years the disease has been transformed from a sinister unmentionable into a cozy fireside word like mumps or measles; its name is a recruit for the bizarre vocabulary of crossword puzzles; school children must learn it if they are to become spelling bee aces and champions. But does this sudden front page popularity mean that syphilis will now start downhill like its twin death, TB?

Over TB—in a true people's death-fight—syphilis has an immense advantage because it will so much more powerfully intrigue the people. Just out of that hiding that has been its best accomplice, the newly mentionable pestilence is at once fascinating and fearsome, ghastly yet dramatic, and why is that so? Because it is tied so tight to sinful romance. Because interest in the various grim rewards of sexual sin is shared by all, even by the pious among the people. The war of our death-fighters against syphilis is a never-ending scandalous, salacious, serial detective story. It is made the more piquant because the trail of the loathsome spirochete leads so often— to the shocked delight of all of us!—from the brothel and the gutter into the houses of the supposedly moral and up to the seats of the mighty.

Syphilis, the disease of harlots, criminals, have-nots, constantly surprises its fighters by the welcome it gets in high society.

Well and good. We congratulate ourselves that the conspiracy of hypocrisy about it has been smashed. But does that mean our fighters for life will now at last set to work to cut down, yes, to obliterate, the corkscrew microbe's life-wrecking terror for good and ever?

By no means.

In spite of the new candor of the people about the sinister sickness, it can truly be said that the mass fight against it is hardly more than a sham battle, a feeble skirmish.

## II

Today there are properly two fights that could be joined against the corkscrew microbe. The one is the fight to cure it, to salvage its present wreckage in a given man or woman, to prevent its awful last consequences to that man or woman or child who is known to be a sufferer. The other battle is immensely more ambitious. It plans to search out all existing syphilitics. It aims quickly to suppress their contagious danger to their fellow citizens. So it hopes to end the plague forever.

The first of these two fights, the cure of the syphilitic man or woman or child, has till lately been scientifically a very difficult one. So far as the actual weapons go, the cure has been much harder than the possibility of its mass prevention. Why? Because it is—by chemical treatment—easy to suppress syphilis so a given victim can't spread it. Yet, that same victim—now no longer dangerous to others—may perish from the last attack by the corkscrew microbe that remains lurking, hidden, in that victim's body. This is not to say that, if the victims are chemically treated thoroughly and long enough, they can't be cured. Most of them can be.

But now the tide in these two fights has turned, to the advantage of the curative science. During the past few years, a new hot science has come to the help of the old difficult, yes, dangerous, curative chemical treatment. The unfolding of this baby science in the past six years has been one of the most stirring of the modern fights for life. Our death-fighters can now prevent the most terrible deadly attacks of the corkscrew microbe in all but the most far-gone rear-guard whose brains or hearts or spines are wrecked beyond repair.

But will its aid in the curing of formerly incurable syphilis make the mass prevention of the plague more hopeful?

If it can so beautifully guard against the plague's last stages, couldn't it also much more rapidly, drastically, suppress the contagiousness of early syphilis, and so speed up the second fight, the battle for complete eradication of the sickness?

Scientifically, that now seems possible. Economically it is still the wildest of dreams in the heads of a few of our syphilis-fighting vanguard. Yet maybe, if our people are informed of its magic power, the fights to cure and to wipe out may become one. If the eradication of syphilis is deeply enough desired by the people.

There is now no longer question that artificial fever, machine fever, has proved its power against the insanity that is the most tragic consequence of the gnawing of the corkscrew microbe. Six years ago this life-saving heat was only at a stage of groping experiment, in the hands of a few enthusiasts who were deemed by scientific authority to be slightly goofy. Your chronicler predicted the rise of this new hot science, with timidity, in the book *Men Against Death*. Then only a few tinkering dreamers dared to turn the friendly fire of artificial fever upon an experimental vanguard of people who were otherwise doomed. They risked burning these people. They did badly burn some of them. To keep a few of them from going mad and dying.

Today, this artificial fever is still outlandish. In the hands of those not expert it is dangerous, yes, deadly. But now machine fever is a proved and practical fighter of the corkscrew microbe, when it is combined with the old syphilis-fighting chemical weapons. Yet, for sad reasons you will come to understand, the hot science must still be called experimental. Because it is still out of reach of the millions of sufferers who have no chance to avail themselves of its life-guarding, strength-giving power.

Why? Well, it is not surprising. Not when you once understand the vigilance, the peculiar new high technique that machine fever's use demands. It is true that it is now possible, by turning a few switches, to stoke up any degree of fever in the body of a sick human being whose physique will beforehand have been found able to undergo the new ordeal. Turning those switches is easy, yes. And so is the carelessness easy. Nothing is more common than the human negligence that may kill the sufferer whom this healing heat could save. To use it, our physicians and nurses must become engineers. You will come to see how it can be dosed, this machine fever, with accuracy that is uncanny. In the competent hands of those who understand it, this fantastic new machinery can light the internal fire needed for a sick one's fight with death, and can hold it constant, to within one-tenth of one degree. It is truly eerie to see this fever—stoked by engineering—record its perfectly controlled course by a quivering needle on a big dial, accurate as any powerplant switchboard.

That's why this life-guarding art is still so experimental, because this fever by machinery demands a new type of nurse and doctor. The amiable, sloppy, old medical hit-or-miss-and-maybe does not go in this new hot science which demands a severity, a discipline, unique in medical practice. These fever neophytes must submit to fierce training, to learn the vigilance to hold their suffering ones safely so close to a heat that can kill as well as cure. It is a revolution in medical care and conscience that is molding your new fever nurse and fever doctor. You say that such machine medicine, such healing engineering, is too inhuman, too perilous for human beings to practice or to bear? Then go visit with the death-fighters in one of America's fever clinics. Or ask a victim saved by it from the doom of syphilis.

You protest it is beyond human for many to undergo the discipline of fever's healing art? Then go to hospitals where this infant science is in the beginnings of mass production of saving life and soothing pain. No, it is only the people's ignorance of it, and it is nothing but the fatal false economy born of such ignorance that now prevents the quick training of thousands of young doctors, nurses. They are ready enough to become fever engineers to man those new death-fighting machines our communities would demand, if they clearly understood fever's life-guarding power.

### III

Of course the start of this death-fighting fever was anything but mechanical. It is history how that genius, the Austrian Julius Wagner-Jauregg, by one terrific experiment changed fever from man's alleged enemy into a new powerful friend— By daring to inoculate dangerous malaria microbes into nine doomed human derelicts, sick with syphilis, with general paralysis of the insane.

Malaria's fever brought three of that doomed nine back to health and working. It was unprecedented. But in his very next try at it—by mistake inoculating a fatal form of malaria—Wagner-Jauregg killed three crazy people out of four. Yet, so fatal, so hopeless, was this brain syphilis that searchers scorned the dangers of the new malaria fever cure. So now there arose in the decades of the 1920's a storm of experiment all over Europe and America. No, it wasn't just malaria that helped cure these doomed people. You could save them—sometimes—from imbecile death by relapsing fever, by rat bite fever, by fever produced by injecting typhoid microbes. And no, it was not the feverish *disease* that fought the corkscrew microbe of syphilis, it was the fever. You could wipe experimental syphilis out of rabbits by simply dunking them for a long time in hot water!

Now the new hot science jumped the Atlantic to stir the imaginations of gadget-minded American doctors, microbe hunters, engineers. In Chicago, Dr. C. A. Neymann cured a few paretic, syphilitic people by the artificial, electric fever known as diathermy. His treatment was dangerous; was terribly uncomfortable; it inflicted hellish burns. You had to be crazy to stand the treatment. Yet its occasional life-saving power was quickly confirmed by Drs. J. C. King and E. W. Cocke, of Memphis.

Was fever, was pure heat, surely the answer to the mystery and could it be made a little safer?

Physicist Willis Whitney of the General Electric Company Laboratories in Schenectady, New York, was told of the curious experience of two of his engineers. Tinkering with short-wave broadcasting gadgets that send the caterwaulings of jazz bands and the proclamations of political orators to the earth's ends, a couple of his myrmidons got hot, got feverish. Not touching those gadgets, just working in the invisible field of the machine's short-wave electric energy. Whitney set microbe hunter Charles Carpenter and psychiatrist Leland Hinsie to proving that fever—stoked by letting victims lie in the field of this short-wave broadcasting apparatus!—would save some of them from the insane doom of syphilis. At Elgin, Illinois, certain insane syphilitics were brought back to reason by getting them hot inside electric blankets. In Rochester, New York, ingenious physiologist Stafford Warren invented a simple hot box that set up a terrific artificial heat in paretic people by a battery of carbon filament electric lights. This seemed to turn the trick as well as the expensive finicky short-wave broadcasting gadget.

For a time certain able American doctors held out for malaria fever as against this machine heat, for the good reason that they were expert at dosing the malaria fever, that they knew how to guard their sufferers against its deadliness. For malaria in all but the most skilled hands is a two-edged sword. Yet there was soon small doubt that it was not at all the disease, malaria, but the plain heat you stoke up in these people that stirs their bodies to fight the gnawing of the syphilis microbe in their brains.

Against this desperate disease, paresis, the new machine medicine while groping to become practical took stern chances. Many a paretic wreck suffered frightful skin burns. Fevers lighted by this or that gadget got out of control, killing not a few who burned to death by an awful internal fire. What kept our American tinkerers plugging along to find a truly practical machine fever? Only the desperate condition of these sufferers from syphilis of the brain, only the fact that, if they did not burn, they would surely stay mad, and die.

The malaria cure had advantages. It was a cheap science, of simply shooting a few drops of malarious blood under your patient's skin or into his veins, then nursing him, then watching him close while his body shook with malarial chills and the malarial fever shook up his murdering spirochetes. It is true that if this malaria fever began to get out of hand, you could cure it quickly with quinine. Yet, in certain hospitals, this drastic treatment killed ten out of every hundred forlorn folks it set out to cure. But in the hands of malaria-masters like old Wagner-Jauregg, like our own Dr. Paul O'Leary at the Mayo Clinic, less than one out of every hundred paretic patients died from the malaria.

So why this excitement about machine fever?

Well, there was more than one good reason. By a good machine fever you could get people consistently hotter and keep them hotter longer than by malaria. By a machine fever you could turn the heat on and off in a sufferer's body at will. You could use syphilis-fighting chemicals to aid the machine fever, which you couldn't with malaria, because chemicals killed the very fire that malaria stoked up in your sufferer. Then too there was the economics of it. Malaria put your victim to bed for several weeks, kept him out of work— if he was still hanging desperately on to his employment —for six weeks at least. Besides all this, ten percent of people refused to develop malaria when you inoculated them, and, if malaria failed to cure your patient the first time, then you were sunk, because after that your patient was immune to a second malaria inoculation—

But now, with artificial fever, ah, yes, with machine fever you could heat and heat and heat your threatened one till at last—maybe—you might save him. If you didn't burn or kill him. Such were the desperate arguments of our fighters for life, of a few fever-cranks, despised and laughed at by many a serious scientist in the early 1930's.

### IV

But there was a much graver reason demanding our syphilis-fighters find a fever that was safe, quick, short, and not too uncomfortable. The malaria fevers and the first machine fevers were stoked up in people already paretic. It was only Viennese Doctor Kyrle, who died too soon, who dared use malaria fever—sandwiched between courses of syphilis-fighting chemicals—to treat syphilis when it was early. And Kyrle's pioneering science was denied, was contradicted, both in Europe and America. Just the same, all agreed to this: that the time to cure syphilitic insanity, paresis, is before it happens! For this is the dreadful, mocking power of the corkscrew microbe: that, after the first ugly signs of its attack, it goes into hiding in its victim's body. Through years there might be no outward sign of the spirochete's evil presence. If only, during those reassuring years, the victims suffered pain, or had hideous sores, or growths on their bodies to remind them! But that was the devil of it. The microbes lurking gave no outward sign. The victims most of them were not strong and well, during those hidden years of their sickness, mind you. They lived strength-sapped, underpar as human beings. Even so, in the majority of them, even if they went untreated, through a long life there might not be visible signs of the pale corkscrew microbe's presence. Or, after lurking for years, whole decades, the microbe might wake up to wreck the unsuspecting sufferer's heart, or suddenly attack his brain to drive him to demented death. Not by any means all, no, only five out of a hundred infected with syphilis were doomed to this fatal daftness. And it was true, too, that there was a scientific test to pick out such candidates for crazy death long before their doom began to threaten—

But here was where the miserably tiny, weak, sinister pale

microbe showed its treacherous power. You understand that the standard treatment of a syphilitic with arsenical drugs and bismuth can cure his sickness if it's shot into him long and thoroughly in the early stages. Yet, in those people whose brains are proved threatened by the weirdly prophetic Kahn test, enormous, yes, poisonous, quantities of these drugs are often powerless to cure—

But look, here was hope brought these people by the malaria treatment of that grand old genius, Wagner-Jauregg. When you fevered a syphilis sufferer at the first ominous, almost no-account sign of his insanity, *and then followed the fever with a moderate, safe, arsenic and bismuth treatment,* you had eight chances out of ten of saving him.

Better yet, if you fevered and then chemically treated such a threatened victim while he was still entirely sane, still fairly healthy, when the only portent of danger was the positive test in his spinal fluid, then the chance to save him rose to mighty near one hundred out of every hundred.

That was now the challenge to our American searchers: to invent a safe quick short not too drastic fever. Here in our country, they knew, were hundreds of thousands of unfortunates for whom insanity, horrible death, was this moment lurking, waiting. The Kahn test could spot them, warn them, yes. But here was a practical question—

How many of that vast army of the maybe doomed could you induce to stand malaria's fierce ordeal, to dodge a *maybe* future peril that they could feel preparing, only vaguely, and then not surely in their bodies?

Here was an economic question: how dared you ask men and women who were so endangered, who were working in a store or factory with family dependent on them, to leave their breadwinning for six weeks, to risk the ordeal of malaria, when there was no provision by their employers to take care of their dear ones, while they lay malarious in a hospital to avoid a future imbecile fate which—*maybe!*—might not happen?

No, for the mass attack upon the last awful consequence of syphilis now awaiting America's hundreds of thousands, malaria was not the answer. Malaria was not the fever to keep ten out of every hundred inmates (who are brought there by syphilis!) out of our insane asylums.

These were the grim facts that were faced by syphilis-fighters Fred K. Kislig and Walter M. Simpson in Dayton, Ohio, back in 1931.

### V

It would have been hard to find two death-fighters more fit to embark, in the years that followed, on this hectic, dangerous experiment of finding a machine fever sure enough, safe enough, sufficiently comfortable, short enough, cheap enough, to offer hope to all of the threatened myriads whose syphilis might not yield to the long drastic arsenic and bismuth treatment. Or who, because of the severity and the expense of this medication, or because of their ignorance, might not follow it faithfully through the eighteen months required to complete it.

Kislig was a strange mixture of hard-boiled and gentle. He understood syphilis, was skilled in its chemical treatment, but, better yet, he understood human beings, and though he was the opposite of mawkish, yet he had affection for the least of people, for the incorrigible sinners and outcasts of humanity, much more than for the well-heeled denizens of Dayton's wealthy suburb, Oakwood. This preference for mankind's underdogs kept him poor, but to Kislig this didn't matter, and no time was too much to take to fight last-ditch battles for the lives of wretches with whom skilled and merely stylish doctors wouldn't bother. Kislig was the kind of doctor patients could talk to. He was a famous listener, and an observer whose eye saw through to the mortal sickness of people who outwardly were healthy. Then too he was a curious blend—too seldom met with—of engineer and doctor. He was a patient electrical tinkerer, a self-taught, homespun engineer and physicist who foresaw how medicine must become engineering because it deals, after all, with nothing but human machinery. He was a big, outwardly robust-looking, kind-eyed man who knew he had not long to live, who knew at the beginning of this work that he would not see the end of it. And best of all Kislig was honest.

Walter Simpson was Kislig's friend, a skilled pathologist, learned in the perils of syphilis to heart and brain. Outwardly Simpson was even more hard-boiled than Kislig, and yet Simpson's rough, tough-talking exterior camouflaged a good human heart. He was a combination of laboratorian and doctor—a type of death-fighter still rare in medicine which is hardly emerging out of its condition of priesthood and struggling to become a science. Best of all he was—when necessary—a martinet. That made him the co-ordinator, the organizer, of the new Dayton syphilis death-fight. And, for the spread of this baby science of machine fever—if perchance it might become really practical—you had to have that qualification.

Such then were the two pioneers who in 1931 embarked upon this strange quest of a hot fight for life. What was the quickest, the surest, the cheapest way to prevent the heart-wrecking, brain-softening doom of syphilis? So that men and women would not have to lose their jobs or starve their families to save their own lives. It would be expensive science, and, for the wherewithal to make this fever hunt possible, Simpson and Kislig had to thank Charles F. Kettering—that amazing blend of engineer and man of high finance.

Till his brain stops remembering your chronicler will not forget the forlorn hope that this particular fever adventure was in its beginning. To stoke their first fevers our fighters used a powerful short-wave broadcasting machine called the

radiotherm. Its working was exasperatingly uncertain. The
fevers it stoked up were now feeble, now ferocious, genuinely
unpredictable, and invincibly uncomfortable. The first forlorn wretches treated in this primitive contraption only
stayed their long hours of imprisonment in its coffin-like
cabinet because for them all hope was gone. Arsenic and
bismuth had poisoned them plenty, failed to cure them, all
but killed them. Young or old they were of humanity's rear-
guard and nothing if not the forlornest sort of human rag-
tag-and-bob-tail.

They were all in despair of living. Even Simpson and Kislig could hardly have induced them to return for their slow,
hot, uncertain torture in the radiotherm. But they were incessantly kidded by the gay kindness of pioneer fever-nurse
Florence Storck. Have you ever seen optimism and cheer-
fulness walking? That was Storcky. In those first hectic
months in the Miami Valley Hospital's dingy fever room this
shrewd young woman laid the foundations for a fever-nursing
art for which she will be remembered as the founder. She was
a teacher, too. It is thanks to Storcky that there now exists
the nucleus of an army of young women, part nurse, part
doctor, part engineer.

Your chronicler is hard put to it to explain how the experiments kept going. As the invisible short-wave electric
energy zipped through the doomed syphilitics' bodies, they
would break out into terrific sweating. Then the electric
energy arced in their sweat pools, under their arms, between
their thighs, all over them. Little buzzing zips of this electric fire burned holes in their skins. It was Storcky who was
alert to try to protect these hot spots. She iced their hot
brows. She watched their bounding pulses for signs of
failing of their hearts. She took their rectal temperatures
to guard against fever that might rise high enough to
burn them up and kill them. She told them stories. She
doped them skillfully and laughing made them forget their

torture in their own half-delirious guffaws. She made them come back to this experimental hell. She led them onward, through ordeal after ordeal, towards that return of life, new strength, that they began to feel after they left the hot torture of the radiotherm. It was a strength many of them had not felt for years. It was a surge of energy that made them forget their burns. But it was Storcky in those early days who kept telling them: "You damn fool, don't you know you're getting better?"

From the first it had been the hunch of Boss Kettering that some way you'd be able to air-condition these sweating people. The first day he was told of the radiotherm he said: "Why, we'll just blow some hot air in there to cool the *outside* of those people down!" He said you ought to be able to evaporate their sweat with dry hot air currents. Then there couldn't be any arcing of the short-wave in the sweat pools. Then the short-wave energy would simply stoke up heat inside them, not burning their outsides.

It sounded simple, as Boss Kettering has a knack of making things sound simple, but the actual attempt to air-condition these hot sick people was the job of Engineer Edwin Sittler. This youngster—it was a crazy pioneering that could only be done by youngsters!—was joined by young Dr. Worley Kendell. They were a team of fever maniacs. Nurse Florence Storck, Eddie, and Worley took the real raps in this new fight for life. Engineer Eddie became a doctor taught by Fred Kislig and Worley Kendell. Nurse Storck became an engineer, soaking in air-conditioning science from Eddie. All of them blended their engineering, nursing, doctoring, into a teamwork of machine fever. It was not the fever machine that dominated them. It was the suffering of the hot man or woman in it.

The fury of their work, their not sleeping, their snatching five minutes for eating, their toiling beyond human limit, brought disasters down upon these workers, but not upon

the patients whose safety and comfort they were straining
for with fanatical persistence. In those dangerous first two
years they killed not one patient. And what could stop their
eighteen, twenty-four hour stretches of working? How could
they forget that first human wreck they'd fevered in the first
of their many clumsy, experimental, air-conditioned contraptions? This far-gone syphilitic had been driven to attempts
at suicide by the pains of his locomotor ataxia. Now he was
strong, now back from one hundred and ten pounds up to
his old one hundred and ninety, now happy with his family
again—and with a better job than he'd had before his sickness hit him.

## VI

They had no sooner completed the building of a beautiful
air-conditioned cabinet of balsa wood—it looked like a baby
war-tank and was truly a wonder to behold—when, one night,
Eddie and his assistant, blind-tired, forgot to turn off a switch.
The elegant machine caught fire. The Miami Valley Hospital and its sick people were in peril. Dayton that night
was in an uproar. Their lovely radiotherm was only a tangle
of twisted wires, broken vacuum tubes and ruined hopes. Just
one week—and their patients were feverish in a new apparatus. What could stop those fighters, amazed at their hot
miracles of healing, proud of this little nine-year-old boy,
blind from eye-syphilis he'd got from his mother, incurable
by chemical treatment alone, now back to school with good
vision? After machine fever.

They lacked all judgment and sense of proportion about
their own welfare. You couldn't blame them. It was far more
fun to work than eat or play or sleep. What was the kick
of ordinary amusement, when you'd just tasted this salt of
life? Of watching the resurrection of that poor devil, bedfast
for months from joint syphilis and syphilis of his nervous
system. Unable to feed himself. Brought into the hospital

months ago to die. Up and about now, able to walk, yes, to run. Back to work now, supporting his family.

Before the first two years were up it was too much for Fred Kislig. Months before he went to bed for good, he had told your chronicler he knew he'd not live to see a real triumph of machine fever. Fagged by the day-and-night grind, urged by all his medical friends to go to Florida to rest his flagging heart, he stayed on his feet, learning engineering from Eddie Sittler, teaching high doctoring art to Eddie and Worley Kendell. Kislig was a god to all the fever patients. So then flu got him, and good Fred died the day Walt Simpson had left for Montreal to read the first scientific paper telling of the Dayton fever team's first triumph—

They'd fevered twelve sufferers from beginning general paralysis of the insane. At the same time they'd given them mild arsenic and bismuth treatment which alone was powerless to keep them from going mad, or demented, and dying.

Eleven of these twelve were well now, and back to their former work.

All these eleven had been given up for lost after the severest arsenic-bismuth treatment.

Such was the type of forlorn humanity that the Dayton fever team had to work with, those early days. Doomed people were the only ones doctors would send them. They toiled with lost people, curing them with fever machines that were makeshift, cranky, undependable, and obviously anything but practical for physicians who were not engineers or physicists. Then one day the radiotherm, the short-wave broadcasting apparatus gave up the ghost in the middle of a fever treatment. The patient's temperature was already half-way up toward the 105 degrees they always tried for. Then, Bsss-t! the complicated system of resistances, wires, vacuum tubes went out of action. Storcky, fever-doctor Worley, both were desperate. These breakdowns were bad for the morale of the patients and now, not removing the patient from the

useless apparatus, they kept him in there, with nothing but
the partly humid hot air playing over his naked body. It was
kidding the patient—

Presto! His fever kept going up anyway, without the short-
wave energy from the cantankerous radiotherm. Just from
that moist hot air blowing on him. That very evening they
began a night-long experiment. With nothing but this circulating moist, very hot, too hot air they fevered nurse Kate
Rife's body. And hoorah. Good-by to the expensive, abom-
inable, finicky short-wave gadget. Such was the accidental beginning of their present simple air-conditioning fever cabinet
with exactly controllable heat and humidity.

Now you no longer needed expert radio engineers to supervise your fevers. And now in Dayton, and presently in more
and more hospitals the country over, machine fever began to
gather life-guarding momentum against syphilis. But the machine's the least part of it. There are various ways of stoking
up human fever, and various machines are now in successful
use in many hospitals in our country. But once the fever's up,
air-conditioning is used to keep it there. From the beginning
the Dayton team worked under this great advantage: *they
were not trying to invent a fever machine to sell at a profit*.
They did not have to fool themselves, kid themselves, lie to
themselves, about some fancied merit of their own gadget.
They worked only for the safety, the greater and greater comfort, of those hot, terribly uncomfortable, very sick men and
women and children.

Now their progress toward safe fever became fantastic. It
was the new kind of nurse, the new kind of doctor-engineer
and engineer-doctor, that made all the difference between torture and comfort, between life and death, in this dangerous
hot healing. For them it was not the fever machine, the particular type of cabinet at all. It was simply how you used this
moist hot air you circulated round the sufferer's body. And
your first, absolutely sacred rule was—vigilance.

Not for an instant during the four, six, sometimes eight hours the patient passes through this now no longer very serious ordeal in the hot box, not for a second does the nurse leave the patient unattended. Her lunch is brought her on a tray. Her fingers never stray far from the pounding pulse at her charge's temple. Her eyes hardly ever leave the trembling needle on the big dial over the patient's head. This indicator —wired to a rectal electric thermometer—tells exactly how hot this threatened one lies dozing, or smoking, or listening to the music that pervades the fever rooms.

The old nightmare of bad skin burns worries the death-fighters no longer. The terrific blasts of hot air that at first were used to stoke up fever are no longer needed. The moister the air you blow round your sufferer, the less hot it needs to be to heat him to any degree of fever his sickness demands. And to hold his fever there—for as many hours as you want!— you keep him surrounded by moist air that's not as hot as a hot day in Yuma, Arizona! With their heads in the cool air outside the cabinet, breathing that cooler air, the patients do not mind too much the hotter air playing round their bodies. The cramps that used to harass sufferers as they crossed the hurdle from their natural body temperature to high fever are now quickly quieted by shooting a calcium solution into their veins.

The fever given by experts is no longer a terrible experience.

### VII

Yet a modern fever treatment is not less serious than a major operation, so says Walter Simpson. And so it is that, taking such demanded precautions, the Dayton workers have now fevered more than eight hundred people for a total of more than forty thousand hours of fevers within a few degrees of death. And of all of these, only one—a sufferer already soft-brained with rapidly progressing syphilis—has died

because of this fever treatment . . . Or would the stroke he
suffered in the fever cabinet have felled him anyway, even if
he had not come to Dayton to take this last chance for life?
That's debatable, but Simpson and his workers acknowledge
this as a death due to fever.

There is now no longer any doubt—in 1937—that what was
a dream in the heads of our fever fanatics in 1931, is a dream
no longer. Now your sufferer with the overhanging doom
of brain syphilis does not have to stay for weeks in a hospital so that malaria fever may remove this danger. After
his machine fever has been cooled, at most he has to stay in
the hospital overnight. Next morning he is back home, can
work, and is none the worse for his hot ordeal. Experience
with many such threatened people proves that forty or fifty
total hours of fever—hardly ever any more—are enough to
check the menace. The fevers are always combined with mild,
harmless doses of arsenical drugs and bismuth—the same
drugs which in big, often dangerous doses often fail to prevent brain-softening by the syphilis microbe.

Out of twenty-seven sufferers from early general paralysis
of the insane who have passed through the now safe fever-
plus-mild-chemical-treatament, twenty-one are now completely well, have remained so, and are working— Without
fever they would all be dead, or demented and on the way
to dying— None who've shown improvement have relapsed
again to madness.

Of seven syphilitics not yet insane, but with tests of their
spinal fluids showing ominously positive, all given this safe
fever-chemical treatment are negative now, and healthy.

Five sufferers whom malaria's fever had failed to cure are
well now, and working after the machine fever. They might
yet relapse, but none have done so, and every month that
passes makes this grim possibility more remote. So it now
seems certain that the tragic last attack of the corkscrew mi-

crobe upon human brain and nerve stuff can be forestalled by
mild chemical treatment supercharged by the new machine
fever science.

### VIII

By now you're asking why this safe fever-chemical treatment hasn't already been tried out, on a large scale, upon
people who suffer from early syphilis? If the sinister sickness
is hardest to cure when it's far along; if the fever-chemical
treatment can prevent the brain-softening against which
chemicals alone are often powerless; if it can check oncom-
ing syphilitic blindness and restore people to good seeing
when chemicals alone didn't help them; if you've at last
found a practical treatment for these last stages—

Then why shouldn't this same powerful weapon work best
of all when the sickness is early?

The havoc of syphilis is not confined to the forlorn ones
who make up eleven percent of all first admissions to our insane asylums. It does to death many thousands of our citizens
who are said to have died of "heart disease" not specified as
syphilitic. It saps the energy of hundreds of thousands, makes
them less than half men or women, is formidable in driving
hundreds of thousands into the sad ranks of the so-called unemployables. Shouldn't experiment toward a really practical,
safe, short, powerful, early treatment be demanded?

There are thousands of physicians, and millions of misin-
formed, misguided syphilitic people in our country who
think that a short course of drug treatment—if syphilis is
caught early—is enough. Well, hardly. It is true that, if all
those infected could be diagnosed early, and then given a
full, ideal, adequate course of drug treatment, eighty-six percent of them would be cured. That way, too, you'd reduce
those able to spread the sickness to others to a minimum.
This is the plan of the great campaign for syphilis control,
now led by fearless Surgeon General Thomas Parran, of our

Public Health Service, and this battle has the support of every true death-fighter.

Yet Doctor Parran himself would hardly admit that the best weapon to fight early syphilis has been found.

Why is it that so many people lapse from this "adequate" drug treatment, and then become heart-wrecked, or blind, or go crazy, and die? Why is it that eighty-four out of every hundred who seek treatment in five of the largest, best syphilis clinics in America, do not even continue their drug shots till they've been freed from danger of infecting others?

Famed syphilis-fighter Joseph Earle Moore puts the difficulty in a nutshell—

"It must be recognized," he says, "that even given more clinics, better clinics, and free clinics the control of syphilis by present day treatment methods is still far from satisfactory. Treatment is too prolonged, too painful, too dangerous, too expensive. Efforts of investigators to develop better and especially shorter methods of treatment should be encouraged."

The tragic fact is this: the drug treatment has a deceptive trick of abolishing the first ugly outward signs of syphilis. It drives the pale corkscrew microbe under cover. Then with a feeling of safety, and because of the expense of the long treatment, or because of the animal-like way they're treated in many a clinic, sufferers are prone not to come back for that grueling, once-or-twice-a-week treatment that takes nearly two years to finish. But there's a grimmer reason why so many fail to complete this chemical ordeal, powerful though it is to guard them from ultimate syphilitic disasters—

The drugs are poisons. The margin between the amount of them you've got to use to kill the syphilis microbe and the amount that may be deadly for that microbe's victim—is perilously narrow. There is no published record of the number the powerful arsenicals have killed.

Now in Dayton young Worley Kendell made a curious discovery, by accident. Certain syphilis sufferers are so sensitive

to arsenicals that they can't stand the smallest doses without
the possibility of severe, even fatal skin inflammations. You'd
say that among such unfortunates, the combination of high
fever and arsenic poison would be surely deadly. Kendell
found the happy opposite. Shoot the arsenical into the arm
veins of such people when they're at the height of their machine fever and they stand the arsenic as if they were ordinary mortals.

Simpson and Kendell don't try to explain this lucky mystery, but it takes no scientist to understand its promise for
our syphilitic myriads—

A bold experiment—hopeful—has been under way during
the past four years in Dayton. Worley Kendell began it by
talking heart to heart with certain sufferers from early syphilis. He asked them to take a chance, to become his human
experimental animals. They felt the true physician in this
son, grandson, and great-grandson of Ohio doctors. They felt
his open-faced honesty and kindness. Yes, they would string
along with him. And they did as they promised. Just before
they entered the fever machine (some with the chancre that's
the first stage of the sickness, others with full blown secondary
syphilitic rashes, but all in the first year of their danger) Kendell injected a shot of bismuth into their bottoms. Then at
the height of their fevers—105—he squirted a very moderate
dose of arsenical drug into their arm veins—much less than
the arsenic demanded by the old standard drug treatment—

By this system Simpson and Kendell hoped the drugs and
the fever would work most powerfully together to smash the
corkscrew microbes.

### IX

For four years now Simpson and Kendell have followed the
fates of their human guinea-pigs with unprecedented close-
ness, with exact keeping of all records. What their experiment lacks in numbers of its patients is more than made up
for by their relentless follow-up of the fate of all of them.

Only four years, so far, granted, and admitted, too, that syphilis is of all plagues the most patient in its treachery, most prone to relapse out of a clear sky to fell its victims.

But already the results of the trail-blazing experiment are portentous. By this combined machine fever-chemical treatment the outward signs of all their people's syphilitic sickness vanished with a speed that was remarkable. Among their thirty-two patients, only two showed signs of dangerous relapse after their fever-chemical treatment— And these both had suffered malignant syphilis incurable by strong chemical treatment for almost a year preceding the beginning of their machine fevers— And a few more fevers, plus mild chemical injections, brought both of these rapidly back to health again, and to this day they remain strong and well.

All of the first thirty-two sufferers are now in excellent health. Yet that is not the only good news this experiment brings to our syphilitic population. All of these thirty-two have been followed, during all their years of treatment, by a new kind of blood and spinal fluid test. It is the most drastic, the exactest, the most subtly informative about the secret gnawings of the spirochete, of any test ever invented. Everybody knows how the old blood tests, the Wassermann and Kahn tests, tried to gauge the intensity of syphilis. You're negative, or one, two, three, or four-plus. When you're four-plus you're supposed to have syphilis good and plenty.

But these tests are only the crudest kind of indication of the hob the corkscrew microbe plays in the human body. Syphilis-scientist Reuben L. Kahn, of the University of Michigan, has devised a really exact test—quantitative. Measured in units, it gives you good or bad or most ominous news of the secret battle between the spirochete and his victim. The ups and downs of these units trace the ups and downs of the way the human body defends itself against the corkscrew microbe's savagery. The test has the kind of precision with which the blood sugar test measures the ups and downs of diabetes.

Now this test by Kahn units shows that a mere "four-plus" doesn't tell the whole stern story. Four-plus is the worst you can be sick by the old tests, but that may mean only forty units by the new test, or it may mean ten thousand units— indicating that the battle between the human body and the corkscrew bug is ominous and full of foreboding. Syphilis fighters relying upon the old chemical treatment don't use this tell-tale unit test generally and one of them, quizzed by Worley Kendell, answered—

"Why should we use it? It's too often tough enough to get that four-plus down to two-plus or to negative. If a guy stays four-plus in spite of our treatment we'd rather not know the number of Kahn units!"

Simpson and Kendell were hard-boiled about their new experiment. They proceeded to follow the fate of these early syphilitic sufferers—machine-fevered plus arsenicals in their arm veins and bismuth in their bottoms—by the curve of Kahn units on charts telling the exact tide of battle in their fever-fight against the corkscrew microbe.

The story the new unit test told was fantastic.

At the first fevering of these sufferers from early syphilis there was a tremendous kick-up in the number of their Kahn units. It was as if this new attack by fever plus arsenicals and bismuth stirred these corkscrew demons to bewildered new savagery, to murderous anger. The curve of the tell-tale units shot up to an ominous peak on the blood and spinal fluid test-charts. But then lo and behold. Now watch those charts, follow that curve as these lucky people go through their fevers—usually ten in all. By the second fever (in this first experiment they were fevered once a week) the units start tumbling downward. In almost every case, *within five weeks*, the units had slid down to zero. The curve had flattened out on the bottoms of the charts—

Never again to go back upward. Excepting in those two people—malignant syphilis—who relapsed, and in one fellow who didn't come faithfully for his fever-chemical treatments.

Those unfortunates who showed ominous positive tests in their spinal fluids—prophetic of later brain syphilis—became quickly negative, and have remained so. Those sufferers whose spinal fluid was negative, never developed foreboding positives.

It must be underlined and explicitly stated that Simpson and Kendell regard this new treatment of early syphilis as experimental and do not, for one moment, advocate that it can yet be applied to our early-syphilitic millions. But this cannot be denied: that the new combined machine fever-chemical treatment enormously shortened the fight against the syphiltic sickness of these people. It's true that Simpson and Kendell played ultra-safe. After the ten weeks of fever-chemical treatment were over, they tapered off on all their sufferers with twenty weeks of mild chemical treatment alone. Without fever.

But that was thirty weeks in all—compared to almost two years demanded by the standard arsenic and bismuth drug treatment of early syphilis!

And have they come to the end of their success in notably shortening the old terrible two years' ordeal? It does not seem so. In this first experiment with these thirty-two experimental human animals, they fevered these people at 105 degrees, ten times, for five hours each time, once a week.

Now Simpson and Kendell are hard at a new experiment giving early syphilitics only three hours of fever twice a week —plus the mild drug treatment! The tell-tale Kahn units go down to zero just as quickly—

What would happen if, when the five weeks of ten three-hour fevers are over, no more chemical treatment would be given? (With the sufferers alertly, faithfully followed by the Kahn units test?)

And what would happen, if, instead of fevering their patients three hours, they were brought up to a peak of 105 degrees, and then immediately allowed to coast down to normal temperature? The success of such an experiment upon sufferers from early syphilis is here predicted.

Experimental trials have shown Simpson and Kendell that fever alone—without chemicals—doesn't do the trick. But other experiments tell them that, so long as they fever their sufferers, much less of the dangerous arsenic is needed and their health returns and their Kahn units go down just as quickly when the bulk of the drug given consists of the much less poisonous bismuth.

The possibility of a true revolution in the too long, too painful, too poisonous present drug treatment of syphilis is here suggested.

In the light of all this, why isn't a large scale test, on thousands of early syphilitics, demanded by doubting doctors? Simpson and Kendell can't do it in Dayton—they haven't enough patients at their disposal. But, granting that the mass treatment in the new great campaign for syphilis control must be chemical right now, why shouldn't a mass experiment to check this hopeful Dayton experiment now be run—directed by our Public Health Service syphilis-fighters at their clinic at Hot Springs, Arkansas, where syphilitics in all stages come in thousands?

Your chronicler will not forget the words of super-accurate Dr. Worley Kendell, who has been the front-line fighter, experimenter, observer in this pioneering machine fever-chemical experiment at Dayton.

"From what I've seen right now," said Worley, "if I had to have one of the major diseases, and could choose which one to have, it wouldn't be TB or diabetes or cancer or pneumonia. I know which one I'd take."

"And that would be—?"

"Syphilis," Kendell answered, smiling.

X

Yes, machine fever has come of age now, and it is most encouraging that, of those thirty-two people, all but one of them went through their fever-ordeal without interruption. "There was no trouble selling them on coming back to the end of it," said Worley Kendell. "It isn't only that they feel so good, so quickly, but you can get them interested in the science of it. They keep asking me, Doc, what are my units this week?"

And that is not surprising, because this is fundamental: the more exact, more scientific any fight with any death, the less mysterious do doctors have to be with their suffering people. The patient becomes a co-experimenter.

Yes, machine fever in less than ten years has become a new powerful hot science—and not against syphilis alone. In dozens of hospitals our country over, fever now fights gonorrhea, St. Vitus's dance and the arthritis and even the heart-wreck caused by the rheumatic state. Eye infections that might otherwise progress to blindness are checked by fever's infection-fighting power. And victims of that curious disease, undulant fever, that comes from drinking unpasteurized milk of cows sick with contagious abortion, are now quickly returned to health when machine fever is added to the natural fever of the sickness. Keen searchers in Rochester, New York, at the Mayo Clinic, in Omaha, Denver, Detroit, Cleveland, and other cities are hot on new trails to test machine fever's power against many a human ill where the human body's natural fever *is not quite enough*—

But these future fights with death and pain and suffering, hopeful as they are, do not here concern us. It is the power of this hot young science against the wreckage of syphilis that we deal with in this story. Our economic order being what it is, what today is the chance of our fighters for life to use machine fever's friendly fire against the suffering of the mass of our citizens?

This, alas, must be acknowledged: before machine fever can become a widely used weapon in the syphilis fight, hundreds of fever teams—composed of these ultra-modern fever nurses, doctors, engineers, laboratorians—will have to be trained and made available to our hospitals and clinics. Fever clinics—existing in mere dozens now—will have to be organized all over. Safe, dependable, comfortable fever machines—their style or make is of secondary importance—will have to be installed in these institutions.

As of today then, what possible chance is there for the stricken syphilitic mass to benefit by this new hot healing?—Your chronicler has the evidence of letters by thousands from people desperate, wanting this new machine fever—

But you see the fever machines are expensive, cost several hundreds of dollars. And a nationwide investigation of the feeble number of dollars in the budgets of the majority of our hospitals and clinics would give you figures that would make you laugh, if the situation was not so tragic.

Do young doctors, nurses, engineers, exist who are qualified to receive this training? There is a glut of them, ready and eager.

It all boils down then to this, that here again the fight is a people's death-fight or it is nothing. It is worse than nothing. It is cruelty at its most exquisite to tell our suffering syphilitic myriads of this new hope for strength and life, and then to make it available at best to a few thousands.

Yet here is the dilemma: before the people can demand this new machine fever, they must know of it. But, now informed of it, will the rulers of the people take action?

Yes, the young nurses, doctors, engineers, microbe hunters, will join the new science. But while they're being trained for it, they have to eat, to be clothed, to have decent shelter, and security of that well-paid livelihood afterward which their life-guarding contribution to society demands.

What will be the answer of the rulers of our communities,

when they are asked to spend the wherewithal to train and then to support the hundreds of new fever teams by which alone this new fight for life can be brought to the people?

Let's face this fact: with the poverty of our hospitals and universities deepening and becoming more desperate, with our rulers, comptrollers, budget-balancers, bellowing economy, there is small chance that this wherewithal will be forthcoming to train the new type of death-fighter.

"But wait," you protest, "these hundreds of thousands of syphilitics, heart-wrecked, dilapidated, drained of energy, sapped of strength, unable to work, ending demented in asylums—"

But who ever accused the generality of our rulers, comptrollers, budget-balancers, economy-bellowers, of believing or even understanding the black and red of their own bookkeeping?

CHAPTER THIRTEEN

# WENGER AGAINST SYPHILIS

**B**UT our leaders in the fight for life know death does not wait for our rulers to be de-fuddled of their false economy. So our syphilis-fighters do the best they can with the miserable means they have. They do not sit wringing their hands because of the general lack of the most modern, powerful weapons against the corkscrew microbe. They do not stop (for long) to curse out the stupidity of a system of society that is impotent to let them fight for our lives with every last bit of the science they know. They're like minute men fighting with scythes and flintlocks not moaning because submachine guns are denied them. They know that even with the old chemical weapons syphilis could be conquered, can be wiped out—in a fight that will be pretty rough on its victims— without the new hot science that could make the battle shorter and more simple.

But can it be that at last a general war has been declared upon syphilis in our country? Walter Simpson says the first shot of the battle is the broadcasting of a slogan: "LET'S CALL IT SYPHILIS AND LET'S GET RID OF IT!" There's no question we're beginning a yelling of that call to arms. But do we mean it? One hard-bitten healthman, O. C. Wenger—veteran syphilis-fighter of our Public Health Service—has thrown down the challange to one great midwestern city. Will it now at last be met?

Is the battle to begin finally, in earnest, as it has against tuberculosis in Detroit? Or are the committees of dignitaries, the newspaper headlines, just a fad, a flash in the pan, only some more of the old American ballyhoo? Can it be that there

284

is now to be an end to curing a few out of the millions of victims of syphilis all the while we fail to stem its wrecking of the lives of myriads? The tools are ready. Our lab men know the spirochete, the corkscrew microbe culprit. Their blood tests can reveal the germ's lurking in folks not seemingly sick, yet dangerous to others. There are chemicals powerful to suppress this contagion, much more quickly and cheaply than you can suppress the contagion of tuberculosis.

O. C. Wenger has told his simple strategy of fighting syphilis to the healthmen and doctors of Chicago. He says: "Syphilis is catching. Spot all who've got it. Treat 'em till they can't give it to those who haven't it. *Uncover and treat!"* That boils down all the eight dollar words of scientific battle plans of the fight that has existed—till now—only on paper.

If it is that simple, you ask, what has been stopping us? Why has no community in the nation—with the now possible exception of Chicago—begun the battle? The answer is easy. Just which men and women, in any community, and how many of them have syphilis that is contagious? Doctors don't know. Health experts can't tell you. All statistics are guesses, nothing more. Is syphilis on the up or downgrade? Massachusetts healthmen believe their fight is driving the death downward—but how prevalent was the sickness when their battle was begun? They do not surely know. For our country as a whole from the facts now known it is impossible to tell the tide of battle. You ask how then is Chicago going to begin to fight it? If Chicago doesn't know how much syphilis it has now, how shall its healthmen tell, five years hence, if their fight shall have been effective, or utterly in vain?

What we do know now is something but by no means all about the consequences of the deviltry of what O. C. Wenger calls the back-stabbing gangster among human pestilences. We know something of the babes the corkscrew microbe kills; of the children it maims or leaves with dim half-seeing and sightless eyes; of how it sends good citizens into sudden frenzy

and makes them murderers of their dear ones; of how it helps
to jam our overflowing madhouses; of the scores of thousands
of people it heart-wrecks in their prime of life; and we try to
guess at, but cannot truly estimate the number of good workers by hand and brain that syphilis turns into jobless, unem-
ployable derelicts.

This panorama of misery, despair, waste, sapping of energy,
death, is the ever-growing aftermath of millions of human
disasters preventable at their beginning. Wenger asks: What
is early syphilis but a fire? The masses of its halt, maimed,
blind, heart-wrecked, imbecilic rear-guard, are only the gut-
tered ruins. Of millions of little fires that, caught early,
might have been kept from spreading.

Then where are the fighters of this fire of early syphilis?
Blood tests can detect this fire while it's at its most spreading
stage, all the time that it is catching. Then why haven't these
blood tests been used as they ought to be and could be?

What are doctors if they are not death-fighters? What is
syphilis if it is not one of the worst deaths that plagues us?
How is it then that a large part of the doctors of America
are not now capable of expertly drawing blood to make these
tests, for all? Could they be taught the technique of mass
drawing of blood? Yes. Are they willing to learn? The vast
majority would be eager if they could be taught it without
their having to jeopardize their earning of their legitimate
bread and butter. Then why are they not now in training
for the first drive, the first wave of the attack, the mass blood-
testing without which the hoped-for fight will be nothing?

America has enough nurses who could be rapidly trained
in public health nursing, and enough epidemiologists—disease detectives—to search out, to track down, all those exposed
to syphilitic contagion. Then why is it that they are not now
being trained—nationwide—for this sleuthing?

Arsenical drugs and bismuth are magic bullets to shoot the
evil spirochete, to damage him at least enough so that he

cannot go from syphilitic to healthy people. Why is it that
so many of our physicians are not now trained in the com-
paratively simple art of making these injections into the arm
veins and the bottoms of our syphilitic masses? It is unfortunate that you have to shoot these chemical bullets many
times into sufferers to make them not-contagious. You have
to keep these people coming back for the powerful, somewhat painful ordeal of this chemical treatment. But public
health nurses—who are famous for their sympathy, their humanity—could be quickly trained to see to it that such people
keep coming back till they're no longer a menace to their
wives, their children, their loved ones, the community. Where
are the training schools for the needed thousands of nurses?

The battle is a mass-fight or it is worse than nothing. And,
so far, only Chicago—stirred to it by O. C. Wenger—has
begun to face the fact of why there is now no national
chance to train these various soldiers for a nationwide war
against the pestilence. Yet, nationwide—*and without any
change needed in the set-up of the way medicine is now
practiced*—there are thousands of physicians, healthmen,
nurses, willing to be recruits for front-line fighting—

If we, the people, had enough regard for their human
dignity to give them a decent living while they waged the
war.

There are expert syphilis-fighters in the U. S. Public
Health Service who could direct the battle. But generals
they remain—absurdly—without any army. Because we—as
citizens—have only gossiped, gabbled about the horrors of
syphilis but have not taken action. These public healthmen are our hope. When the word syphilis could be hardly
so much as whispered, men like Thomas Parran and O. C.
Wenger unearthed the scandal of the neglect of this mass
murder. Now Wenger has drawn up a plan of battle. Can
it be true that Chicago is going to allow them to begin the
fight in earnest? Parran and Wenger promise to wipe out

the plague, stamp it out of our nation if we will let them. But you are from Missouri, and that is your right, and you now ask—

By what searchings did Wenger first get a hint of the extent of the terror of this till recently unmentionable menace?

Are Parran and Wenger justified in their faith—it haunts them and burns in them—that syphilis can be stamped out?

## II

Of the experts of the U. S. Public Health Service, O. C. Wenger is the true pioneer, the veteran in the length of time that he has been fighting syphilis. He was already at it in wartime in the army, when there was pious panic about the number of recruits discovered infected. At that time there were means to fight it because young men thus tainted do not make good killers of their fellowmen. But the funds lavished for the fight against every kind of sickness that might kill our young killers dried up when it was no longer demanded that they kill Germans. So it came about that when, in 1920, Wenger set out for our Public Health Service as a surveyor of the extent of syphilis among our civilian masses, his situation—if he had not been Wenger—would have been called ridiculous.

For a brief postwar time there was whispered public hysteria about the ill's widespread ravages. There was actually an Act of Congress. It permitted the (temporary) doling out of a miserable couple of millions of dollars, yearly, for a few years, to try to determine the extent of a sickness that was suspected (albeit vaguely) of costing our nation hundreds of millions of dollars annually. The weapons recommended for the actual fighting of the sickness were fearful and wonderful. Our youth was to be guarded from getting syphilis by inducing it to peruse pamphlets. In addition it was to be herded into lectures—adults only!—in which the retailing of its ravages would dampen its collective sexual ardor!

Now after a couple of years of this fatuous shadow box-
ing against the sickness, the Public Health Service and the
American Social Hygiene Association regretfully had to report to Senator Reed Smoot of the Senate Finance Committee that the pamphlets and sermons hadn't stopped the pestilence, that its ravages were not yet known, that they were
worse, even, than had been suspected. So that elder states-
man cut off the money provided by the Act of Congress—

No, the money hadn't been entirely wasted. Because of
O. C. Wenger. In the course of his probings our country over,
in honkytonks and mansions, in high places and low, Wenger
had found more syphilis than our most frantic viewers-with-
alarm had dreamed of. Best of all, in the course of his wan-
derings Wenger came to Hot Springs, Arkansas. Hot Springs
jerked Wenger up short. Hot Springs became the preliminary
proving ground of Wenger's battle plans to wipe out the
plague. In 1921 he came to this famous spa to make a syphilis
survey that was to take him ten days maybe. He stayed six-
teen years.

Instantly here at Hot Springs he saw that there was a
unique advantage for him, alone as he was in his guerilla
warfare, and with a most ridiculous pittance of death-fighting money to support him. Here he didn't have to go out
to find the secret sickness. At Hot Springs a terrible parade
of its victims came to him, from every state in the Union.
It was a spa for all diseases, but it was a Mecca for the sufferers from the sickness of the sinister name. They came here
in Pullman drawing rooms, by blind baggage, or by the then
new form of transportation now known as hitch-hiking. But
it was only the lowly who concerned Wenger. And at the
Government Free Bath House he now took up his station.
He quizzed—quickly intimate with everybody and like one
slightly luckier comrade trying to help another—a bedraggled
procession of sick people, pilgrims all to the alleged magic
of hot water.

Here came paralytics from all causes, and wretches twisted with arthritis. These rubbed elbows with the tuberculous and he saw an occasional leper. Each made his or her own diagnosis. None could afford a doctor. The ticket of admission to the bath house was the pauper's oath, because this particular house of hot water was only for "persons poor, needy, in want, or without means of comfortable subsistence. "

Here Wenger found syphilis, epic.

Now immediately Wenger wangled a little government money to found a U. S. Public Health Service Clinic. He got it by an argument that was perfect in our plutocratic paradise. He said: "Looka! These self-treating paupers are a menace to the three hundred thousand prosperous visitors who come here every year for pay baths!" He indulged in no sniveling nonsense about the pains and misery of those paupers. Of course nobody had ever before—America's ragged individualism being what it is—regarded these paupers, medically, as human beings. Wenger so regarded all of them, intensely, but hid it deep down under his hard-boiled outer shell. "But listen!" he told the government authorities, "these transients are not only a local but a national danger!" Some, believing they themselves malarious, spread typhoid fever. Then there were desperate women wandering in and out of the bath house, and, because hunger is no help to chastity, these were a danger.

Himself building his own laboratory benches, with one lab man, a clerk, one nurse, to help him, Wenger organized a mass production of spotting and treating syphilis that is one of the wonders of the scientific world and even our motor magnates could get pointers for their belt lines from its smooth operation. At that Government Free Bath House, to sieve out the syphilitics from the parade of paupers who suffered every kind of sickness, Wenger now stretched a dragnet. Out of this he made a daily haul of those infected from among sufferers from every ill from eczema to cancer.

His dragnet was nothing but the blood test. It was the one quick sure way to spot the spirochete. No arm, not the most pious, was safe from Wenger's syringe needle.

The result? Astounding. Though at this time the majority of poor people came to hot-bathe for sickness not venereal, in the first year of the clinic's operation Wenger found thirty-three out of every hundred to be syphilitic.

A super-high voltage machine of human energy, Wenger bit off more than he could chew and the work swamped him. He buttonholed the prosperous docs of Hot Springs, saying, "Listen! Looka!" begging their volunteer aid to give the powerful 606 and mercury treatment to all paupers found infected. They made the objections doctors all over our country make today against public free clinics, said Wenger's clinic was doubtless full of chiselers, that they'd be working against themselves, taking pay business out of their own offices. "Looka, you guys," Wenger said, "come and take anybody you can get a dime out of to your own office. If you can get money out of 'em, fine, fine!"

They couldn't find chiselers. And twenty-seven of the city's doctors became Wenger's devoted, unpaid assistants. To mass-inject his horde of sick ones, Wenger invented a curious long table. Over it there hung, from a long iron pipe, in a gleaming row, a battery of fifty glass cylinders, from which through rubber tubing there flowed the clear, yellow, dangerous, spirochete-destroying 606—into the veins of the arms of fifty people at one time. It was nothing for a shuffling parade of one hundred and seventy-five sufferers to get hip-shots of mercury in an hour. And to Wenger it didn't matter at all that these sick ones believed their new strength was not thanks to this powerful chemistry but to their baths of hot water. Many of these citizens were tough babies, but Wenger was tougher, and he kept them in line, and kept them coming back by threatening to take their bath tickets from them.

This way for seven years he toiled—his energy is legendary

at Hot Springs—at a self-taught apprenticeship to make himself a master of the secret sickness. He learned why it is that syphilis has its great reservoir among humanity's have-nots and underdogs. Yet he said: "I'm always surprised where I *find* syphilis." And he insisted the reason he kept working at this disreputable sickness was that it kept him meeting so many fine people, but by this Wenger didn't necessarily mean rich or aristocratic people.

This was what these seven years taught him: have or have-not, underdog or topdog, it didn't matter. It was only by the blood-test dragnet that you could find all syphilitics. By mass treatment you could make them safe, ninety-nine times out of a hundred.

### III

But that was just in Hot Springs. What of the millions, syphilitic, hidden in the nation? A queer accident in 1927 took Wenger and his dragnet out of Hot Springs, out into America, out among a section of our population that was underdog enough to be suspected—all of them!—of syphilis. You recall Joseph Goldberger of the Public Health Service, fighting pellagra that summer of the big flood of 1927, when Bill De Kleine first fed the yeast cure? Well, Goldberger was puzzled by Mississippi doctors who insisted upon shooting 606 into the veins of pellagrous Negroes, claiming they were curing them of this pellagra that Goldberger knew could be conquered only by good food or yeast.

So he sent for his Public Health colleague, Wenger, whose gray eyes looked sharp through narrow slits at the assembled blacks' hands and arms. Wenger swore and snorted. Pellagra? Maybe. But syphilis. Amazing how much. Terrific. But how much in this Mississippi County? Nobody knew. Nobody could say how much in any county in all America. Now co-working with Dr. Paul S. Carley, Wenger got permission to sweep a whole county—yes, of course only the colored part of it!—with his blood-test dragnet. Churches, schools—

the Jim Crow ones of course—were their clinics. Failing these they took their tests at ends of rows of cotton under the hot sky. The Julius Rosenwald Fund furnished them the money. "FREE BLOOD TEST BY GOVERNMENT DOCTORS AND FREE ICE WATER." That big sign brought the dark people to their auto. Sundays, to get them in bunches, Wenger and his crew marched into Negro churches; in the middle of the sacred service asked the pastor to step down from his pulpit; had the shepherd of the flock roll up his sleeve first of all; then gentlemen, ladies, and pickaninnies; then thanks very much, good-by, and go on with your sermon.

"What I'd like to see is facts, not figures, about syphilis," Wenger was always saying and here at last were facts—

In that county, one Negro out of every four was infected with syphilis.

Here without question was a menace much more formidable than malaria, hookworm, or pellagra.

Talliaferro Clark, then Assistant Surgeon General of the Public Health Service, saw that here was true pioneering and got the Rosenwald Fund—solicitous about Negroes—to put up half the money for a big dragnet to see if this scandalous situation was in any way general. So now, in six counties in six different Southern States, 1930-'31, Wenger, the health officers of the counties, a few nurses, a few volunteer doctors, dragged a giant syphilis seine through Negro populations. To every last Negro found with bad blood, they offered shots: FREE TREATMENT BY GOVERNMENT DOCTORS AND FREE ICE WATER. Never before had the sickness been treated so vastly, informally, in country stores and churches, in schools and under trees at the edges of fields of cotton, with the mammies—matriarchs—rounding up the cotton pickers for Wenger.

The results were terrible and terribly hopeful.

Of thirty-three thousand Negroes tested one out of every five was found syphilitic.

In counties like that of Albemarle, Virginia, where the Negro has a little money, some education, knows how bad blood is caused and how it can be fixed—here less than one in ten was found infected.

In Macon County, Alabama, where black poverty is most exquisite, there four out of every ten were found tainted—one child out of every three—one young adult out of every two!

Now Wenger had facts to blow the old figures to smithereens. In 1926 such figures had been assembled by the American Social Hygiene Association's survey—it was a one day census among doctors and looked impressive because it represented the doctors taking care of 25,000,000 of our population. It was a kind of dragnet—but with holes that would let the fish slip through it. The doctors were asked how many patients—as of this one day of the census—they had under treatment or observation for syphilis. It didn't seem alarming—

Four out of every thousand for whites.

Seven out of every thousand for blacks.

That was the alleged prevalence—of the syphilis the doctors saw or said they saw. Now here were the facts from Wenger's blood-test dragnet: two hundred out of every thousand for Negroes—

Twenty-five times the syphilis reported by the doctors. But aren't Negroes notoriously syphilitic? What would a mass blood test show for white people? Not that awful? Of course not. Yet— What would be the facts? Nobody knew— Would you find any syphilis at all among the better class? No? But here was an ominous piece of news: when the blood test was applied to candidates for West Point, these boys—no human scum certainly—were found infected, one out of twenty.

Wenger grinned and said: "That's not surprising. Sissies aren't the ones who get syphilis!"

Here was the best news from Wenger's giant experiment in
the southland: it proved the power of mass treatment with
606 and mercury; it showed the eagerness of the black people
to get rid of this ill that sapped their life, their strength. A
year after the experiment, Thomas Parran, now in the thick
of the syphilis fight, journeyed through the region mass-
tested and mass-treated by Wenger and his workers, and
what he found was no different from what Henry Vaughan
is now finding out about the tuberculous Negroes of Detroit's
industrial wasteland—

"The rural Negro . . . responds to gentle treatment when
convinced of the interest of doctors and scientists in his welfare," reported Parran. Negroes were human beings. And
their masters, the planters, showed human intelligence. What
gratified Parran and Wenger was the enthusiasm of those
white planters, not that they loved the Negroes, not on any
humane grounds but on the ground of business. One Alabama planter had been dead against this sucking blood out
of the arms and squirting 606 into the veins of his bucks
and black women at the experiment's beginning but at its
end he most handsomely acknowledged the corn. "Why, there
were niggers on his plantation who'd never done a day's
work in their lives. Before those shots. Now look at 'em!
And his doctor bills for 'em had been cut in half!"

Wenger knew the reason. Master observer of the sinister
sickness, he understood how when there's no outward sign
of it at all, long before it strikes at your heart and brain, how
it makes you feel less than half alive, tired for no reason,
fagged when you get up in the morning, feeling as if you
had a steel band round your head and as if there was something terrible working deep inside your bones at night. So
now it was no wonder that one planter expounded to Parran that this syphilis was "mighty bad business," yes, he
meant business. His plantation was the largest in the world.
It had veterinarians to mend its sick mules. Each year these

vets examined all mules, sold off all unfit for service, replaced them with healthy three-year-olds— "But now I ask you, Doctor," said the planter to Parran, "is it good business to hook up a healthy mule to a syphilitic Negro?"

So amid the mutual congratulations and the hoorahs of everybody—county officials, planters, physicians—and oh, yes, let's not forget the Negroes—this experiment came to its triumphant end. It petered out at the moment it should have just begun. Because—there was no more money. That's America for you. Influential citizens agree with you that syphilis is bad business and that you are economically sound if you spend some money *now* to save much more money in the not far distant future. They say yes, yes; and then they don't spend the money.

You certainly can't blame the Rosenwald Fund for being appalled at the enormity of the problem of finding all the syphilis in the black South and treating it to non-contagiousness. You couldn't ask the Rosenwald Fund to take the financial burden of re-conditioning all the South's Negro human machinery . . . There were maybe ten million black people down there and what private philanthropy could be asked to blood test all and then treat the very likely one out of five of all that ten million who would be found syphilitic?— And the Public Health Service? Mind you, this was 1931, this was the Hooverian epoch of most intense rugged individualism. And Parran's Venereal Diseases Division of the Public Health Service had a budget of $80,000 a year to fight this ill that was costing America an annual nobody knew how many hundreds of millions of dollars.

Yet hope smoldered in Parran and Wenger. What they'd done, said Wenger, was very much like taking a teaspoonful of water out of the Atlantic and carrying it coast to coast to pour it into the Pacific. What they had done was nothing. Yet what they had found was in its little curious way hopeful. In counties like Albemarle in Virginia—where for years

early cases of syphilis had been pretty well treated in quite
a number of Negroes—the prevalence of the sickness was
four times less than in benighted Macon County, Alabama,
where syphilis had been medically neglected.

You couldn't laugh that one off. Now, if a great dragnet
could find all early cases, black and white, all over our nation? And if you then mass-treated all cases thus found? Well
then!

This was the dream of Wenger and Parran, forerunners.

### IV

But, alas, where in 1931 in all America was there a chance
to use this powerful blood-test dragnet on the general population? Even if you had the laboratories, the doctors to take
the blood, the lab men to make the tests, wouldn't your white
people, your better class white folks, be insulted by the suggestion that they might be tainted? Parran and Wenger had
to face this fact: that the Negroes—unashamed and childlike
—were far ahead of the mass of their white brothers and sisters in this just-emerging people's fight against syphilis. So
Wenger retreated to Hot Springs.

And towards Hot Springs there trekked this terrible pil-
grimage that was the consequence of our nationwide hypocrisy and folly. As the depression deepened, this awful
procession grew in numbers, dragging toward Hot Springs
to the dirge of "Brother-can-you-spare-a-dime." From the
four corners of our country, on freight trains or highwaying
it or walking—whole families walking behind fathers pushing
wretched family belongings on a rickety wheelbarrow—there
converged an ever-growing parade of sick, desperate ones,
blistering their feet, shot at by railroad yard detectives, going
hungry, walking in the cold and rain, going to Hot Springs,
to Wenger, to hot water, to 606, to beg to be let live again.
Wenger must have regretted his wisecrack about liking to
treat syphilis because he met so many fine people. Because

now, as America grew poorer, the kind of sick pilgrims who came to him grew finer. Now in 1932 the grim migration to his clinic grew desperate, and swamped his facilities to take care of it. Wenger was saved by Regina Kaplan, head nurse of the Leo N. Levi Hospital at Hot Springs. This woman, remarkably resourceful, always managed to find room in this fine hospital supported by the B'Nai B'rith, for one more of Wenger's desperately sick people. Even, in Wenger's words, "when she already had patients hanging out the windows of her overcrowded joint." Many of these sick pilgrims were starving, and Mrs. Wenger and her neighbors improvised a soup kitchen in the garage in Wenger's back yard, feeding those who were absolutely penniless. Families, with little children, slept under trees, invaded empty houses and abandoned shacks, so that they could stay at Hot Springs to get the healing hot baths, 606, and mercury. 1932—nearly forty out of every thousand of all those thousands who sought new life, came to Wenger without a nickel, without a soo markee.

It was then that Wenger must have coined his most famous gag, about his idea of heaven. "My idea of heaven," he said, "is unlimited syphilis and unlimited facilities to treat it."

He did have unlimited syphilis—

But you could not down Wenger. Mass poverty, the near-collapse of our economic order, could not down this dauntless warrior. Now to fight the murderous poverty of his pilgrims Wenger invented an intense, continuous treatment for syphilis—squeezing an ordinary year's treatment into three months! Here lay the one salvation for the sick man, his wife, his children whom he might endanger: intense chemical treatment without let-up. And the free hot baths without a question made the powerfully poisonous treatment safer, and very likely to some extent—though not as greatly as machine fever could do it—supercharged the chemical treatment's

syphilis-smashing power. Marvelous. Congratulations for
O. C. Wenger. Hoorah for science. But what would these
poor pilgrims have to eat while science saved them?

Heaven knows how Wenger and his worshiping, devoted
helpers faced it, kept standing it, kept order in that milling
crowd of sick ones clamoring to take their pauper's oath for
a new chance to live. Hardly a day passed that Wenger, after
a terrific day of mass-treatment, didn't carry home with him
tragedies that kept him sleepless. Like the sad little saga of
the family from Louisiana, husband 21, wife 20, with two
babies aged one and three. Their capital upon arrival at Hot
Springs was $3.90. Both parents had early, infectious syphilis.
Both babies were still free from it. Treatment began. In a
week the $3.90 was gone. For a few days already over-strained
local charity bought milk for the babies and then the jig
was up. The little family did a fade-out from Wenger's care,
hitch-hiking homeward, the parents a danger to their babies,
and the fate of future children if the mother had them, unmentionable. Wenger lay awake with it: in a few years the
father and mother would be underpar to a point where they
would be a burden to the tune of thousands of dollars to
their county, their state, the nation—

Month after month unending, such was the fierce focus of
the end results of our nation's hypocrisy, cruelty, and folly.
For the concentration of this tragedy upon Wenger the Federal Government was responsible, absolutely. It offered the
free curative baths to these indigent ones. Wenger faced it
that he, too, was responsible because the fame of his free
powerful treatment had been broadcast by that mysterious
grapevine radio of the have-nots, the underdogs the country
over. Now at last, 1933, in response to a powerfully written
statement by Wenger, and thanks to the true humanity and
the insight of Aubrey Williams and to the quick action of
Relief Administrator Harry Hopkins, our government recognized that poor syphilitic people were—people— At least

while they were under Wenger's care at Hot Springs— The government admitted that untreated syphilitic people were dangerous. Now quickly Camp Garraday was built, lovely among the oaks and pine trees just outside Hot Springs. Here the sick thousands, if they had contagious syphilis and while being treated till no longer dangerous to others, were well-housed, amply fed, in return for five hours of light work a day—

—Your chronicler will not forget a vision of the mass-power of Wenger's science, the contrast of the look of the milling throng of suppliants for life that waited for their pauper's oath, and the look of people under treatment living at Camp Garraday. Clamoring to enter the clinic you saw a parade of humanity in the last stages of physical dilapidation. Now regard this khaki-clad crowd of young men, husky, tanned, strong, looking like CCC boys, or shock troops filing into Camp Garraday's dining hall for supper. It was 606, it was bismuth, that in a few short weeks had so transformed them. It was Wenger—

And deep in his heart and in the bottom of his brain Wenger knew that this was nothing. Burned into your reporter's memory is Wenger, syphilis master, talking to a pretty seventeen-year-old girl, here for treatment of syphilis and gonorrhea. With that genius Wenger has of showing his people how—on a level of absolute comradeship with them— he understands their tragedy, he quizzed this bit of human flotsam. She had been a waitress in a restaurant in a small Oklahoma city. Her total take, including tips, had never been more than $2 a week. In spite of her sickness she had a sort of defiant flippancy about her and that morning, going through the routine of her examination, she had ogled the orderlies and even the doctors. Completing his cross-examination, made with Wenger's own unique brand of rough and ready, tough-talking comradeship, he turned from that little girl to Rhea and your chronicler. He seemed to forget that the little girl was there, or that she even so much as existed. He generalized—

"Now looka!" he said to us. "Look at this kid. What chance did life ever give her to be really self-supporting and decent? Listen! We'll treat her here. Yes. We'll cure her. She'll be well-fed, have a good clean bed and shelter out at the camp while we're fixing her. Then what'll she do? She'll wrap up all she's got, her toothbrush and nightie in a bath towel. She's got no money. She's got absolutely no place to go. We've cured her physical disease, yes, okay! But now who's going to make a decent citizen of her? Look at her. She's a fine kid, well-built, pretty. She's got some brains too, I can tell it. But when she's cured, what'll she do? She'll wrap her next-to-nothing that she owns in that bath towel, stick it under her arm, and hit the highway, to go—"

Suddenly this forlorn waif, this little slip-shoe lovey, burst out crying, and Wenger cut short his blasting denunciation of man's inhumanity to man. Her tears stopped Wenger and he put his arm around her shoulder while she cried and cried incontinently—

This was Wenger the teacher. This was Wenger, not the doctor but the agitator. For the reason for this little apprentice loose-woman's tears was plain to Rhea and your chronicler. They were not for herself. Yes, she'd get along, somehow, get another job, get men again, get syphilis again maybe. Her tears were tears of a mental awakening. They were not tears of self-pity. They revealed emotion she felt at a flash of illumination, of understanding of herself as a marcher in the great rear-guard of victims of America's injustice.

Yet, despite this hatred of man's inhumanity to man that raged in Wenger, he was first and last a fighter of syphilis. He was not so much obsessed with syphilis as totally possessed by it. This gnawed at him: his treatment was powerful. Excellent. A step in the right direction. But, for the thousands cured, made safe at Hot Springs, there were millions, he knew, abroad in America, dangerous. This for Wenger was the grim question: Why did these sick pilgrims come to Hot Springs anyway? Why couldn't they be treated by private physicians or public health authorities in their own communities? Now at last we come to the answer and it is as simple as it is infamous—

It is poverty. It is national lack of wherewithal. Reach down in to the grab bag of the tragic histories of any hundred of these sick suppliants. Why did they have to come?

Out of any hundred, twenty-five came because there were no facilities for diagnosis, treatment, in their home places.

Nine, because when blood test showed them infected, their own physician referred them to Hot Springs because they could not pay him for curing them.

Thirty-two, because their doctors had treated them till their money ran out. Then Hot Springs was the only place they had to go.

And so on: to sum it up seventy-four out of every hundred came because they themselves and their communities were powerless to buy them life—

And impotent to keep them from being spreaders of new pestilence and death.

### v

It was the great pioneering merit of Wenger and his comrade Thomas Parran that they understood this: that nowhere in our land had syphilis been fought as a contagious sickness, like TB is now in some places fought, as smallpox is fought all over. There had been sermons against syphilis, yes, but not the blood tests to find it. There had been pious moralizing, sure, but not 606 and bismuth to abolish it. Vast sums had been outlaid, granted: for asylums, for blind schools, for jails, for poorhouses, for the relief rolls that its last consequences helped to fill to the consternation of all who now fill the land with their wailing about high taxes. But when Parran, Wenger, begged for money, then from everybody, from presidents all the way down to city aldermen, there was indifference, there was silence. In a furious memorandum Wenger reiterated the lack of the one weapon, far more powerful than 606, than bismuth, yes, than their combination with machine fever—

"Money, money, and more money!" roared Wenger.

This was the deadliest enemy of the spirochete.

## VI

Then came Surgeon General Thomas Parran on a new adventure. 1936—he dared at last to speak out from his high position as generalissimo of our nation's healthmen. Writing in *The Reader's Digest* what was before mumbled only in the halls of science, he courted disgrace because what he sought to fight was in itself so shameful, unmentionable. He found this fact: that the mass of America's people are not stupid if only you do not act as if you so regard them. Parran now at last did say to millions: LET'S CALL IT SYPHILIS AND LET'S GET RID OF IT. He did not conceal its horror. He told how full half its blight fell upon the innocent. He did not shrink from revealing that it spreads, chiefly, because of that human imperfection which is at the same time vigorous animality, that not yet firmly controlled but powerful human reproductive instinct that goes by the old silly name of sin. So upon the sneakings of the corkscrew microbe Parran turned the clean bright beam of universal knowledge and now, 1936, America woke up one morning to tell itself this is a contagious sickness, nothing more.

Chicago was the first of all cities of America to try to take up Parran's challenge. June, 1937, that city, where anything may happen and usually does, began the launching of what it was hoped might turn out to be the most formidable people's fight for the people's life ever attempted by any American community against any sickness whatsoever.

This attempt to fight syphilis in America's second city

began not in Chicago at all but in a little hillbilly town in
Arkansas in the foothills of the Ozarks. To this town, one
evening, June, 1937, O. C. Wenger had gone to meet with
the County Health Officers, the public health nurses, the Arkansas State Health Commissioner, and the physicians of the
county's medical society. With un-Wengerish restraint and
politeness he asked these doctors whether they in their practices would take a syphilis blood test, as a routine, on every
last patient they saw in their offices or in the patients' homes,
no matter what the patient's sickness—on every patient from
babes to oldsters, whether they had cancer or nose-bleed or
fallen arches or housemaid's knee. Wenger assured them
they'd be true pioneers, that this would be the first universal
county dragnet in America's history—

The obviously big-shot doctor of the county demurred.
"Yes, ahem, speaking for myself and I believe my colleagues,
we will consider doing it. But we cannot tell our patients
for what their blood is being taken. Otherwise, ahem, *my*
class of patients would not stand for it. Not if they knew.
You see, Doctor Wenger, we as physicians can do nothing
that will jeopardize our private practices!"

It was the first time your chronicler had seen our doughty
Wenger frustrated, yes, completely flummoxed, at a loss for
any answer. But it happened that Rhea de Kruif was there,
and she whispered to us: "Well, that doctor must have an
awfully dumb class of patients!" Then at Wenger's urging
Rhea spoke up in meeting. What would happen, she asked
the big-shot doctor, if the people, all the people of his county,
were asked by referendum whether they would be willing
to have a free blood test FOR SYPHILIS taken in strict confidence by their own family physician?

That simple question was the beginning of Chicago's syphilis fight. For Wenger, after the purport of this innocent question sank in, forgot about that Arkansas backwoods county,

blazed into action, and early the next morning, back at Hot Springs, stormed up and down a hotel room and said—

"We'll put that question before the people of Chicago!"

Within forty-eight hours Wenger took his audacious proposal to Chicago's famed Health Commissioner, Herman Bundesen. Did *he* dare to put the question to the vote of Chicago's millions? It was a challenge never before faced by any healthman in our country's history. The vote was a two-edged sword. If the citizens said "no"—this would mean that Wenger's great dragnet scheme to uncover syphilis was not practicable. If they said "yes" overwhelmingly, that they did want the free confidential blood test—then how would Herman Bundesen and Wenger find the wherewithal to set up the great blood-test machine that would be needed?

Bundesen's answer was as quick as it was bold. And this fantastic vote was sponsored by the U. S. Public Health Service, the Illinois State Department of Health, and the Chicago Board of Health—

"IN STRICT CONFIDENCE AND AT NO EXPENSE TO YOU, WOULD YOU LIKE TO BE GIVEN, BY YOUR OWN PHYSICIAN, A BLOOD TEST FOR SYPHILIS? —— NO —— (PLEASE CHECK ONE)"

This historic ballot was mailed to nearly a million property-owners of Chicago, thanks to the quick action of Assistant Administrator Howard O. Hunter of the Works Progress Administration. With his seemingly so-effortless energy this man who is one of our not-enough-appreciated public servants transformed a part of the WPA into an emergency death-fighting army. In less time than it took to tell it, Hunter set machinery going that got the ballots printed, and produced a great force of clerks, of expert statisticians, to analyze the returns of this vote by citizens of Chicago.

A hundred thousand replies rolled in. These ballots represented the possibility of blood tests for between three and four hundred thousand people of Chicago, because the voters spoke for themselves and their families. The sentiment ex-

pressed was an overwhelming yes—*in a proportion of twenty
to one of all those voting.* And when the "no's" were analyzed, a great majority of these were explained by messages
written by the no-voters on their ballots. They didn't need
the blood test because they had just had one. Or they had
syphilis and were now under treatment. Or they were 80
years old and didn't think they needed to have their blood
examined! Only a few no's were genuine ones from people
who protested that this was or should be a private matter
between themselves and their physicians. The real majority
of those who said yes, we'll take the test, was close to ninety-
nine out of every hundred.

This was the first step for Wenger. This was the voice of
Chicago's people. There remained no doubt that they would
be back of their healthmen, their doctors, if only a great
effort could now be made to find Chicago's hidden syphilis,
to begin the working of Wenger's dreamed-of blood-test dragnet, of putting Chicago's population through a giant syphilis-
finding sieve—

Now how to do it? Wenger's plan for it was hardly different from the simple one he had proposed to the doctors
of that remote Arkansas county. Wenger went before the
Council of the Chicago Medical Society and that body voted
unanimously that it was in favor of making Chicago's doctors public healthmen—of asking Chicago's doctors to draw
Chicago's blood in their offices, their practices—

Dr. Reuben L. Kahn, most famed of America's blood-test
scientists, inventor of the Kahn test for syphilis that today
is the simplest, cheapest and most accurate yet devised, now
came to organize Chicago's laboratories for a giant campaign
of blood-testing. Now the WPA printed coupons, hundreds
of thousands of them, which should be distributed to various
groups of Chicago's citizens—high as well as low—that would
entitle them and their families to the test. Already the hue
and cry of the vote campaign—with airplanes flying over the

city drawing great banners—VOTE TO HELP CHICAGO
STAMP OUT SYPHILIS—had begun to stir a clamor for
the blood test. Physicians were bedeviled by patients tele-
phoning to them for blood-test appointments. Two thousand
youngsters of the National Youth Administration marched
through Chicago's Loop carrying banners—FRIDAY THE
THIRTEENTH IS AN UNLUCKY DAY FOR SYPHILIS.
And the echoes of this hullabaloo reached out over the Mid-
west—Dr. William F. Lorenz of Wisconsin reporting that
bloods to be tested for syphilis at the State laboratory had
jumped two hundred and eighty percent in number—

But would it be more than ballyhoo? Bundesen, his able
and gentle Venereal Diseases Director Dr. Louis Schmidt,
Wenger, Howard Hunter, all of them had to face this fact—

That, before you offer the blood test to three million, five
hundred thousand people, free, before you get the blood,
you have got to get the money.

It is true that this began to be recognized—if somewhat
dimly—by Chicago's city fathers, because at the very beginning of the excitement her Mayor and Council placed
$50,000 at the disposal of Doctor Bundesen.

But this was only a drop in the bucket. They were told
that it was costing the city of Chicago many millions of dollars, yearly, to maintain the ghastly luxury of syphilis. To
keep the victims of syphilis in hospitals, jails, blind schools,
asylums, and to support a great army of unemployables—who
couldn't work because they had syphilis!—on welfare lists, relief rolls.

It was the Detroit TB story all over, and no different. For
the amount of money needed to begin the uncovering and
treating of all syphilis was nowhere near the amount now
yearly spent to support its wrecking of the lives and sapping
of the strength of Chicago's people. Spend the needed yearly
millions for, let's say, a generation. Place those millions in
the competent hands of Chicago's healthmen and physicians

who could be trained for the death-fight, and by the end of that time there'd no longer be any need for such syphilis-fighting expenditure—and, at the same time, the enormous expense of the ghastly luxury itself would have vanished.

That was the common sense of this new public health economy, and, in Wisconsin there was already evidence of its working. 1916—the Wisconsin State Laboratory under direction of psychiatrist William F. Lorenz, had begun offering free blood-test facilities to all of Wisconsin's doctors outside Milwaukee County. They were encouraged to blood-test all their patients, then treat them if they were found syphilitic. That year, 1916, syphilis was responsible for thirteen percent of all the admissions to Wisconsin's asylums outside Milwaukee County. The blood-testing grew in popularity during the twenty years that followed— And, 1936—syphilis was responsible for only six percent of admissions to those asylums—

And what Wisconsin had saved, in good hard money, was an amount several times greater than the entire budget of the State's Psychiatric Institute, of which the State Laboratory was only one small division.

### VII

Then came disaster. Wenger was the sparkplug, better yet the dynamo of this new Chicago death-fight. The magnificent dragnet idea was Wenger's brain child. It was Wenger who saw through and all round the wastefulness and the tragedy and the simple way to fight it, saw how the sickness was a public, a communal, and in no sense a private question between individual patient and private practicing doctor. Syphilis, early contagious syphilis, said Wenger, was no different from a fire. Millions of Chicagoans could not pay for blood tests, nor for the treatment that would make them no longer dangerous to others. All right, no argument—

Then what would be sillier, if you wanted to save your

community, than only to put out fires in houses where individuals could pay for the fire department to come?

But you have to pay for pumpers and hook-and-ladder apparatus and you have to pay the firemen a decent wage.

Then shouldn't Chicago's physicians, too, be well-paid for the time they'd have to take for instruction in drawing Chicago's blood, and in treating the hundreds of thousands who would be found syphilitic? And shouldn't they be well-paid, too, for the blood-testing and the treating of the dangerous people—when a sufficient number of them had been turned into part-time public healthmen?

The city was empowered by state law to pro mil tax itself to fight contagious sicknesses and this was already the way Chicago was financing its fight—inadequately—against tuberculosis. Why not raise the $2,600,000 yearly—which Wenger estimated would be adequate—the same way?

Wenger, indomitable, could single-handed have carried to victory the fight for this money without which the new death-fight would only be farcical, without which it would be nothing.

Wenger, selfless and without personal ambition, equipped with the wherewithal that is the supreme killer of the spirochete, could have organized the great continuing campaign of teaching all of Chicago's people how they could co-work to fight the menace.

Wenger, aflame against this waste and horrid heartbreak, could have brought it about that Chicago's citizens, its Women's Clubs, its civic groups, its employers of labor and the millions of those who worked for them, its people on work relief and welfare rolls, all the mass of its haves and have-nots—he could have brought them for the blood test.

Wenger, master student of the disease in man, and because of his great experience, his common sense, and wisdom, respected by all physicians worth the name, could have organized Chicago's doctors into a front-line shock brigade against the terror.

—Get the vote—get the money—get the blood—that way find all people whose syphilis is contagious, then treat them till they're no longer dangerous—

That way Wenger could truly have begun the wiping of syphilis out of Chicago.

September, 1937, death-fighter Wenger came to the end of his tether as a front-line fighter, as a leader first over the top in every battle. Only fifty-two years old, in life's prime, the heart of this never-tired man grew tired and your chronicler will never forget him, gray-faced at the end of that hot September day when he'd watched those two thousand N.Y.A. youngsters carrying their strange banners towards Chicago's city hall—

"FRIDAY THE THIRTEENTH IS AN UNLUCKY DAY FOR SYPHILIS."

Wenger himself had coined that slogan.

Friday, September 13, 1937, was an unlucky day for O. C. Wenger. That day a letter came for him, from the Public Health Service, from Washington, from the GHQ of this syphilis battle of which he was the chief veteran.

"What the hell!" said Wenger. His old ruddiness was gone and he was slumped, gray-faced, in a chair in his little office. "What the hell! I know I haven't long to go. But what of it? I don't want to quit. I'd rather die with my boots on—"

Stricken with heart-wreck that gives its sufferers an average of two years to live—if they live not generously, fiercely, like Wenger but with care—this fighter that day got his orders, irrevocable, to leave Chicago's battle.

Can Chicago now fight syphilis? Has it all been ballyhoo? Will our country have to go back to asking feebly, wistfully, "Why don't we stamp out syphilis?"

There is only one Wenger.

Will the people rise to demand of their rulers that the death-fight be started? By the hundreds of young fighters for life who could begin it if, inspired and stirred by the life and work of Wenger, they were given a chance to begin to stamp out syphilis?

CHAPTER FOURTEEN

# THE MARCH OF LIFE

WENGER would be the first to laugh at any pessimism at his own passing from active service in the syphilis fight. He knows other Wengers will rise at the demand of the people. He knows how on every front the fight for life will grow in power exactly as fast as the people understand it and demand it. De Lee may die but by masses our citizens now begin to realize that mothers can be saved from child-bed death. Charles Armstrong may break his death-fighting arm but millions at this moment are joining to make it possible for other searchers to conquer infantile paralysis. The lives of bold Pat O'Brien, Bruce Douglas, Henry Vaughan, might be snuffed out tomorrow. Yet myriads already understand that the white death's doom is mainly a matter of voting a sound economy that will give us all the death-fighters needed to complete the victory. Wenger's own heart-wreck may cause Chicago's syphilis fight to flag for a while. But everywhere in our nation there are citizens stirred by knowing that our country can be freed from this ghastly luxury— when enough people once realize that this is what syphilis is, and nothing more. So Wenger does not despair. He knows that the fight for life must gain in power because of this new great growth in the people's understanding. That's what begins to make the forward march of human life unstoppable, inevitable.

Now that the people themselves begin to understand this, that, and another death can be conquered by science, by the hunt for truth, and by their own clear understanding of this truth—what will be the limit of this new people's fight for life? Our searchers' adventures now begin to compete, on newspaper front pages and by radio and in the movies, with the exploits of mass-murderers of humanity. Millions now flock to see "The Life of Louis Pasteur" (who was against death) and "The Life of Emile Zola" (who was for truth). And at the same time the people boo out of our country the fat young baby-killer who boasts of his bombing of the innocent. The people are getting ready to choose between the promises of warmongers on the one hand and their fighters for life on the other. The baby-bombers may yet have their innings. But in the end there's small doubt whom the people will follow in the onward mass march of life.

It is most stirring of all to the courage and the optimism of the people that the scientific fight for life is right now so fantastically growing in its power. For the adventures that have been here recounted, of science against mothers' death, children's maiming, TB, and syphilis, are only a part of a general fight for life that every year is gaining in breadth and momentum. At this very moment, using a new chemical death-fighting discovery, our searchers are getting ready to strike a blow against another deadly cohort of man's microbe enemies. Against streptococcus and his evil brothers and cousins that are to be counted among the most formidable murderers of mankind.

Not three years ago your chronicler sat in a session of scientific philosophizing and yarn-spinning with certain top-cut microbe hunters. We laughed at the notion that such a chemical death-fight was possible. Today sulfanilamide—magic microbe-shooting chemical shotgun though it is already acknowledged to be—is only the first hint of a whole new world of life-guarding chemical science.

## II

The accident by which sulfanilamide's power was discovered will probably remain a mystery because this chemical

death-fight was not born in any university laboratory where
science is an open secret. No, for finding it the great German
dye trust, *I. G. Farbenindustrie,* Elberfeld, must have the
credit. Now for industry's own defense the truth, the whole
truth and nothing but the truth must take a back seat at
the demand of profit. So the new chemical made its bow in
a manner the opposite of scientific. 1933, the first whisper of
the microbe-smashing virtue of the strange medicine came
to physicians with no fanfare at all. That year a certain German, Doctor Foerster, at a meeting of skin doctors at Düs-
seldorf, brought news of a mysterious drug, patented and
trade-marked as "Streptozon."

Foerster said the drug had worked wonders for a child
blood-poisoned by staphylococcus.

Then the next year this drug changed its trade-name to
"Prontosil." Now in Germany it began to stir up medical
excitement. Quickly came medical reports—not very scientific
—that prontosil acted against skin diseases caused by the murderous streptococcus. It could cure rheumatism of which this
microbe was the evil author. It could cool childbed fever in
a way truly wonderful!

To American searchers there seemed something fishy about
these first reports of the virtues of this orange-colored dye.
Never a word, those first two years, about laboratory science,
about proof of its curing streptococcus sickness of mice, to
justify its use for men. And what wonder? So, smiling and
rubbing their noses, asked hard-boiled microbe hunters all
over. Since the pioneering microbe-hunting days of great
Robert Koch, himself, all searchers had failed to find any
such magic chemical— You could find 606 against more complicated bugs like spirochetes and trypanosomes, but a killer
that would work in the human body against the simpler bacteria? Never. Beginning with grumpy old Robert Koch,
chemicals like carbolic acid, corrosive sublimate, and many
a dye had been found to kill bacteria—in test-tubes. But

when germs like this streptococcus began playing havoc in the bodies of men, and you then tried to use these chemicals to cure, it was the mouse or the man these antiseptics and germicides killed, and not the microbe!

But now, 1935, Professor Gerhard Domagk—professor in a dye factory at Elberfeld, Germany!—brought news of one mouse experiment and what an experiment. He claimed every mouse injected with surely deadly streptococcus stayed chipper if you only treated him with this orange dye, prontosil. All not-treated mice died pronto. This was almost worse than if the German dye-makers had published no scientific experiment at all. Domagk's lone experiment was too, too perfect. Furthermore, the time of its publication was in the highest degree mysterious. Here it was 1935, with all kinds of human cures reported for two years, and why was Professor Domagk's test dated—on his protocol—way back in December, 1932? What searcher in the whole scientific world, if he'd found a cure of this streptococcus mouse-murder, would wait so long to give such genuinely world-shaking news to the world of science?

That was only a beginning of the commercial mystery of this alleged discovery. Domagk said that this prontosil was harmless to streptococcus when you mixed it with cultures of the bug in glass dishes. It only walloped the varmint when he was already at his deviltry inside the body of a mouse or a man. What then could have been the clue to the death-fighting discovery? From the dye trust came no answer.

Now from the Pasteur Institute in Paris came news of a yet more Alice-in-Wonderland-like topsy-turviness. Mr. and Mrs. J. Tréfouël—working for famed French chemist Fourneau—reported that you didn't need the complicated, patents-applied-for dye at all to cure this hitherto incurable streptococcus mouse sickness. Yes, you could cure it. But you could take this prontosil, chemically reduce that dye to whiteness, break it up chemically to something much simpler, get out of it a mother-substance with which the German chemists must in the first place have started. A fairly simple organic chemical compound. Not patentable. An old coal-tar chemical that had been kicking round for fifty years. Para-amino-benzene-sulfonamide. Now called sulfanilamide. Why had the German covered it up with all that gingerbread of colored chemical complexity?

Why hadn't they tried the simpler sulfanilamide on the sick mice in the first place? Or had they?

Again from the German dye trust, no answer. The answers to all these questions remain—regrettably for truth—trade secrets, but let that pass. The good news for mankind was this: that for doomed mice this cheap, easy-to-make sulfanilamide did have definite microbe-fighting virtue.

III

Now the German dye-chemist Dr. Heinrich Hoerlein—he must have prime credit for beginning the whole death-fighting project—made an impressive speech to the bigwigs of the Royal Society of Medicine in London. He sold them. Immediately there began a buzzing in British laboratories. There was un-English, pop-eyed amazement at surely doomed blood-poisoned mice not dying. Saved by this fairy-tale patent medicine prontosil. Now in Queen Charlotte's Hospital there was medical excitement at women saved from the mortal fire of childbed fever. Keen English searcher Leonard Colebrook, Rockefeller-supported for ten years, all that time groping for something to cure childbed fever, cold-blooded scientist that he was, could hardly believe his eyes when he saw mouse and woman getting well. Yet nobody could doubt the exact experiments of Colebrook, master-searcher.

Now it was summer, 1936, and young American Dr. Perrin H. Long and his co-searcher, the no less able Dr. Eleanor A. Bliss, both of them from the Johns Hopkins Medical School in Baltimore, have come to the microbiologist's Con-

gress in London and they are experts in the deadliness of
mouse-murdering streptococcus and they are from super-
scientific conservative Johns Hopkins. Long missed Colebrook's speech about protonsil because he was getting his
friend J. Howard Brown into a London hospital after being
hit by a car. But what were these rumors about this patent
medicine, prontosil, about this formerly no-account coal-tar
chemical sulfanilamide? Long had been confused by the more
or less scientific reports geysering out of Germany—whose
rulers publicly admitted that German science was no longer
primarily a search for truth. But here were Arabian Nights'
yarns, truly. Claims of cure, not only of streptococcus rheumatism, erysipelas, blood-poisoning, childbed fever— But
also surely fatal Hodgkin's disease, not caused by a microbe!—
And of TB meningitis— All cured by this patent prontosil—
Horsefeathers!

It was by chance that Perrin Long didn't pass this whole
prontosil business up as pseudo-scientific moonshine. He'd
missed Colebrook's speech, but what began as a polite chat
with English microbe hunter Ronald Hare ended up with
Long in an excited dither. Hare had accidentally infected
himself while he was playing on death's doorstep with streptococcus in his laboratory. He'd got critically sick with streptococcus blood-poisoning. He'd very nearly checked out. He
should by rights have died. He'd been dragged out of this
valley of the shadow.

Yes, by prontosil.

Now Perrin Long has been criticized for his enthusiastic
nature that is alleged not to be suitable if you want to make
science. Yet it is not the drab men who always find the
truth and now Long dispatched cables and letters, right
away, across the Atlantic this August and here it is September 1, 1936, with Long back at the Johns Hopkins, to find
on his lab table bottles—of the red dye, prontosil S, and of
the simpler powder, sulfanilamide. Here, too, all ready to

begin work on, bang, right away, are four big batches of white mice. They've been infected by his lab boy and are now nicely on the way to dying because all these four batches have got in their bellies, each batch of them, four different savage families of streptococcus.

—For two years before this, Long and Eleanor Bliss have been trying to cure mice with specific streptococcus serums. Never have they seen a mouse survive who has been infected with one thousand fatal doses of any of these bugs, if they waited more than four hours after injection to give him serum—

How could Long plunge so impetuously into these new experiments without consulting high Hopkins authorities? For this he could thank the Chemical Foundation, and particularly Mr. Francis Patrick Garvan who had given Long and Bliss the wherewithal for their researches. It was Garvan's notion that the Foundation should not dictate the problems to be worked at but should pick a good man and let him go it on his own. And Garvan's own daughter, Patricia, had been killed by streptococcus—

Now here lay these four batches of mice already very sick in their glass jars. They had been infected for eight hours. Their blood was already alive with streptococcus. Doomed they were surely. Under the skins of part of them Long shot the red dye, prontosil S; into the mouths of another part went the simpler sulfanilamide. While half of all the sick ones were left to their mouse fate.

No, it was no moonshine. Out of every ten of the treated mice, eight lived. All not treated died. Now again Long became impetuous—

Here it was only the 8th of September with this one experiment finished and he jumped from mice to men. This day a baby doctor came to him telling him of an eight-year-old girl. She was "damn sick," he said. With erysipelas—fever 106. He'd transfused her, given her antitoxin. She was going to die. No, Long personally had no experience or knowledge of possible poisonous effects of this new-fangled sulfanilamide, or prontosil, but yes, he'd be glad to try it out. Doctoring was in Long's blood. His father today is a practicing doctor in Bryan, Ohio, and his grandfather and great-grandfather were doctors before there was such a thing as medical science. Doctoring now dominated Long's scientific caution and within eight hours the red flame on the doomed little girl's skin stopped and in thirty-six hours all fever had left her—after prontosil every four hours.

This event set off a queer combination of high science and plain doctoring in the Johns Hopkins Hospital. The little girl had the honor to be the first human being reported as treated—and the first human life saved?—by the red dye in the U. S. A. It stirred a terrific toiling among hundreds of white mice by Perrin Long and Eleanor Bliss while Long punctuated his mouse experiments by jumps from those mice to doomed men before he'd got clear in his head the why's and wherefore's of the new chemical's man-curing or even mouse-curing power.

Long concentrated on the cheaper, simpler, easier-to-give sulfanilamide. Did it save life, really? Wouldn't that first little girl have taken a turn for the better without it? By November, 1936, Long and Bliss reported at a big scientific meeting that they had treated some seventy severely sick people with sulfanilamide. Several had had blood-poisoning, overwhelmed they were by microbes swarming in their blood and the way they'd up and got better—all but four—was astounding.

Of the four who'd died, all but one had had one foot in the grave when the treatment started.

It was so simple. Unless the sick person was too far gone to swallow, these people just got pills of the new drug by mouth. Like aspirins. And yet and yet! Was their cure happenstance? After all bad streptococcus sore throat doesn't by a long shot always turn into blood-poisoning and blood-poisoning sometimes gets well when all you've given it is a prayer. And what is more frequent, more notorious, more tragic, than the fooling of doctors by the glitter of new remedies? And shouldn't we beware of Perrin Long—enthusiast?

So here it was December, only three months after they have started. Here was a six-year-old girl, sick with a streptococcus infection so deadly that the most hare-brained optimist could hardly be fooled by an alleged cure for it. This girl suffered the almost surely mortal streptococcus meningitis. Here was one disease about whose fatality there was little doubt. It killed ninety-nine percent, plus, of all its victims, no matter what any doctor or surgeon might try to do. This was a deviltry of the streptococcus from which, during fifteen years at the Johns Hopkins Hospital, not one victim had come back to tell the story.

In all medical record only fifty-five of its victims were reported to have recovered.

Here, when a child's earache, or running ear, or mastoid sickness progressed to high fever, to delirium, to vomiting, to convulsions with head drawn back in a spasm and with awful headache—such a child had not more than a Chinaman's chance to live.

So on the 7th of December, Dr. Francis Schwenkter, aided and abetted and cheered on by Long, began to give this doomed six-year-old girl sulfanilamide.

On the 25th of that month—some Christmas present—she went home cured to her father and mother.

In that same month out of four doomed with this same mortal sickness, three were made sound and well by the new medicine, and, in less than a year's time, out of forty-three cases of proved streptococcus meningitis of which Long has record—thirty-six are now alive and healthy. Thanks to those simple pills of sulfanilamide swallowed, and to its solution injected by expert physicians into these people's spines.

We need no longer smile at Perrin Long's enthusiasm.
In Europe and America there is now hardly a question that,
already, thousands of lives have been saved from childbed
fever, erysipelas, and the blood-poisoning caused by streptococcus; but the final proof of its life-guarding power is this
miraculous band of thirty-six youngsters and grownups who
have no right now to be living . . . Who, except for sulfanilamide, would have been one hundred to one shots to
die.

IV

But how did this seemingly harmless chemical save the
lives of mice and men? The unscientific secrecy imposed
upon commercial science gave Long and Bliss no hint about
how Hoerlein and his myrmidons had happened on to it.
Now Long snatched hours from his treatment of doomed
people, and helped Eleanor Bliss—who worked day and night
busy as a boy killing snakes—at hundreds of mouse experiments. Yes, the Germans were right. In a glass dish, in a
test-tube, this sulfanilamide did not kill streptococcus. No,
but wait, here was something the Germans hadn't tried out:
the chemical did check their growing for eighteen, twenty
hours maybe. Then they got over it and multiplied to beat
the band, so that in a couple of days they were swarming in
the tubes in dangerous millions—

So what of it? Bliss and Long jumped this growth-checking
experiment from the test-tubes to the insides of the bellies
of living mice, sick mice. It was beautiful and mysterious
and new in all microbe-hunting science. You infected your
mouse, shooting strept into his abdominal cavity and in three,
four hours the bugs began to swarm in there. Eight hours—
you gave the beast his first dose of sulfanilamide. You kept
sticking your syringe needle into your mouse's belly hour
after hour withdrawing a drop of the deadly germ-swarm-
ing fluid to examine under your microscope how the strept
were ruining the mouse and now—it happened very sud-

denly—six hours after that first dose of the magic chemical, good-by bugs! Suddenly on the battlefield inside that mouse there appeared an attacking wave of phagocytes, of microbe-eating white blood cells, who'd been perfectly willing to stay away from there till now, who suddenly screwed up their phagocyte courage and began gobbling up those malignant streptococci right and left . . . It seemed as if, after a while, after a few hours, this funny sulfanilamide—not in itself deadly to the strept assassins—softened them up just enough so the white blood cells got up their nerve to make hash of them. It was no one-shot miracle though. If you didn't keep on giving that mouse dose after dose of the magical chemical—

If you left off treating him before every last streptococcus was gobbled it was too bad for Mister Mouse. It was certainly a long way from the one hundred percent cure that German Domagk claimed it was. Many a mouse they thought they'd cured, who'd stayed perfectly healthy for thirty, sixty, even one hundred days, then suddenly relapsed, sickened, turned up his toes, died. So Perrin Long hatched a theory—novel but seeming very sound—of the chemical's life-guarding magic. Sulfanilamide simply and only checked the strept's growing. Not growing, the microbe does not pour out its poisons. (That is not theory but long-known fact.) Not pouring out its poisons the strept becomes defenseless against the white blood cells.

Everything seemed too good to be true, those exciting autumn days of 1936; it must have seemed to Bliss and Long as if fate had relented from perpetuating a part of man's ages-old suffering and death. Sulfanilamide had other virtues besides its microbe-checking action. Pharmacologist E. K. Marshall reported that it was astounding the way this chemical—even when you took it in pills by mouth—quickly spread itself into every nook and cranny of your body, wherever a strept might think of lurking to bite you. Marshall cooked

up a test so that at any given instant you could tell precisely
how much sulfanilamide there was in the blood of a treated
mouse or dog or man. This gave the new curative science
an unheard-of controllability, a scientific precision, possessed
by no other cure whatever. A man's dangerously sick, blood-
poisoned. You give him quick big doses of the chemical but
you don't have to shoot in the dark because you can measure exactly how much is staying in the man and how much
is leaving him—or is being sucked up by the microbes attacking him. You can keep boldly looping sulfanilamide to him
to keep it in his blood at a high level. Till he begins to get
better. Here was science; not the old hit-or-miss-or-maybe
dosing of medical quacksalvers.

## V

Those days of autumn and winter, 1936-'37, it was as if
cruel nature had given a moratorium on its debt to death.
It seemed as if the Germans were right when they reported
this prontosil was all but harmless for human beings—
Almost unbelievable . . . Shades of old Paul Ehrlich with
his magic bullet 606 that was loaded with poisonous arsenic!
The cure which, when you used it to kill the syphilis spirochete, sometimes killed the man . . . Now from England
came news that was still better. Searcher G. A. H. Buttle reported this same sulfanilamide powerful to prevent dying of
mice infected with other microbes besides the deadly streptococcus! The meningococcus—microbe of epidemic cerebro-
spinal meningitis—was hardly more than the remotest cousin
of strept. Yet the chemical could prevent the dying of mice
shot with a million fatal doses of what the lab men call
meningo!

Yes, it would cure the mice when they were already infected—

Again Long egged Dr. Francis Schwenkter on to take a
new jump from mice to men. Ten out of eleven youngsters

dangerously sick with epidemic meningitis—meningococcus!
—got spectacularly better after Schwenkter had shot sulfanilamide into their spines, given them pills of it by mouth. This
was as good a record as the best serum could show . . .
Maybe better than any serum? The after-effects of serum are
sometimes very serious, often extremely disagreeable, even
though they've saved the sufferer's life.

Now Perrin Long took a Steve Brodie. What germ's the
blood brother of this meningococcus? No less than those bis-
cuit-shaped bugs that cause gonorrhea. The evil microbes
of this—for men!—semi-comic sickness have in their time
blinded myriads of newborn babies, and still blind many of
them in spite of the preventive drops of silver nitrate. They
have wrecked the lives of countless women, innocent as well
as sexually "guilty." Tiny torturers they are, twisting limbs
into terrible deformities, racking with the most hellish of all
rheumatic pains the untold thousands now suffering from
gonorrheal arthritis.

But now for Long there was an obstacle to any laboratory
experiment with it. Mister Gonococcus was cantankerous,
refused to sicken any lab animal from mouse to monkey.
How then could Long scientifically test the new chemical's
possible action against gonorrhea? Perry Long is notorious as
a genial yet pretty sarcastic kidder of his colleagues and now
for weeks he kept at a campaign of joshing the resident staff
of the Brady Institute . . . You might as well use dishwater
as what urologists used, to irrigate gonorrhea victims . . .
The fact that there were a dozen irrigations, alleged cures,
proved that there weren't any . . . They thought Long was
a wild man . . . At last Drs. John E. Dees and J. A. C.
Colston had to listen to this pestiferous Perry Long. They'd
show him. They were veterans in the futility of using any
chemical to cure gonorrhea, by irrigations or by injections.
About all chemical cures they were disenchanted. High artificial fever, machine fever—107 degrees!—could cure it, yes.

But dangerous. And, for the wiping out of gonorrhea, of the millions of cases of it in America, who dared to propose such mass-fevers as practical?

"Come on, give sulfanilamide a try-out," wheedled Long— not telling them the wonders he had seen it work on three cases of gonorrheal rheumatism—

June, 1937, at the annual meeting of the American Medical Association, our "profoundly impressed" Dees and Colston reported that, in thirty-six out of forty-seven people to whom they'd simply fed pills of sulfanilamide—no irrigations and no injections!—in that thirty-six all painful, dangerous, gonorrhea-spreading discharge had disappeared within five days.

There had been only three relapses.

In not one of all the forty-seven had there been any of the otherwise so frequent painful, disabling progression of the sickness.

This news threw the assembled experts into an uproar of mixed enthusiasm and denial of the possibility of such a miracle.

That was June, 1937. Today there is a fury of treating gonorrhea with sulfanilamide. Among this lucky eighty percent whose painful, disagreeable discharge so quickly vanishes, has the evil biscuit-bug really been wiped out? In many, it begins to seem so. Dr. Loren Schaffer reports that in the experience of the Social Hygiene Clinic in Detroit, it appears as if sulfanilamide, for gonorrhea, closely parallels the contagion-suppressing power of arsenical drugs for syphilis.

Yet our searchers must be cautious. For it is not the man with active gonorrheal discharge who spreads the sickness so much as the man who thinks he's cured, but in whom a few dangerous microbes may yet, invisibly, be lurking.

But now comes scientific news yet more encouraging for the unlucky ones whom sulfanilamide does not cure—

Dr. Edgar G. Ballenger and his co-workers in Atlanta, Georgia, report that three mild fevers—only 103 to 104 degrees, not dangerous or very uncomfortable—plus sulfanilamide, cure people incurable by the drug, and difficulty curable by the dangerous high machine fever when it is used alone—

## VI

Almost as powerful as its curative action is this chemical's virtue of preventing infections, by streptococcus, by meningococcus, in mice in the laboratory. All right. Excellent. So for the curse of gonorrhea you may think there is now a simple way for erring people to dodge the reward of their sins? A short time ago a microbe hunter heard a bar-boy asking the bartender whether he'd heard about these new "G. C. pills?" You just swallowed a couple of them before you went out for a night of fun. This practice is now spreading in America, for sulfanilamide can now be bought by anybody in all drugstores and here is the first cloud in the sky of this new science—

German dye-chemist Heinrich Hoerlein, in 1935, in London, had astounded English doctors with what seemed a scientific fairy-tale of a chemical so deadly for microbes, yet so gentle for men. And when Long and Bliss began making martyrs of hundreds and thousands of white mice, the only effect of this chemical—except its power to cure—seemed humorous. Give a mouse too much, and he got drunk, sashaying comically round his cage. But he didn't die. Better yet, nothing serious happened to the first few hundreds of sick people they'd cured by the coal-tar chemical. Long saw the lips and finger nails of many of them turn blue, but this vanished often, even though he went on treating them. Like the inebriated mice, certain men and women became giddy, nauseated, and dopey after heavy treatment with the new drug. But let up on it and they felt better pronto. The same was true of the fevers it gave them, and their rashes.

So Long kept giving heavier and heavier doses the more serious the streptococcus sickness, more and more boldly. Then, out of a clear sky, March, 1937, a man getting beautifully better from strept infection came down suddenly with a devastating anemia. Blood transfusion saved his life. A few days later, another, terrifying. Again transfusion and instant withdrawal of the chemical. Worse yet to come. In June, from the blood of another man under heavy sulfanilamide treatment the white blood cells began to vanish—and that's a blow which for six people out of ten is mortal—

This blasting of the red blood cells and vanishing of the white blood cells is not common, it's true. But, already, deaths have been reported, and Long knows of unreported deaths that have occurred. Doctors have issued grave warnings against self-treatment with sulfanilamide and they are right, without question. Physicians only should use the powerful chemical death-fighter, yes, but how many doctors are any more competent than lay people to employ it?

## VII

What are the dreams this powerful new chemical science now stirs in those of our searchers and physicians who believe it their duty to relieve all possible human pain and misery and to guard mankind from all death that is preventable?

There now need be no more streptococcus mastoid disease, and its consequence, the deadly streptococcus meningitis.

The thousands of yearly deaths from streptococcus childbed fever could probably right now be made evil memories only.

Sulfanilamide can prevent all the life-wrecking and deadly consequences of hemolytic streptococcus infection that follows epidemics of milk-borne sore throat; and, used skillfully and in time, it can cure the streptococcus blood-poisoning that is so often fatal.

The high death rate of epidemic meningitis should now be lowered to less than ten out of every hundred stricken, and maybe sent still lower if the sickness could only be spotted more quickly, and caught in its beginning.

For the first time in human record there is the chance now for our healthmen to set out to obliterate the curse of gonorrhea.

Dread rheumatic fever, rheumatic heart disease, is almost certainly an aftermath of the poisoning left by streptococcus sore throat. From October to May, hundreds of thousands of our children in northern latitudes live under the shadow of this peril. What would happen to this heart-wreck death rate if—under expert medical and nursing supervision—such threatened children were kept on little daily doses of sulfanilamide? To prevent their sore throat infection?

In New York and Baltimore such experiments are already in their hopeful beginning.

Sulfanilamide has been found to cure mice infected with the Welch bacilli that cause dread gas gangrene. This is a limb- and life-destroying consequence of muscle and bone-crushing wounds in motor and industrial accidents, and in war. Already there is reliable report of how sulfanilamide saves gas-gangrene sick human beings.

The drug is a strange microbe-shooting shotgun, truly. For at the Mayo Clinic, and elsewhere, it is found to conquer serious and sometimes deadly infections of the bladder and kidneys that are caused by staphylococcus, and by colon and proteus bacilli.

But this is what we must face, this is the bitter fact: that lay people are not the only ones incompetent to treat themselves with this powerful chemical. How many doctors know how to detect—by laboratory tests—the first signs of sulfanilamide's occasional blood-wrecking action?

And, if they do not themselves have this skill and these laboratory facilities, how many doctors feel justified—the poverty of the mass of their patients being what it is!—in adding to the charge for their own services those laboratory bills which change the cheap, fifteen-cents-a-day sulfanilamide to a treatment far beyond the average citizen's power to pay?

And in how many counties in our country are there laboratories, county medical centers, quickly available even for the minority who can pay the laboratory bills—let alone the mass who have not the wherewithal to buy the science now existing, to buy the life now purchasable?

It's the plainest sense—you don't have to be a doctor to understand it—that, before you use a powerful cure for a microbic sickness, you should first be sure of the microbe causing it.

How many of our rank and file doctors have the skill or time for such microbe-hunting practice? And should our doctors be asked to be microbe hunters? And, if not, how many of them have instant access to free laboratories where experts can give them this information?

How many practicing physicians in our country have the knowledge to tell the difference between sulfanilamide that is safe to use and sulfanilamide so dolled-up, chemically, that it is deadly?

But surely such dolling-up of this drug is not permitted? Yes, in our country, there's no law against it; you can mix sulfanilamide with any other chemical—and so long as there's no explosion—you can peddle it to the public (and to physicians) for a profit.

So it came about that this marvelous cure—in the hands of doctors not the people—became a killer.

It was not the curative chemical itself that killed. Plain sulfanilamide came in tablets, like aspirins; mightn't some people and doctors like it better out of a bottle? As an elixir?

The di-ethylene glycol in which the sulfanilamide was dissolved to make this fancy elixir was deadly and could not this have been found out in available scientific chemical literature?

But if knowledge of this danger did exist, the compounders of this elixir did not find it, and so it came about that this elixir of life became in the hands of doctors an elixir of death—killing seventy people this 1937 autumn.

The complete absence of government control of remedies sold for profit had its part in this tragedy. And so did the ignorance of the physicians who prescribed the fatal nostrum, who hadn't the rudiments of knowledge to distinguish a chemical that cures from one that kills.

Yet it is beside the mark to blame the doctors, who are victims of the system under which they must make their livings. Perrin Long has told many a County Medical Society the news of sulfanilamide's life-guarding power. He has seen the rank-and-file physician's eagerness to use this so easy-seeming yet so complicated and dangerous science.

Long knows that the average doctor would rather cure his suffering people than kill them. Yes.

Then why—

# CODA

THE time has come when the fight for life can be a people's fight. It must be that, or it is worse than nothing. Death does not wait for a gradual extension of life-giving art and science. And death and suffering of the people—while life is within reach—is the most exquisite of all human cruelty, is an affront to mankind's conscience.

The fights against mothers' death, the maiming death of infantile paralysis, against tuberculosis and syphilis, and for the skilled use of sulfanilamide, all these are fights for the whole nation. But you say wait, don't be impatient, let it come gradually, remember the triumphant way in which Detroit has now begun against tuberculosis—

Yes, that is here kept in mind. But can Detroit wage the battle at the same time—adequately—against syphilis, too? No. Henry Vaughan admits that while his city is appropriating its ample money for TB, on the basis of it-costs-us-money-to-die, it cannot do the same for syphilis. Though the city's economic loss from syphilis is as great as that from consumption. Even though the wiping out of this syphilis loss would cost less money.

It is the same the country over. Chicago may now pro mil tax itself to begin a truly adequate fight against syphilis, but it could not be asked to increase its TB tax to make the same TB fight that Detroit is making. And your chronicler's own State of Michigan cannot find the funds to begin the wiping out of TB as its city of Detroit is now doing. And as for syphilis? Well, a feeble $100,000 was appropriated by Michigan to fight syphilis in the midst of the syphilis-excitement, spring, 1937.

This amount was cut down to $25,000 this autumn by legislators howling for what they call economy.

.    .    .    .    .    .    .

No, death does not wait, and none of the deaths here chronicled can be conquered by the horse and buggy medicine of the oldtime doctor with the beard and the bedside manner—though this is not to say that the bedside manner has not its place in the art of healing. But in the fight against the death of mothers, in the attempt to prevent infantile paralysis and to minimize its wreckage, in the battle to wipe out tuberculosis and conquer syphilis, the old art of healing is now nine-tenths of it no longer art but science.

How many of our physicians have the birth-helping knowledge to guard mothers against the streptococcus infection, the bleeding, and the eclamptic poisoning that kills them?

How many rank-and-file doctors are technically trained to apply the new chemicals that may guard children from the maiming death's invasion? Or skilled in early diagnosis, or the use of the physiological rest treatment, that can now prevent the horrible deformities of infantile paralysis when it is applied early in the acute stage of the sickness?

Can the average doctor take the x-ray film that alone detects early, minimal tuberculosis, and faced with such a chest film, does he know whether or not he sees tuberculosis?

Many doctors are capable of drawing blood from the arm veins of our population for the Kahn test dragnet that is now going to be used to uncover early syphilis. Yes, but how many can do it, how expertly? And how many are skilled in the injection of the arsenical drugs into the arm veins and the bismuth into the bottoms of syphilitics so that they may be no longer dangerous to the people?

And how many physicians—in your community—know and can use the blood-testing science that alone can make sulfanilamide treatment safe, and the microbe-hunting technique that alone can make it scientific and powerful to wipe out streptococcus and gonococcus sickness, crippling, and death?

The laboratory has now become the heart of all these death-fights. It is knowledge of the use and meaning of this science that our doctors lack. This does not mean we will have to replace the doctors we have now. The majority of our physicians could become front-line fighters in these battles. In the Detroit TB-fight they are actually doing so. But nationally they must be given the wherewithal for scientific training, and the wherewithal for the livelihood of themselves and their families while they are learning.

None of these fights are local ones. Babies are born in Maine as well as in California. TB is a killer the nation over. Syphilis is rampant everywhere. All these battles are mass-fights, fights to prevent further death, or they are nothing.

.        .        .        .        .        .        .

Well and good, but do our physicians, healthmen, microbe hunters, believe that these various battles are now part of the whole people's fight for life? Excepting in Detroit against tuberculosis, for the rank and file of physicians your chronicler does not here presume to speak, but experience of the past three years has taught him the feeling of many of the leaders.

"Tuberculosis is no longer the primary concern of the medical profession," says Pat O'Brien. "It is the people's death-fight. Tuberculosis was not created to put money in the doctor's pocket," says Pat, the dynamo of Detroit's fight with TB death.

"You'll never win until you take the doctor bill out of syphilis," says O. C. Wenger. "Or at least not until you make the doctor bill a direct charge upon the whole people."

And when the veteran birth-helper, Joseph B. De Lee, is confronted with the cost of building safe hospitals for mothers, and the expense of training our physicians to bring babies safely, he answers: "I know only this, that nothing compares in value with human life."

All over our country, in regard to the question whether these are private matters between individual people and their bedside counselors, or whether they are now the people's fight for life—all over there is a great stirring among top-ranking healthmen and physicians. There is the beginning of a revolt of the competent. This year, 1937, there has been issued a new medical declaration of independence—signed by four hundred and thirty of our nation's death-fighters.

They make bold to say that the health of the people has now become a direct concern of the government; that the first step in this people's fight is to cut down the risk of illness and death by prevention—which means mass prevention or it means nothing. They demand that our public health services, federal, state, and local be so expanded and organized as to become the general staff of the people's fight for life against death, now mass-preventable.

Do you question seriously whether the rank and file of our physicians would follow competent leaders if, without basic change in present medical practice, the people, taking action, would demand that our best men of medical science be given their chance to begin the battle?

If the medical rank and file were given the opportunity, the wherewithal from time to time to leave the grind of their practices, to become part-time public health officers, to become skilled in the rudiments of the use of the new life-guarding weapons, would they follow such leaders?

Why cannot our U. S. Public Health Service be entrusted with co-ordinating in the instances of these now preventable plagues, the people's fight for life? You hear the wail that this will breed a new bureaucracy. Let this then be remembered: we have an army and a navy, supported by the government, by all the people—to defend our nation against threat

of human invasion that becomes real not once in a generation. They are bureaucracies, granted.

But is it anywhere advocated that the army and the navy
be turned over to private hands, that the defense of our
country be left to us as individuals armed with scythes and
shotguns, because the army and the navy are' bureaucratic?
Human enemies threaten us from outside once in fifty years,
maybe . . . Who then objects to the organization of a death-
fighting army against the far more dangerous subvisible assassins in ambush for all the people—always?

Yes, a truly powerful national health program against preventable deaths would be bureaucratic. And your chronicler,
for one, would feel comfortable in the matter of the lives of
himself and his own, in the hands of a bureaucracy manned
by such death-fighters as Thomas Parran, Goldberger, Armstrong, Edward Francis, O. C. Wenger and the other death-
fighters of the U. S. Public Health Service.

.     .     .     .     .     .     .

Today there are headline howls for economy and bellowing about the need to have done with national spending. It
is deplorable, doubtless, that twenty-five percent of the national income is eaten up by taxes. And you may well ask
where our President and the Congress, bedeviled as they now
are by this wailing, will get the money to finance the people's
fight for life?

You may ask, too, where does all of the people's money
come from. And the simple answer is now more and more
widely known. Now, when we are threatened with war, the
President and Congress do not hesitate to go to those bankers
who buy the nation's bond issues. The bankers snap them
up amid the blaring of the brass bands in the loan drives.

It is notorious that war is no economy. It is well known
that war debt is a debt that can be amortized with great
difficulty and that it is a burden upon the people for gen-

erations . . . There is even rumor that some war debts are never paid at all.

And now if our President and the Congress go respectfully to those bankers who buy the bonds our government must sell to get the people's wherewithal, and they tell those bankers: we can show you this most sure and rigorous economy—

If you allow our death-fighters—we can assure you they are competent—the money to wipe out such and such and such deaths that cost us billions to maintain, within a generation there will no longer be this drain upon the wealth of our nation. Of all ways to ease our awful tax burden, this is the sure one.

Would our bankers consider this basic investment for our country's stronger future? Would they buy the people's health bonds, the paying off of which is as sure as tomorrow's sunrise?

.    .    .    .    .    .    .

It is the wisdom of all great leaders of the people, it is the wisdom of our President not to go too far ahead of the people in their march of life. But in the matter of the getting of the wherewithal for the people's fight for life, basing the getting of it on the common sense that it costs us money to die, would our President require a mandate of the people before he proposed the new death-fight to the Congress?

A referendum showed that the people of Chicago were not against the plan of its healthmen to rid the city of the ghastly luxury of syphilis.

Would a nationwide vote have to be taken, from people like that Negro mother saved by science in the hands of the young birth-helpers of the Chicago Maternity Center; like the thousands given new life at Hot Springs by science in the hands of syphilis-master O. C. Wenger; like Detroiters saved from the white death's doom in Detroit by Pat O'Brien, Bruce Douglas, and Henry Vaughan?

Do the people want to die if they can be truly told that they do not have to?

.        .        .        .        .        .        .

Death does not wait and the people are beginning to know it. In the matter of their being ill-fed they are told to be patient because if enough food were raised to feed all of them, that would drive down the price of pork and milk and beef and wheat. They are told that not enough cotton and wool can be raised to clothe all of them because that would drive down the price of wool and cotton. Good houses cannot be built for all of them because this would disturb the landowners and drive down the price of building materials that would be needed.

Granted. These are serious economic questions and demand long waiting by our ill-fed, ill-housed, ill-clothed millions.

But what economic obstacle is in the way of giving the people life, when it is costing our whole nation—its rulers and owners included—billions to keep the people only half-alive and to let them die?

Will the people wait, will they be patient when they know there is not even a rotten economic reason why their dear ones should drown in the blood of consumptive death, perish with childbed fever, go blind, become heart-wrecked, and go mad with syphilis?

The people are beginning to know that life is no longer a question of do *I* live or do *I* die. No, in their onward march of life it now becomes do *we* live or do *we* die.

.        .        .        .        .        .        .

You say the cat is out of the bag now. You protest that all urged in this story of the fight for life—though seeming to defend our present economic order—is at bottom bolshevik?

Then your chronicler must here make confession. This is his credo—

That the relief of suffering and the prevention of dying cannot be best served, for all, so long as there remains any money consideration between the people and the fighters for their lives.

This reporter believes that all considerations of private profit are not only wasteful but infamous if they frustrate the fight for life, if they deny the right of one human being to live.

*Wake Robin,*
*Holland, Michigan,*
*November 12, 1937.*

# INDEX

Abortion, 55, 71
Adair, F. L., 61
Adam, 51
Addison, Thomas, 64
Agriculture, Dept. of, Federal, 18
Alger, Horatio, 87
American Medical Association, 325
*American Medical Association, Journal of*, 55, 200
American Social Hygiene Association, 289, 294
Anesthesia, in childbirth, discovery of, 49-54
Armstrong, C., 175-197, 205, 206, 208, 209, 211, 212, 213, 215, 312, 335
Artificial fever, 260-283; arthritis, treatment of, by, 281; becomes practical, 272; danger of, 269, 272; gonorrhea, treatment of, by, 281; prevents consequences late syphilis, 273-274; rheumatic state, treatment of, by, 281; syphilis, treatment of, by, 260-283; undulant fever, treatment of, by, 281
Aycock, W. L., 167, 170

Bach, J. S., 132
Beethoven, L., 130, 132
Bell, Blair, 40
Benaron, H. B. W., 94-139
Bergenholtz, Doctor, 146
Birth control, 35, 131
Birth-helping, as science, 43-44
Bliss, E. A., 316-321
B'nai B'rith, 298
Brodie, M., 169, 170, 174, 182
Brown, J. H., 317
Bundesen, H., 211, 305, 307
Burns, Bobby, 80
Buttle, G. A. H., 323

Cancer, 280
Carley, P., 292
Carpenter, C., 261
Caesarean operation, 101, 107, 138
Chemical Foundation, 318

Chicago blood-test referendum, 305-306, 336
Chicago Lying-in Hospital, 87, 88
Chicago Maternity Center, 84-139, 336; discipline of, 105; low death rate record of childbed fever, 116-127; low death rate record of, in eclampsia, 94; low death rate record of hemorrhage, 96-99, 113; low maternal death rate record of, 85; poverty of, 114, 139; prevention of childbed fever by, 115-127
Chicago Medical Society, 306
Chicago syphilis fight, 304-310
Childbirth, natural, 45-47
Clark, T., 293
Cocke, E. W., 260
Colebrook, L., 316, 317
Colston, J. A. C., 324, 325
Cookingham, Doctor, 72
Cotret, 107
Cottrell, H., 25, 26, 27, 28
*Country Gentleman, The*, 231

Dale, H. H., 106
Dees, J. E., 324, 325
De Kleine, W., 11-24, 214, 292
De Kruif, R., 300, 301, 304
De Lee, J. B., 39-62, 83, 86-91, 100, 101, 108, 111, 112, 117, 118, 119, 121, 122, 129, 137, 312, 333
*Detroit News, The*, 232, 233, 236, 238, 240
Detroit TB fight, 224-252
Diabetes, 280
Douglas, B., 227-246, 312, 336
Dragnet for syphilis, 292-294, 306
Draper, G., 163, 164, 165

Eclampsia, 84; low death rate of Chicago Maternity Center, 94; prevention of, 91-95
Elliott, C. R., 63-83
Elliott, Lillian, 67, 69, 70, 71
Elixir of sulfanilamide, 329-330

339